The Clare in the Community Collection

Harry Venning

Clare may have been do-gooding in The Guardian for twenty five years, but she actually made her debut in a free magazine called Care Weekly posted out to social workers. I had got the job through a friend in Care Weekly's publishing house who tipped me off that their regular cartoonist was leaving. Had there been a vacancy in Yachting Gazette or Artificial Insemination Today, history would have taken an altogether different course.

I didn't choose social work, social work chose me. In fact it is true to say that I knew almost nothing about it. But a freelance cartoonist will never let anything as mundane as ignorance stand in the way of a regular paid job and I set about listing the few things I did know about the profession: they are always stressed out, the media vilify them, they wear sandals and they talk in jargon. I then proceeded to draw a cartoon on each of those themes - unkind souls may suggest I just repeated the cycle for the next quarter century- and Karen In The Community was born. That was her original name before it occurred to me that there was a much smoother pun out there.

I was away. Only I wasn't. At the time I was something of a Curse Of The Monkey's Claw amongst cartoonists, insofar as every publication I joined would go out of business soon afterwards, and Care Weekly was no different. But I recognised the germ of a good idea in Clare, and sent the few strips I had drawn to Malcolm Dean, editor of Guardian Society. Thankfully my employment by The Guardian didn't sink it, although sales did go into a terminal decline soon afterwards. Maybe it was me, maybe it was the growth of the internet. We shall never know.

It took a while for Clare to find her face and physique - her nose changed shape more often than Michael Jackson's- but she eventually settled down into her recognisable form. Handy hint to novice cartoonists: If you are creating a character give them a distinctive article of clothing to make them instantly identifiable when everything else about them is in a state of flux. I put Clare in a stripey top. When the cartoon went to colour I made the stripes blue and white as a tribute to my football team QPR who, I think it fair to say, can do with all the help they can get.

Even Clare's.

1995

Media

The Guardian

Receivers called in after £500m goes walkabout □ Mayhem feared in markets

Barings Bank goes bust

Big fight injury prompts attack on safety delays

Major woos vote of Euro-rebels

2006

theguardian

From Monday: a new, smaller Guardian, the UK's most colourful national paper

2019

Flame on
Barbecue secrets of top chefs

Who killed Sweden's most controversial prime minister?

The Guardian

Probation will be renationalised after disastrous Grayling reforms

MPs launch inquiry after reality TV deaths

Anger at near-total abortion ban in Alabama

Europeans fear EU may collapse in a generation

Apology; I was unable to provide every year with four Guardian front pages, as originally planned, due to the Guardian archives being inaccessible during Covid. All gaps have been filled by extra cartoons. Every cloud...

1997 **Start small..**

2001 **a larger size...**

2019 **and finally colour!**

Guardian 2

- How a trader with Barings threatened a meltdown in the world's money markets
- Profile: Graham Kelly, the FA's chief executive

Plus television, radio and weather

With hundreds of jobs

Media

Tabloid pages 13-37

Analysis

Can Tony Blair win the battle for the middle classes?

Page 18

45p
Monday
February 27
1995
Published in London and Manchester

The **Guardian**

Receivers called in after £500m goes walkabout ☐ Mayhem feared in markets

Barings Bank goes bust

Patrick Donovan and Alex Brummer

BARINGS Bank, the oldest and most esteemed of British merchant bankers, was forced into receivership late last night after the Bank of England failed to put together a City rescue operation to help cover share trading losses of over £500 million.

The announcement came after the heads of all of Britain's major banks had attended an all-day crisis summit at the Bank of England's headquarters on Threadneedle Street, central London.

The failure to effect a rescue means that Baring Brothers will be forced to default on a series of huge derivatives contracts in Singapore and Tokyo. The deals were carried out by a single trader in Barings' Singapore office and are under investigation by local police.

Derivatives are highly complex trading instruments which speculate in changes on future market conditions.

The news sent shockwaves across the world's markets, with sterling plunging to an all-time low when dealing in Australia opened early today. Shares fell to a 14 month low on the Tokyo Stock Exchange. Dealers are bracing themselves for a sharp fall in London share prices and for the pound to tumble on the foreign exchanges.

One senior trader last night said he expected the FTSE share index in London to plummet by at least 100 points in early trading, wiping billions of pounds off investments.

The markets have been plunged into turmoil because the share deals could involve unlimited losses. The Bank of England warned that several contracts entered into by Barings in the Far East are still open, thus exposing Barings to "unquantifiable further losses until the contracts expire or are otherwise closed out".

One banker close to the failed rescue talks said: "This is a hole of indeterminate size."

The £500 million "black hole" in Barings' account was traced yesterday to rogue share deals secretly carried out by one 28-year-old dealer. The trader, named by sources as Nick Leeson, was understood last night to have left Singapore for Kuala Lumpur, Malaysia.

Sources say the transactions involved the purchase of up to 20,000 packages of share contracts, priced at £120,000 apiece, which were based on predicting movements in the Tokyo Nikkei 225 Stock Market index. The losses snowballed as the Tokyo stock market fell over the past two weeks.

Banking sources said it was too early to say whether fraud was involved or a "double or quits" strategy to trade out of losses that badly misfired.

Ian Perkin, chief economist at the Hong Kong Chamber of Commerce, said earlier the disclosures made him "sick in the pit of my stomach. You wonder what else may emerge."

Barings is one of the biggest players in the Pacific rim. The bank recently announced that it had made a 54 per cent increase in its profits to nearly £55 million for the first half of its financial year, and senior banking sources said it was due to report record results for 1994 today.

The Bank of England, which confirmed in its statement last night that the losses at Barings had been caused by "massive unauthorised dealings by one of its traders in South-east Asia", was forced to step in as it became clear that confidence in world stock markets could be thrown into jeopardy.

Last night, the Bank went before a High Court judge to ask accountants Ernst & Young to take on the complex task of managing Barings' books as it seeks to quantify the losses.

In a statement issued last night, the Bank pledged to provide liquidity to keep Barings going. Despite this promise to provide all the cash that was needed, however, the statement was seen as falling far short of what was required to prevent tremors from sweeping across the global financial markets.

In its statement, the Bank revealed that Barings, the oldest institution in the City, had run up an astonishing debt of £500 million on irregular tradings in Singapore and other South-east Asian markets.

The Bank of England had hoped to find weekend buyers for large parts of Barings as part of its support operation. But it bowed to the inevitable and allowed the creditors to put it into administration.

Bank insiders described the situation as one of the blackest days in British banking. Schroders' director of Asian operations, Gerry Grimstone said it was "the stuff that novels are made of. This is not some boutique firm going under."

It is the first time that the Bank of England has allowed an institution of such importance at the heart of the City of London, and a member of the exclusive Accepting Houses Committee, to go under.

The Governor of the Bank of England, Eddie George, yesterday called the heads of all the high street and merchant banks to a summit at which they pledged to inject fresh capital into the collapsed bank.

Although a rescue operation appeared within its grasp, the Bank of England failed at the last minute to secure the deal. The rescue consortium refused to concede a Bank of England demand that it take on the full and unidentified exposure arising from the derivatives trade in Singapore. Even though the Bank of England had found a willing buyer for the suspect contracts, in the end the price demanded was too high.

Despite the announcement, the Bank of England pledged that the London markets would open as normal today. It underlined that the decision to allow Barings to fail should not be seen to have implications for other banks operating in the London markets.

Shares and sterling plunge, page 10; Curbs go back to top of agenda, page 11; Leader comment, page 10; Panic in the Pacific, G2 cover story

Taking Barings

- Barings is the oldest merchant bank in the City, founded in 1762 by John and Francis Baring, and has the Queen as one of its clients.
- In 1890 Argentinian loans brought the bank to its knees, and the Bank of England had to rescue it.
- Barings finances the Baring Foundation, supporter of hundreds of charities.
- Barings acts as adviser to Wellcome, which is fighting a takeover bid from Glaxo.
- Barings employees average £100,000 a year in pay.

The end of one day, as Eddie George leaves the Bank of England having failed in his rescue bid; the beginning of another as shares plunge in Tokyo

Big fight injury prompts attack on safety delays

Vivek Chaudhary

THE Professional Boxers Association criticised the sport's governing body yesterday for failing to implement safety measures as American Gerald McClellan remained in a critical condition following his knock-out by Nigel Benn.

Barry McGuigan, president of the PBA, said it would hold a joint inquiry with the British Boxing Board of Control (BBBC) following Saturday night's WBC title fight, after which McClellan collapsed in the ring. Surgeons operated for almost an hour to remove a blood clot from his brain.

McGuigan said the PBA had made a series of safety recommendations to the BBBC last year to increase the safety of boxers but these had still to be implemented. "The BBBC have been very slow in responding to us. We need to bring in the changes as quickly as possible. They will not prevent boxers from being injured but they will ensure that they get the best possible help and as quickly as possible if something was to go wrong. You can't ever totally rule out the possibility of there being a serious injury in the boxing ring."

John Sutcliffe, who operated on McClellan, said the next 48 hours would be crucial for the boxer, who remained in a critical condition on a life support machine at the London Hospital, east London.

He added that McClellan, aged 27, could end up disabled and will never box again. The boxer would have died if he had not received immediate treatment. "Gerald is in a very critical state at the moment and we have had some trouble maintaining normal pressure inside his head, but so far we appear to be winning that battle."

Mr Sutcliffe also operated on London boxer Bradley Stone before his death in April last year.

Mr Sutcliffe, who is a member of the BBBC committee which is due to report on medical care for fighters later this year, said he did not believe boxing should be banned. But he added: "I wondered at the end of the first round if Nigel Benn was going to be the candidate I would be seeing."

Benn said: "I'm very sad at what happened. My thoughts are with Gerald and his family and I'm praying he will make a full recovery."

Angela Brown, McClellan's girlfriend, his mother, Stacey, and aunt Linda Shorter arrived in London on Concorde last night to be at his bedside.

As their car sped off, it hit a photographer's leg and the driver was cautioned by police.

Saturday night's fight has led to calls for boxing to be banned or for greater safety measures to be implemented.

A British Medical Association spokesman said: "How many more cases do we need of boxers playing roulette with their brains before the Government and the BBBC take seriously what we say about the cumulative danger that boxing does."

The Liberal Democrats' sport spokesman, Menzies Campbell, said: "It's surely time to ask the serious question whether the sport of boxing can be permitted in a civilised society."

The Health Secretary, Virginia Bottomley, said: "We will have discussions to make sure that the proper precautions are being taken." Labour's sports spokesman and former boxer Tom Pendry called for full reassurances that the BBBC was doing everything in its power to minimise the risk of injury.

Boxing's future, page 3; Sport, page 16; The Noble Art, page 18; Leader comment, page 10

09
9 770261 307316

News in brief

Clause 4 setback

Tony Blair's campaign to ditch Clause 4 suffered a serious setback when London Labour Party voted to retain it. Page 3

Runaway found

Peter Kerry, aged 14, who ran away to Malaysia with his father's passport and credit cards, was found safe yesterday. Page 3

Hooligan laws failed

The Government's get tough laws on football hooligans have failed. Page 5

MoD contracts

The MoD is giving most consultancies to firms that have hired its senior staff. Page 6

Inside

Major woos vote of Euro-rebels

Patrick Wintour
Political Correspondent

THE Conservative Party chairman Jeremy Hanley held out a battered olive branch to his Euro-rebels with a clear hint that they may be speedily returned the party whip if they back John Major's European policies on Wednesday.

The Prime Minister weighed in by lending his name to the foreword of a radical rightwing manifesto calling for the abandonment of the Maastricht timetable for a single currency. Although he did not endorse the specific demands of the European Research Group's document, he called its contribution lively and thought provoking, seen as a move to persuade the nine whipless rebels to stick with him.

The rebels also came under pressure yesterday from a leading rightwinger, Sir George Gardiner, not to vote against the Government, but to use a rare act of loyalty to restore relations.

In the first sign that the rebels may scale down their demands in Wednesday's vote, Sir Teddy Taylor said he wanted Mr Major to give a commitment that he would tighten Britain's immigration controls at the 1996 inter-governmental conference, and that he would hold a Commons vote before considering rejoining the Exchange Rate Mechanism.

If Britain were to meet the Maastricht timetable to join a single currency by 1999, Sir Teddy said the crunch would come earlier since the country would be required to sign up to the ERM two years in advance, possibly only four months before a general election.

"Neither of these suggestions would undermine in any way the Government's basic policies but would help to remove concerns," he told a meeting in his Southend East constituency.

Although Sir Teddy acts as the informal whip for the nine, the Euro-rebels are often unpredictable in their voting behaviour. The best bet nevertheless is that they will abstain on the Labour motion and vote for the Government's amendment.

Mr Hanley said: "Those who do vote for the Government on Wednesday will be in a different position from those who do not. That is clear. It will be a step in the right direction if they support the Government."

Ulster Unionist MPs, still angry over Anglo-Irish peace plans, said they would find it difficult to back the Government.

The position of the sceptics was given heavyweight support yesterday when the former chancellor Lord Lawson, an advocate of the ERM, attacked the Chancellor Kenneth Clarke by restating his view that a single currency would mean a European government.

Speaking on ITV's Dimbleby, he said: "Those who push the idea of monetary union are those who wish to see the European Community change into a single federal United States of Europe. The single currency is the means they see for that. The whole legitimacy of government would come into question."

1995

.... Sometimes I just don't think I can go on, I feel utterly crushed by the relentless round of desolation and despair....
I know, I know...
Don't patronize me! How can you possibly know the inner turmoil I suffer, day in, day out....
Look, this is obviously a bad time for you. Perhaps it would be better if we arranged another meeting.
Good idea. Come back next Tuesday and I'll finish writing up your care package.
HARRY VENNING

My god, Frank, what's wrong?
I can't do it, I just can't do it.
It's completely beyond me, I can't cope, nothing adds up anymore. I'm at the end of my tether and don't know what to do.
Yes you do, Frank, you turn to us, your friends and collegues for help and support. All you have to do is ask.
Clare, will you help me balance my care budget?
Care budget? No fear, mate, you're on your own.

Just look at all those people queueing for the lottery!
NEWSAGENT
PLAY HERE
I despair!! It's like this every Saturday.
Most of those people standing in line are either unemployed, pensioners or in low paid part-time work. Won't they ever learn....
....that they've got all week to buy their tickets.

The latest books and CDs
FridayReview
Bye bye Blur: Is Britpop really dead?
Voice of the century
Richard Williams on Sinatra
What's gone wrong at Poundbury?
Charles and the dream that died
Deyan Sudjic on fogeys and follies

45p
Friday
December 8
1995
Published in London
and Manchester

The Guardian

EU pact could sideline Major

Kohl and Chirac agree to fast lane

Ian Traynor in Baden-Baden and Paul Webster in Paris

GERMANY and France last night launched a joint drive for fast-track European integration, proposing that faint-hearts and Eurosceptics be allowed opt-outs that would leave European Union enthusiasts to push ahead on their own towards political union.

"Temporary difficulties of a partner in keeping up must not impair the union's capacity to act and its opportunities for progress," Chancellor Helmut Kohl and President Jacques Chirac said, in a pointed reference to John Major's government.

The Franco-German agenda calls for more majority voting in the Council of Ministers, a common immigration policy and more powers for the European parliament as part of a renewed drive towards political union. It also puts into sharp relief Britain's isolation in Europe and reveals the extent of the disenchantment with which other leaders view Mr Major's increasingly Eurosceptic policies.

In the Commons yesterday Mr Major said he would oppose the extension of majority voting and "massive" new powers for the European Parliament at next year's inter-governmental conference.

Dramatically seizing the initiative, Mr Kohl and Mr Chirac issued an open letter in the south German spa town of Baden-Baden before next week's EU summit in Madrid aimed at banishing suspicions that Europe's central alliance was in trouble.

Although Mr Kohl denied this would lead to a "hardcore Europe" — saying, "We don't want to exclude anyone" — the Franco-German initiative poses a clear challenge to Britain before the next election: sign up for closer integration, or be relegated.

The two leaders committed themselves to a single European currency before the end of the century, and more common European foreign, security and interior policies.

Referring to next year's review of the Maastricht treaty, the letter said: "Because of experiences hitherto, we consider it desirable and possible to insert a general clause in the treaty giving countries who want to and are able to the chance to strengthen co-operation."

Earlier in the day in the Bonn parliament, Mr Kohl outlined his new pick'n'mix model of European integration, arguing that variable groups of EU members should be able to opt in and out of differing policy areas.

"It must not and cannot be that — France and Germany see this similarly — the slowest ship determines the pace of the convoy. If certain partners are neither willing nor able to join in specific integration moves, the others should not be prevented from going forward and developing greater co-operation," he said.

With a huge political crisis at home and grave doubts about the social cost to France of the European project, President Chirac took a gamble yesterday. Shedding his Euro-scepticism by agreeing to the EU reform proposals, he was nonetheless at pains to stress that the austerity policies that have brought hundreds of thousands of French on to the streets in protest had not been forced on him by his keenness to qualify for a single currency.

While Mr Chirac met Mr Kohl in Baden-Baden, a top-level revolt in his government's ruling party, the Gaullist RPR, was surfacing in Paris, with critics demanding delay in the European single currency.

The two leading Gaullist anti-Maastricht campaigners, Charles Pasqua and Philippe Séguin, who won nearly half the votes in the 1993 referendum, boycotted an RPR executive meeting called to support the beleaguered prime minister, Alain Juppé. The former premier, Edouard Balladur, also stayed away.

Desperate attempts were being made yesterday by Mr Juppé to find a formula to end two weeks of strikes which public sector workers are joining in growing numbers, according to official figures.

The Franco-German proposals, which are anathema to the British government, aim to strengthen common EU foreign and security policies, intensify co-operation on interior policy, and improve the union's capacity to act — probably by abandoning the national veto among other measures — and more authority for MEPs.

"We want to make clear our common engagement for European unification and acquaint our partners with some basic ideas on the aims of the inter-governmental conference," said Mr Kohl. "There is no cause for Euro-pessimism or Euro-scepticism."

Kohl-Chirac letter, page 14; Peter Preston, page 19

The Princess of Wales leaving the Savoy Theatre after her controversial speech yesterday PHOTOGRAPH: DYLAN MARTINEZ

'Political' Diana upsets Tories

Major on defensive after princess rues 'wasted lives' of homeless

Edward Pilkington

THE Princess of Wales yesterday put John Major on to the defensive over the politically sensitive issue of homelessness, in her first set speech since she launched her bid for an independent "ambassadorial" status.

The princess inflamed backbench Conservative opinion in an address to the annual meeting of the homeless charity, Centrepoint. She spoke in emotive terms about the "wasted lives" of young homeless people and said teenagers were being forced into begging and prostitution in order to survive.

Patrick Cormack, Tory MP for Staffordshire South, told ITN that the princess had shown a lack of judgment. "Either she is very badly advised or she doesn't take advice."

Anthony Steen, Tory MP for South Hams, said that by agreeing to appear on the same platform as Jack Straw, the shadow home secretary, the princess had shown "how vulnerable she is to the influence of those who want to exploit her unique position for party political ends".

Buckingham Palace played down the suggestion that the princess had strayed into political waters, saying the engagement, at London's Savoy Theatre, was arranged several months ago. But the impression of a rift between the princess and the Government was heightened when the Prime Minister was forced in the Commons to defend the Government's housing policy. He said there had been a "remarkable reduction" in the number of people sleeping rough.

Princess Diana's speech is likely to have been guided by Centrepoint, of which she is patron. She is also known to have received help with speeches from Peter Settelen, a former Coronation Street actor.

Princess Diana said society must ensure young people were given the chance they deserved. "I have listened to many young people whose lives have been blighted by their experiences."

Teenagers aged 16 and 17 were forced to resort to begging, "or worse prostitution to get money in order to eat". She said young people were attacked in the street and faced the "indifferent stares of passers-by who have no idea how brave they are or how much they have suffered.

"It is truly tragic to see the total waste of so many young lives — of so much potential. We, as part of society, must ensure that young people, who are our future, are given the chance they deserve."

A speech focusing on such a political hot potato is bound to be interpreted as a provocative gesture, two days after the Prime Minister's weekly audience with the Queen at which they are believed to have discussed the princess's demand for an ambassadorial role abroad.

Some Tory MPs expressed anger at the princess's decision to appear alongside Mr Straw. Neil Hamilton, former minister at the Department of Trade, said: "She was very ill-advised. Jack Straw used it as a political platform to attack the Government."

Mr Straw pointed out that the Queen had opened Centrepoint's Drury Lane project in central London in July and that the guest of honour at the charity's previous annual meeting was Michael Howard, the Home Secretary.

Street life divided, page 5; Bel Littlejohn, page 19

IRA rejects surrender of weapons

David Sharrock
Ireland Correspondent

THE IRA last night ruled out any surrender of weapons in a highly damaging snub to the British and Irish governments' efforts to unblock the peace process through an international body on illegal arms.

In a statement issued at midnight to the BBC in Dublin, the IRA said there was no question of meeting what it called the "ludicrous demand of the surrender of weapons either through the front or the back door".

The timing appears intended to inflict maximum damage to the newly established "twin-track" approach of the British and Irish governments. The deal between John Major and the Irish prime minister, John Bruton, was struck only a few hours before President Clinton began his morale-boosting visit to Britain and Ireland last week.

The IRA statement comes on the eve of the first meeting in New York of the three-man independent commission chaired by former US senator George Mitchell, which has been established to look into the question of paramilitary arms.

The commission, which includes a Finn and a Canadian, is set to begin its work in Belfast and Dublin on December 15. The IRA's hard-line statement appears to have put the strategy's success further into jeopardy.

Mr Major and Irish foreign minister Dick Spring meet in London today to discuss the twin track process, which establishes an international independent commission to consider how best to remove illegally held weapons from the political question, in parallel with preparatory bilateral talks between the Northern Ireland parties and both governments.

But the deal looked flawed from the moment of its announcement when Mr Bruton admitted he disagrees with Mr Major over the need for a token handover of IRA weapons as a confidence-building gesture. Both the main Unionist parties have also refused to participate. Sinn Fein president Gerry Adams said the Major-Bruton agreement was not a document he would have negotiated.

This morning's statement, in the name of P.O. Neill, says: "It is a matter of profound regret that rather than fulfilling its responsibilities, the British government, presented with this historic opportunity, has sought only to frustrate movement into inclusive negotiations and has erected an absolute barrier to progress with its untenable and unattainable demand for an IRA surrender.

"This demand, which has been elevated into a precondition for the commencement of all party political negotiations, blocks the inclusive dialogue essential if the causes of conflict are to be removed. It is also a demand which the British government has stridently and repeatedly made even over the course of the last week.

"We noted that British Prime Minister John Major, at the press conference to announce the twin track approach, actually rejected it as a means of removing preconditions. It is also obvious that Mr Major is actively encouraging the Unionist proposition of a return to Stormont and actively reinforces the Unionist leadership's refusal to engage meaningfully in the search for a negotiated settlement."

The statement concludes: "British bad faith and Unionist intransigence has raised a huge question mark over the potential of the twin-track approach.

"As we stated on September 29, there is no question of Oglaigh na h-Eireann meeting the ludicrous demand for a surrender of IRA weapons either through the front or the back door."

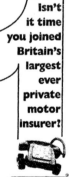

Wheelie-bins rolled out as safety menace for Yorkshire pensioners who break with clean traditions

Martin Wainwright

NORTHERN hospitals coping with the double threats of meningitis and flu are now facing a new epidemic — the fracture menace of household wheelie-bins.

The jumbo-sized containers have combined, dramatically, with the local housewives' tradition of keeping everything like a new pin, to create a health hazard in the Yorkshire town of Pontefract.

"Over the last three months, nurses have noticed a significant rise in fractures, particularly among pensioners," said Virginia Asquith, departmental manager of orthopaedics at the town's general infirmary. "It was all a bit of mystery until we had discussions over coffee, listened to patients' chat and finally tracked down the culprit."

This proved to be the wheelie-bins. They were introduced to the tidy-minded residents of Pontefract exactly three months ago and almost immediately, pensioners began falling into the bins after leaning over the rims with mops, spraining ankles when they climbed on the rubbish to stamp it flat, and being blown away in windy weather as they wheeled bins out and refused to let go of the handles.

"I think the problem has come to light here because of the tradition of keeping bins clean, especially among older people who seem to be suffering most," said Ms Asquith.

The accidents add a new chapter to the lore and legend of wheelie-bins, which have been blamed for traffic accidents — when they break loose — and crime, with burglars using them to block householders' drives to gain time to escape if disturbed.

"It's funny in a way, but also a serious preventative health matter," said Ms Asquith, whose nurses have been commended for spotting the reason for the rise in breaks. "We are now running a drive for everyone to follow Wakefield council's wheelie-bin instructions to the letter — for instance, laying them on their sides if you have to clean them, and arranging for the binmen to wheel them out if the weather is gusty or you are frail."

Wakefield council last night set up a telephone wheelie-bin helpline to remind callers of its instructions for cleaning the containers, which were issued with the new bins in September.

49
9 770261 307354

1995

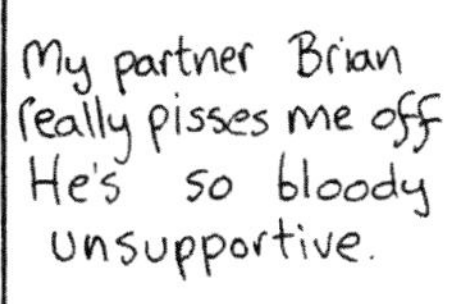
My partner Brian really pisses me off He's so bloody unsupportive.

After a day on the Emotional Frontline it would be nice to have someone to come home to who shows an interest in what I've been doing.

I try to talk to him but it's a waste of time. He thinks Social work is just a regular job like his.
What does Brian do?

Oh, he's a librarian, or an accountant or something. He did tell me once...

... and another brilliant thing about doing this counselling course is the way it's really improved my listening skills....
SHAC
HARRY VENNING

As social workers we spend our working day trying to help people. This takes its toll.

Which is why, when our shift is over, like now, it is essential that we say: "I CAN GIVE NO MORE, THIS IS MY TIME"

If we don't make this distinction we would become emotionally exhausted, a pair of burnt out wrecks of no use to ourselves or our clients...

...otherwise, Gran, we'd be out there like a shot.

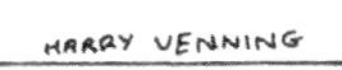
HARRY VENNING

SAVE THE POLITICAL METAPHOR DRAGON
IGNORANCE
POVERTY
INJUSTICE

Weekend magazine

A hurting business
One man's life in boxing

Norway gets serious about Eurovision

Nul points no more
Outlook, Arts page 26

Joe Queenan on those wild Kids

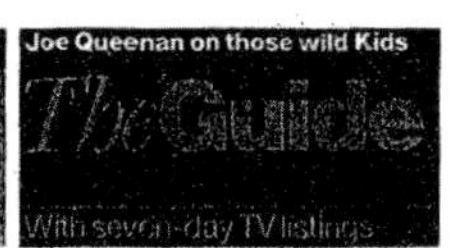

60p
Saturday
May 11
1996
Published in London
and Manchester

The Guardian

'We still believe in decency, hard work and fairness'

Blair defines British dream

Michael White
Political Editor

TONY Blair unveiled the centrepiece yesterday of Labour's campaign to end 17 years in the political wilderness when he accused the Thatcher and Major governments of creating an insecure majority among voters who would turn against them "with a vengeance".

Speaking in Swansea, the Labour leader contrasted the British dream with the world of job insecurity, higher taxes and fears of homelessness and crime in which most people now lived as a result of ministerial ideology and error.

"You still believe in the British dream. You still believe in British values, in decency, hard work, and fairness. You still long to do better for yourselves and your family and you long for Britain to do better too. You are proud to be British but too much of that pride depends on history and nostalgia and not on what Britain is today.

"It is Labour that offers the new British dream now. Labour that can build a new Britain that is fair, efficient, and can regain our standing in the world."

With one eye firmly on disenchanted middle class voters — and their wavering Conservative MPs — he even called New Labour the party of one nation radicals, capable of reuniting the country with a devolved democracy, an efficient economy and a reformed welfare state.

But Mr Blair's intention to launch a "lost generation" campaign next week to highlight the plight of jobless and unskilled people ran into fire from senior Conservatives seeking to exploit concern that the shadow chancellor, Gordon Brown, may decide to abolish child benefit for 16 to 18-year-olds, without recompense for needy families.

Deriding Labour's efforts to appeal to the middle class, Peter Lilley, the Social Security Secretary, accused Mr Brown of inventing a "teenage tax" and proclaimed the Tories to be "the party of the hard-working classes. We don't care if they have blue collars or blue blood."

Stirring what he undoubtedly saw as real discontent among Labour MPs over the child benefit scheme's potential impact on post-16 education, he challenged them to support Mr Brown's review publicly. Mr Blair did that unequivocally in Swansea.

With ministers like Mr Lilley using the Scottish Tory conference in Aberdeen to test themes for the election, the Labour leader used his party's Welsh conference to do the same. He mocked John Major's prevarications over the Westminster council scandal as proof that a degenerate party governed Britain.

As ministers struggle to rekindle the feel-good factor, he argued that 17 years of Tory electoral success "was based on their willingness to tolerate an insecure minority. But it is the majority that feels insecure today.

"The electoral battlefield was portrayed as Labour for the poor and disadvantaged — against the Tories as the party of the secure and comfortable majority," Mr Blair said. "It has changed. It is Labour that now speaks up for the insecure majority and puts forward the policies that meet their concerns. And it is the Tories who speak only for the privileged few."

The Labour leader added: "It is today's thirtysomethings and fortysomethings that now fear both for their children and for their parents."

This week's Guardian/ICM poll, however, saw Labour's lead slip 4 per cent in the Liberal Democrats' direction, a move which Lib Dem strategists believe reflects emerging voter mistrust of Labour rhetoric.

The post-16 child benefit row is a case in point. Yesterday Mr Blair stressed it was still only an option to see if the money could be better spent along with that spent on the assisted places scheme.

"Insufficient numbers of our young people stay on at school. There are large problems of youth unemployment. A lot of our young people are not getting properly skilled or educated," he said.

Blair signals deal on gays, page 7; Notebook, page 34

Visions

'The Germans have an image of organisation; Italy has one of flair. At the moment Britain does not have an image. We need to get an image again both as a nation and a football nation.'
Terry Venables

'I had a dream of Britain and it was that the Labour leader would stop colluding with bigoted military chiefs, who support the ban on lesbians and gay men in the armed forces.'
Peter Tatchell

'I am glad that he is naming the lost generation but I think that we need to give them an entry point to tell us their dreams and disappointments.'
Susie Orbach

'I would like to see the word caring put into any dream of Britain. The divide is widening between those who have and those who have not.'
Max Clifford

'Streets filled with laughing, happy, frolicking scousers.'
John Peel

Tony Blair unveils the "new British dream" at Labour's Welsh conference yesterday PHOTOGRAPH: GARETH LLEWELLYN WILLIAMS

Diana gives divorce ultimatum to Queen

Alex Bellos

DIVORCE negotiations between the Prince and Princess of Wales appeared to have broken down yesterday when it was confirmed that the princess had met the Queen and raised the prospect that the marriage may drag on for two more years.

It is understood the princess asked the Queen to spur Buckingham Palace's lawyers into action by threatening to withdraw from the talks, which have stalled because of wrangling about the settlement. It is believed that both sides can not even agree on some of the most minor details.

After a meeting with Prince Charles in February, the princess agreed to a "quickie" consensual divorce, but the deadlock may cause her to change her mind and wait two years for the formal no-consent five year separation period to elapse. The couple officially separated in December 1992.

The princess is known to be frustrated with the slow pace of negotiations, because she wants them resolved before she raises her public profile as a goodwill ambassador. She is currently accepting very few public engagements.

Since the Queen in December ordered the Waleses to divorce — because their public scrapping was embarrassing the monarchy — both sides have constantly disagreed about several details of the settlement including money, homes, and the princess's title. She is thought to want a clean-break package that would give her a substantial annual income, but it is doubtful the prince has sufficient capital to afford such a settlement without help from the Queen.

He wants a "drip-feed" allowance which would give him more control over his ex-wife and is more affordable in the short term.

The princess is expected to continue living at Kensington Palace but the prince is resisting her desire to retain an office at St James's Palace, close to his London apartment.

It is understood another sticking point is his refusal to her request that he should sign a confidentiality or "gagging" clause in the same way as she was being required to do. The prince considers that his word not to divulge details of their life together was good enough.

There has also been speculation about the title Princess of Wales and whether she will continue to be addressed as Her Royal Highness. It is most likely that in future she will be known as Diana, Princess of Wales, but without the HRH — and so no longer commanding a curtsy on greeting.

She saw the Queen on Wednesday after meeting her solicitor Anthony Julius, of London law firm Mishcon de Reya, who reported that negotiations were still bogged down. It seems that Mr Julius and the prince's solicitor Fiona Shackleton, of Queen's lawyers Farrer & Co, cannot even agree on some relatively minor details.

Both sides have consistently declined to comment on matters concerning the divorce after a request from the Queen that talks should be private and confidential.

Details of the meeting between the Queen and princess were leaked to the Sun, which was also leaked the December letter from the Queen that ordered a divorce. It is believed that the letter was given to the paper by someone close to the prince.

The princess flew to Majorca yesterday with a female friend for a few days in the sun, said her spokeswoman Jane Atkinson.

Whoever wins the Cup, Wembley will make a killing

Liverpool defender Phil Babb flies the flag at Wembley

John Duncan
Sport Correspondent

MANCHESTER United earn almost as much in gate money from their average Premiership match as they will from today's FA Cup final, the biggest match of the season.

The owners of Wembley stadium may make twice as much out of the match as either United or their opponents, Liverpool.

Each club receives £700,000 from the gate, £100,000 more than the average Old Trafford match. They also claim a share of the television pool, which takes their income to about £1 million, but players' win bonuses and hotel expenses eat heavily into that, leaving them with about £600,000 each.

Wembley plc makes a profit of about £1.5 million. The Football Association's deal with Wembley, struck in the 1980s, allowed the company to make huge profits from FA events at the stadium through pitchside advertising, car parking, catering and the matchday programme.

From total gate receipts today Wembley will receive £840,000, to which is added its share of the £1 million TV money for the final — in 1995 that gave it £333,000. Add to that a share of the £460,000 matchday programme profits (£6 each, expected sales of 80,000), £56,000 in car park receipts (7,000 spaces at £8 each) and money from catering contracts, and Wembley will be about £1.5 million better off tomorrow morning.

Wembley admits that the Cup final is its biggest pay day but argues that the money subsidises other games. "Not every event is a moneyspinner like this," said Martin Corrie, the Wembley spokesman, "but in order to hold other smaller events we need to get income from the bigger events. We have a contract with the FA which reflects a recent partnership agreement. How the money is then allocated is their responsibility."

The FA is diplomatic over the Wembley deal. "You can't look at the Cup final in isolation from the other events," said Mark Day, FA director of finance. "The next day they have the Vase and they won't make a killing out of that. However, clearly, if we were doing a deal now rather than 15 years ago it would not be the same. No one could have foreseen the growth in TV money and sponsorship."

BBC's 'Best feet', page 9; Schmeichel the screaming saviour, page 18; United in search of triumph, page 20; Vincent Hanna, page 28

Inside

Home Some of Beethoven's best known themes may have been stolen from other obscure composers, according to one of Britain's leading conductors **3**

International The presidential elections in Uganda look likely to produce a landslide victory for the present incumbent, Yoweri Museveni **12**

Finance Lloyd's of London insurance market has boosted by £1.2 billion its offer to those Names who have suffered financial losses **34**

Sport Ruud Gullit, the former Dutch international, was last night appointed player-manager of Chelsea. He succeeds Glenn Hoddle **19**

1996

I'm really glad you and Brian are back together.
Yeah, but we've got a lot of stuff to work through yet, Megan.
Which is why we both decided to go to couple counselling. So we can re-assess and explore the nature of our relationship in a supportive, constructive, non-judgmental environment.
How long do you think you'll go for?
Until the little bastard admits it was all his fault.

I'm a social worker.
I'M a social worker
I'm a SOCIAL worker
I'm a social WORKER.
An acrobat! How fascinating....

For Goodness sake, Brian why don't you spend a bit less time sulking and a bit more time listening to what I actually say!
I never said your problems weren't important. Of course your problems are important, as important as mine, my clients or anybody elses.
They're just not as interesting

1996

Derek Malcolm on Mission: Impossible
Cruising for a bruising
Screen pages 7/13

45p
Thursday
July 4
1996
Published in London and Manchester

The Guardian

Howard's £2bn jail cover-up

Secret costings block Learmont proposals to improve security

Alan Travis
Home Affairs Editor

THE Government is to shelve key parts of a package to bring Britain's jails up to recommended minimum security standards because it cannot afford the £2 billion price tag, according to internal Whitehall documents seen by the Guardian.

The papers also show that the Home Secretary, Michael Howard, is being advised to cover up from Parliament the failure to find the money for the security work, and to introduce a much delayed scaled down security package.

The need for an extra £2 billion of public money to provide the minimum security in the jails recommended by the official inquiry into the Parkhurst prison breakout has remained a Whitehall secret since February. The scale of the funding problem facing ministers is similar to the cash needed to bail the Government out of the BSE crisis.

The disclosure comes as prison governors claim that record prison numbers recently led to to inmates having to sleep on mattresses on the floor at one prison.

Home Office ministers told Parliament on December 13 Mr Howard would make a statement "in the spring" on his progress on implementing most of the recommendations of the inquiry report by General Sir John Learmont. Decisions on some specific proposals such as the "super-maximum" security prison would left until later this year.

"There is a presentational problem," says an internal Whitehall submission to the Home Secretary written earlier this year. "Ministers would not wish to indicate that implementation of a significant security report was contingent on achieving adequate funding."

The document suggests alternative devices for omitting to tell MPs that he has not secured the necessary Treasury funding for Learmont's main recommendations.

The £2 billion bill spread over four years covers 73 of Learmont's 127 recommendations. They include bringing all prisons up to a minimum standard of security with strengthened perimeter fences and new closed circuit television systems; training for prison officers 14 days a year instead of the current five; replacing dormitory accommodation with cells; introducing electronic and magnetic locking systems; improving searching of visitors; and building a new "supermax" prison to hold the most dangerous inmates.

The documents say the costings are "ballpark figures" but say even if more work is done on them the total sums "will remain large, well beyond our ability to handle in the forseeable future . . . we need to take a view on the priority we attach to the different elements of the Learmont report".

The Prison Service must decide which elements to press ahead with and which "it can put on the backburner indefinitely".

The documents suggest to Mr Howard he can delay making a full response until November — a year after Learmont reported — as long as "there is not undue political pressure".

The senior civil servants admit that there is a "tangible tension between the expectations generated by the Learmont report, which ministers broadly supported, and the realities of staff and capital cuts which followed.

The document says that since the "dreadful Whitemoor and Parkhurst events" the prison service security performance has been much improved with a sharp reduction in the number of escapes. The senior civil servants suggest that the Treasury is pressed for an interim high priority package to upgrade the high security prisons, costing a total of £118 million.

Harry Fletcher, of the National Association of Probation Officers, said it was now clear why the real costs of the Learmont report had not been made public. "These costings in the current financial climate are not possible. The Learmont report will be one security measure that this administration just cannot afford. Cuts and minimum levels of security are clearly incompatible."

Whitehall tips, page 6; Leader comment, page 16

Russia puts Yeltsin on course for second term

David Hearst and James Meek in Moscow

BORIS Yeltsin was poised last night for a decisive vindication of his uncompromising struggle against a Communist comeback through the ballot box.

But the effort of beating Gennady Zyuganov, the Communist leader, in the final round of presidential elections may have damaged the president's health too severely for him to savour the victory.

Early results from the Russian Far East, Siberia and the Urals showed Mr Yeltsin building a solid lead over Mr Zyuganov on a strong turnout. Results from the mainly communist "red belt" of southern Russia were still to come, but the trend pointed to a final Yeltsin lead of between 3 and 10 per cent.

The outcome came as a relief to the Yeltsin camp after a day of low turnout fears and desperate attempts to disguise the fact that the sick and awkwardly moving president had cast his vote from a private sanatorium.

With about 35 per cent of the nationwide vote counted, Mr Yeltsin was given 54.44 per cent to Mr Zyuganov's 39.48 per cent. Mr Yeltsin narrowed the first-round gap on his rival in areas where the communists are strong, such as the Siberian coalfield region of Kemerovo.

Significantly, early results from Yaroslavl, one of the regions where Alexander Lebed did best in the first round, showed Mr Yeltsin picking up virtually all the former general's votes, justifying his strategy of appointing him secretary of his security council.

The first communist reaction to the results sounded like an admission of defeat. Anatoly Lukyanov, a leading member of Mr Zyuganov's team, said: "The National Patriotic bloc [Zyuganov's coalition] will keep its electorate and be a weighty opposition force."

In 14 regions which had closed polling by 8pm, the turnout was a little over 62 per cent, just above the level that presidential supporters calculated would give Mr Yeltsin a clear lead over Mr Zyuganov, though down on the first round.

A win of the scale being predicted would not be the large margin predicted in the opinion polls, but enough to stamp his authority over feuding factions in the Kremlin and the increasingly loose cannon of Mr Lebed.

The day started with a public relations disaster for the presidential campaign as Mr Yeltsin, who had disappeared for a week amid conflicting reports about an alleged "sore throat", failed to show up for the world's media at his local polling station.

The 65-year-old president was filmed by his own cameras casting his vote in Barvikha, the elite sanatorium in which he spent a month recovering after two mild heart attacks last year.

Moving slowly, but managing a smile, Mr Yeltsin said: "All of you, absolutely all of you come to vote! Do not forget your duty!" Later his press spokesman, Sergei Medvedev, tried to explain the last-minute switch in the polling arrangements, claiming Mr Yeltsin had got permission to vote in a different station the previous night.

Viktor Chernomyrdin, the prime minister, continued to insist Mr Yeltsin was all right. "Would I have left the country, had things been otherwise?" he said, referring to his recent trip to the G7 summit in Lyon.

National television gave no hint of the morning crisis, showing a ticking clock with the time left for voters. In an message that became dangerously two-edged, the clock was accompanied by the sound of a human heart beat.

Mr Zyuganov arrived at his polling station in a black Volga limousine, surrounded by armed guards. Referring to Mr Yeltsin, he said: "Apparently his state of

turn to page 2, column 3

Knobbly liver? page 2; Russian election, page 13

Sir Cliff Richard, with 'backing group' of (from left) Pam Shriver, Rosalyn Nideffer, Martina Navratilova and Gigi Fernandez, entertains at Wimbledon yesterday PHOTOGRAPH: BILL ALLEN

Sir Cliff to serve – with throwbacks

Richard Williams on how rain halted play and pop's sedate golden oldie held sway

JUST when Tim Henman threatened to bring British tennis into the modern era, up jumped Sir Cliff Richard on to the very same Wimbledon stage to take British pop music back into the dark ages.

Sir Cliff, the nation's number one tennis groupie as well as its oldest surviving pop star, took advantage of a long rain delay on men's quarter-finals day — which saw Henman's match postponed until 11.0am today — to serenade the cold and frustrated Centre Court spectators from his seat in the royal box.

Pete Sampras and his Dutch opponent Richard Krajicek were at two games all in their first set when the drizzle set in. Three hours later, after the crowd had exhausted its repertoire of community singing and party games, Sir Cliff came to the rescue.

Commandeering a microphone, he began his performance with, inevitably, Summer Holiday. "What next?" he asked. "Do you remember The Young Ones?" The faces of the many foreign visitors remained politely blank.

But there were enough genuine Brits in the crowd to ensure that, even after 30-odd years, the hand-clapping was resolutely anchored to the on-beat. John Lennon, Mick Jagger, Liam Gallagher — they seemed to have passed across the face of British culture with no more consequence than Bobby Wilson, Roger Taylor, and Jeremy Bates.

As Sir Cliff swung into Bachelor Boy, an all-star backing group filed into the row behind: Pam Shriver, Martina Navratilova, Virginia Wade, Gigi Fernandez, Elizabeth Smylie and other past and present stars of the women's tennis tour. "The Supremes!" Cliff said proudly. More like Ginny and the Groin Strains, others felt.

Notable by her absence was Sue Barker, Sir Cliff's sometime alleged girlfriend. The 1976 French Open champion and current BBC-TV Wimbledon presenter is generally credited with lighting the fuse of his tennis obsession.

But nothing could hold back Sir Cliff, who at 55 looked almost as boyish as the 21-year-old Henman. All Shook Up and Livin' Doll whizzed by, in the atmosphere — enhanced by the large green canvas tent covering the court itself — of a Boy Scout camp of the 1950s. Sir Cliff announced: "I never thought I'd play the Centre Court."

But it couldn't last. As the crowd swayed in waltz time, the sun came out. Just like Woodstock, really.

Wimbledon reports, page 24

PM set for £60,000 rise as Commons gets free vote on pay

David Hencke

HUGE pay rises for MPs and ministers — including a £60,000 annual increase for the next prime minister — are to be rushed through Parliament next week.

A free vote for MPs to approve a £9,000 increase for backbenchers and pay rises of between £20,000 and £30,000 for ministers is expected to be agreed by the Cabinet today.

The rises would be the biggest for more than 30 years, but will not come into force until after the next election.

Tony Blair, who could benefit from the biggest rise in the prime minister's pay this century if he enters Downing Street, declined yesterday to reveal which way he will vote. So did John Major. But Paddy Ashdown, the Liberal Democrat leader, is to vote against and will back a 3 per cent rise.

Details of the pay rises were revealed yesterday with the leaking to the Press Association of a Senior Staff Salaries Review Board report. The report calls for substantial rises to redress a long period in which MPs' pay has been tied to inflation.

The report recommends salaries of £103,000 per year for cabinet ministers and the Speaker, an increase of more than £33,000 on the present £69,651 a year. Ministers of state would receive £74,125 and junior ministers £66,823, rises of between £15,000 and £20,000 a year.

The report, however, criticised the mileage rates paid to MPs and recommended a substantial cut. It describes the top rate, 74.1p, as "unjustifiably generous" and recommends the level paid to peers, 47.2p a mile.

Reaction, page 2; Leader comment, page 16

Inside

27
9 770261 307347

1996

Why are you here? I'll tell you why: To salve your snotty liberal conscience, that's why...
... You swan in here as if you own the place, with your crappy briefcases and la-di-da social worker ways.....
Well I've got better things to do with my time than be patronised by a pair of po-faced witches. Sod off, the pair of you.
I don't want to rush you, Megan, but we'll be late for work.
I just popped in to say 'Happy Birthday Grandad' and I'll see you tonight at the party.

Therapy? Therapy is self-indulgent claptrap and therapists are a bunch of vultures picking at the bloated carcass of middle class insecurity.
You wouldn't say that if you met Susan, my therapist. Susan's brilliant. She's helped me work through so much, especially after I left that bastard Tom.
Your ex-boyfriend?
My previous therapist.
HARRY VENNING

Clare, I'm so sorry. I'm so ashamed that I raised my voice.
No, No, Megan. It was my fault. I lost my temper and turned an argument into a shouting match.
It's an issue I feel very strongly about....
... and you expressed your opinion strongly. So did I. Little wonder things got overheated.
We could argue till doomsday but neither of us are going to compromise.
We'll just have to agree to disagree...
... you continue using the term 'service users' and I'll keep calling them 'clients'.
HARRY VENNING

KEEP OFF

●Wimbledon latest ●Ruud Gullit interview ●Italian footballers head for Britain
A unique 24 page tabloid with unrivalled coverage of the summer of sport

45p
Friday
July 5
1996
Published in London and Manchester

The Guardian

Grand old man of '38 nurtures wistful hopes that new star will lift 58-year burden

Frank Keating goes back 58 years with Wimbledon finalist Bunny Austin (inset) who yesterday cheered on Tim Henman in the quarter-final. Austin's wish to be relieved of his 'record' as the last Englishman to reach the final was, he feels, merely postponed by Henman's defeat by Todd Martin (above)
MAIN PHOTOGRAPH: TOM JENKINS. INSET: MARTIN GODWIN

THE old man's soft-boiled eyes glistened in anticipation in front of the television in his Surrey nursing home for the beginning on Wimbledon's Centre Court of Tim Henman's quarter-final match against Todd Martin of the United States yesterday.

His enthusiasm would doubtless have remained undimmed when Henman went out 7-6, 7-6, 6-1 in rain-affected match of stops and starts.

"Young Henman seems to me certain to win Wimbledon some time soon. He is remarkably impressive, such beautiful strokes, such an equable temper, and, crucially, he's learning that the bigger the point, then the better you have to play."

This weathered ancient may not be able to walk, but he knows his tennis. No Englishman knows better.

Bunny Austin will be 90 on August 26. He was the last native player to reach a Wimbledon final — 58 summers ago in 1938. He was also the losing finalist in 1932. Before the nurses settled him in front of the television yesterday, Austin said he had been "desperately willing" young Henman at least to reach Sunday's final. "It's been a 'record' which has been round my neck for far too long."

As a losing quarter-finalist Henman will receive £51,025. For beating Austin in the 1938 final, the American superduper star Donald Budge received a voucher for £5 to be spent at the London jewellers Mappin & Webb, and Austin's prize was ditto for £2.10s. "I asked if I could have a voucher instead for Tooths picture gallery. They said 'all right, old boy' and on the Monday I went down and bought a jolly nice little watercolour landscape of the Riviera."

Although he cannot move about his sick-room, the gaiety of his laughter fills it: "Oh yes, those were the days. Vast riches couldn't buy the fun we had. Drive down in the morning, or take the train from the City. Have lunch, play your match. We enjoyed it far more than they seem to these days, although they are all extremely rich people now, aren't they?"

The old man remains in chortling good nick, although those once famously twinkling feet have been immobile for almost two years. "Don't worry about me, I'm generally feeling top-hole, in the pink — except last October, I tripped on my slippers and fell down the staircase when I was staying at my sister's house. Ruptured three vertebrae, so I'm still learning to walk all over again. I have a standing-frame thing and can take one or two steps on it, so everything's coming along fine. Must say, young Henman's cheered me up no end these past few days.

"Henman's play reminds me of my old French adversary René Lacoste — 'the Crocodile' — with his crafty play, his patience, and his killer-instinct when he knew he'd cornered you. He wasn't a power player, but had a very strong will and all the strokes."

In all, of 48 Davis Cup rubbers he played, Austin won a remarkable 36 of them. In the final round of 1929 against Germany in a sweltering Berlin, he

turn to page 2, column 1

Wimbledon reports: Sport 96, pages 1 to 6

Blair lays ghost of old Labour

Michael White
Political Editor

TONY Blair's launch of Labour's five-pledge Road to the Manifesto last night unleashed a propaganda blitz between the major parties which pitted familiar Conservative allegations of extravagance against Labour counter-charges of reckless mendacity by the "Tory lie machine."

In a move calculated to kill off Labour's old "tax and spend" image, bind party supporters to his designated priorities for government, and win over wavering voters, Mr Blair promised a radical but responsible "contract for a new Britain" if he wins the election due within 10 months.

The Labour leader told a crowded press conference: "In government, this will be what we deliver" — and deliver it without breaching Gordon Brown's "strict rules for spending and borrowing".

Within hours of the Labour leadership's official publication of its 10,000-word pre-manifesto statement — to be voted on by all 376,000 Labour Party members before Christmas — Tory HQ had unveiled a 1,000-site "New Labour, New Danger" poster campaign and John Major had warned that the new policies would mean higher taxes, despite Labour assurances to the contrary.

The sharpest skirmish involved the Chancellor, Kenneth Clarke, who picked on one of Mr Blair's five symbolic priorities — to phase out the assisted places scheme and divert funds to cut class sizes to under 30 for 5- to 7-year-olds over three years — to prove that Labour had got its sums wrong.

"Squaring the circle is in fact impossible. This is Houdini economics, the politics of smoke and mirrors," said Mr Clarke, only to be confronted by Labour's new "rebuttal unit" with figures from Mr Brown which accused the Chancellor of missing the crucial phasing of the policy.

The key battleground in the months ahead will, nonetheless, be taxation. Mr Brown's £3 billion windfall tax on the privatised utilities — to finance job creation for young and long-term unemployed — is already under fire, while some City and independent analysts do not believe Labour can deliver many of its declared objectives without raising taxes or borrowing.

In the presence of his shadow cabinet, Mr Blair insisted that past Labour heroes could all have signed up to principles underpinning the statement, even though it reflected changed policies for a changed world. "Yes, there has been a revolution inside the Labour Party. We have rejected the worst of our past and rediscovered the best. And in rediscovering the best of our past, we have made ourselves fit to face the future and fit to govern in the future."

Mr Blair today goes on the broad to start selling his policy statement to supporters and voters, some of whom fear that too many concessions have been made to head off Tory attacks.

But after their disastrous mid-week propaganda initiative — an anti-Labour spoof called The Road To Ruin — Conservative strategists promised to harry him all the same. Mr Major told MPs: "The new Labour Party's policies mean new taxes ... on Scotland, on people with children aged 16 to 18, taxes for living in London, taxes on jobs with the social chapter, and the minimum wage."

The Conservative chairman, Brian Mawhinney, issued his own five points, claiming that Mr Blair's five would bankrupt Britain. His staff issued a 14 page analysis of the Labour statement's weaknesses. Labour HQ countered with a 40 page rebuttal.

In response to the prospect of millions of Labour cards, bearing the five pledges, the Tories issued similar red cards, repeating their own warnings.

The rival campaigns are expected to cost the Tories £2 million and Labour half that.

Sketch and review, page 2; Manifesto details, pages 13-15; Leader comment, page 18; City notebook, page 21

Labour's promises

- Cut class sizes for 5-7 year olds using cash from abolishing assisted places scheme.
- Fast-track punishment for persistent young offenders.
- Reduce NHS waiting lists by 100,000 patients using £100m saved from cutting bureaucracy.
- Take 250,000 under-25 year olds off benefit using cash from tax on privatised utilities.
- Tough rules for government spending; ensure low inflation; keep interest rates down.

MORE than 120,000 people took up the Labour Party's invitation to telephone Tony Blair after last night's political broadcast. The first 1,000 were able to get through, but most could only listen as Mr Blair answered other callers' questions. All were offered copies of the draft manifesto. Mr Blair, who answered calls until 11pm, called it a fascinating experience.

Charles offers '£15-£20m' divorce terms to Diana

Quick end to marriage likely after 10-week deadlock broken

Alex Bellos

THE Prince of Wales offered Princess Diana terms for divorce last night, breaking 10 weeks of bitter deadlock and clearing the way for an end to the marriage this summer.

The princess's media adviser, Jane Atkinson, confirmed that her lawyers had received proposals from the prince's lawyers last night, but declined to comment further. Buckingham Palace refused to comment. The offer opens the last chapter of the couple's 15-year marriage. If Princess Diana accepts the terms, Prince Charles could be granted a decree nisi from the divorce courts within the next few weeks on the grounds they have lived apart for more than two years. A decree absolute, finally ending the marriage, would take a further six weeks.

It is widely believed that the offer is for a clean-break settlement worth between £15 million and £20 million, though the prince would have preferred the initially cheaper option of giving his wife an annual allowance. Although he is able to afford the pay-off in the long term, he does not have the liquidity necessary to make it immediately and will need financial help from the Queen or may seek a multi-million-pound loan.

His annual income of almost £5 million from the Duchy of Cornwall leaves him with about £1.5 million for personal expenses after deducting nearly £2.5 million in official expenditure and £1 million tax.

The prince cannot sell off any duchy assets as this wealth is, in effect, held in trust by him for future heirs to the throne. His personal portfolio of stocks and shares, thought to be worth more than £2 million, would also not cover the cost.

The princess is thought to be ready to move quickly, since in May she expressed her frustration to the Queen over delays.

The Queen and the Duke of Edinburgh are thought to be keen for a swift end to the protracted divorce negotiations. In December, the Queen ordered the couple to divorce.

As part of the eventual divorce settlement, the princess is expected to continue living at Kensington Palace, although though it is unlikely the prince will agree to her request to retain an office at St James's Palace.

There is agreement between the prince and princess that access to Prince William, 14, and 11-year-old Prince Harry, will be shared equally. Both Charles and Diana will continue to have a close involvement in their sons' upbringing.

There has been mounting speculation that the princess, as the mother of a future king, will, contrary to earlier reports, retain the style "Her Royal Highness". But this seems doubtful. It is more likely that she will be addressed as "Diana, Princess of Wales". Agreement must also be concluded, involving 10 Downing Street and the Foreign Office, on the princess's future public role. She wants to be a "goodwill ambassador" for Britain, as well as a "Queen of Hearts" raising funds for charity and comforting the sick and needy.

The divorce settlement will include a "gagging clause" restraining the princess from writing a "kiss-and-tell" book or going public in other ways.

Diana was last night guest of honour at a charity ball held by Imran Khan at London's Dorchester Hotel.

Unitying the knot, page 6

Inside

Home The Archbishop of Canterbury wants two feuding churchmen at Lincoln Cathedral to resign. But they are Crown appointees, and cannot be fired. **3**

International Binyamin Netanyahu, the Israeli premier, was embarrassed with opposition claims he used at least four different names when studying in the US. **17**

Finance A new survey shows commercial lawyers in London earn at least £100 an hour. Partners can earn an average £248 for 60 minutes' work. **21**

Sport Middlesbrough signed Fabrizio Ravanelli for £7 million from Juventus. He will earn £25,000 a week. In Sport96 **8**

Weather 4; Obituaries 20
Comment and Letters 18
Friday Review
Quick Crossword 18
Radio 19; TV 20

27
9 770261 307354

1996

I mean, I find working with older people very rewarding. It makes me so angry the way society disregards them.

They're still people, for christ's sake, and are entitled to the same respect and dignity enjoyed by any other section of the community.

It's a question of awareness, really.

Matthew Engel goes back to school

Eight pages of unrivalled coverage

SportExtra

Frank Keating witnesses the taming of Iron Mike

With 22 pages of jobs

Media

Lord Wakeham: what I couldn't say to Gerald Kaufman

45p
Monday
November 11
1996
Published in London and Manchester

The Guardian

Brown talks tough on Europe

Labour in Social Chapter switch

Larry Elliott
Economics Editor

THE Shadow Chancellor, Gordon Brown, will today seek to toughen Labour's stance on Europe — and weaken its commitment to the Social Chapter — with a promise to veto any attempts to force Britain to adopt common social security policies or give workers the right to a seat on company boards.

In a clear attempt to defuse Tory attacks claiming Labour is soft on Brussels, Mr Brown will tell the Confederation of British Industry conference in Harrogate that Labour shares the concerns of business about these two key elements of the Social Chapter.

After strong lobbying from the CBI, Mr Brown will argue that Labour's transformation into an unashamedly pro-business party means that it will look at European social legislation on a case-by-case basis.

Government ministers have been keeping up a non-stop barrage over Labour's support for the Social Chapter, and Mr Brown's speech — coming after the cooler line on the single currency taken by the shadow foreign secretary, Robin Cook — is a sign of the Opposition's determination to neutralise Europe as an election issue.

The shadow chancellor will stress that Labour has no intention of importing any European legislation that would threaten jobs. Mr Brown hopes to reassure the CBI that Labour's policy of signing up to the Social Chapter falls well short of a blanket commitment and is not a way of introducing Europe's high social costs "by the back door".

He will say: "We must never return to the situation here in Britain where — unlike in America or most of Europe — one party is seen as pro-business and the other is seen as anti-business."

Labour is keen to counter Tory claims that it would agree to an extension of qualified majority voting (QMV), thereby leaving Britain with no alternative but to accept continental-style social laws.

"Some have suggested that we will allow QMV in new areas," Mr Brown will say. "We will sign the Social Chapter, a position that the British people have consistently supported, but we will not allow QMV to be extended to areas where it should not be."

At the moment, there are two sections to the Social Chapter: one governed by QMV, the other requiring unanimity. Mr Brown will say that Labour has no intention of allowing social security and co-determination in the boardroom to be moved into the section where Britain could be outvoted by other member states.

Labour's tough talking on the Social Chapter won the immediate support of business, which is convinced that it can comfortably live with the directives on works councils and parental leave.

Sir Colin Marshall, CBI president, said yesterday that business wanted to see social policy reformed so that it was about "employability of the unemployed" and not about "making conditions better for those in work".

● Mr Brown's new sceptical approach to European social legislation came as John Major prepared to try to turn the Government's anticipated defeat in the European Court tomorrow over the 48-hour week to his political advantage. The court is expected to reject Britain's opposition to the working time directive, which seeks to limit working hours and guarantee holiday rights.

Mr Major will attempt to switch the election battleground back to the economy in his speech to the Lord Mayor's banquet in the City of London tonight. He will say that Britain is regaining its confidence, with its success noted around the world.

Unions' legal push, page 4; EMU squabble, page 15

Heseltine at centre of new sleaze row

Rebecca Smithers
Political Correspondent

THE Deputy Prime Minister, Michael Heseltine, will today be pressed to explain his role in a damaging new "sleaze" affair, arising from evidence that he and John Major sought to undermine the neutrality of the Civil Service by ordering officials to work on "party political" tasks in the run-up to the general election.

In the first big test of the new code of ethics which came into force a year ago, the Cabinet Secretary, Sir Robin Butler, who also heads the Civil Service, vetoed Mr Heseltine's plan for Whitehall officials to set up teams of "cheerleaders" to champion government policy. Sir Robin's action came after concern was expressed by the senior Civil Service union, the FDA.

A copy of a Cabinet Office memorandum, leaked to Labour yesterday, makes it clear that Mr Heseltine had personally proposed that government departments should "identify service providers who could be vigorous and attractive proponents of government policies".

The memo, sent to ministers' parliamentary private secretaries in mid-August, also discloses that Mr Major had rubber-stamped the plan.

Mr Heseltine insisted that the wording of the memo had been misinterpreted. He accused Labour of waging a dirty tricks campaign. Sir Robin's concerns had been dealt with, he said on BBC Radio 4's The World This Weekend.

"Sir Robin pointed out to me that it was very important to make sure that this [the project] was not done by civil servants, and that it should be done by special advisers [who are political appointees]. The moment he did that, I agreed that that was the position. That is what has been happening. All of that is quite clear."

'The Deputy Prime Minister proposed that Departments should identify service providers who could be vigorous and attractive proponents of Government policies'

But Labour will today press Mr Heseltine for further clarification. It is demanding a full Commons statement, but if that is not forthcoming its MPs will ask a series of tough questions.

The fresh controversy comes at the beginning of a week that will be dominated by sleaze. David Willetts, the Paymaster General and former junior whip, will today be questioned by MPs on the standards and privileges committee about why he apparently tried to smother the first "cash-for-questions" inquiry in 1994.

Sleaze in spotlight, page 3; Leader comment, page 12; Conrad Russell, page 13

David Trimble, Paddy Ashdown, Tony Blair and John Major hold wreaths as the Queen arrives at the Cenotaph yesterday to honour the nation's war dead PHOTOGRAPH: GARRY WEASER

Hong Kong minorities in last battle

Andrew Higgins on the 'stateless' former British citizens with friends in high places

AS BRITAIN pauses this morning to remember its war dead, a tacit alliance of the Queen and the Hong Kong governor, Chris Patten, is challenging the Government's stance against granting British residence rights to the families of Gurkha troops who served in the Falklands and to other Hong Kong ethnic minority groups.

There has been widespread dismay in the colony, which reverts to China on July 1 next year, over London's refusal to admit the families of some 750 Gurkhas who are to join the 5th Airborne Brigade based in Britain.

In an unusual intervention, the Queen has expressed sympathy for the plight of the estimated 3,000-5,000 people from Indian and other ethnic minorities in Hong Kong who will become, in effect, stateless after the handover. The letter from Buckingham Palace increases pressure on the Home Secretary, Michael Howard, to relax his stand.

Unlike the Gurkhas, who are nationals of Nepal, most Indians and other minorities resident in Hong Kong were born as full British citizens but later reclassified as "British nationals overseas" with no right to live in Britain.

Mr Patten arrives in London today and is expected to press for better treatment for those affected by the passport restrictions. Similar demands are also likely to be aired in Parliament this week when MPs hold their last formal debate on the territory.

The Royal British Legion believes today's two-minute silence at 11am will be the most widely heeded since shortly after the second world war.

● A man will appear in court today after a minister's face was slashed during a Highland village's remembrance service.

The Rev John MacPherson needed 16 stitches in a wound received during yesterday's two-minute silence at the war memorial at Scourie on the west coast of Sutherland. A local man, Donald MacLeod, aged 52, was taken into custody.

Silence will be honoured by millions; knife attack, page 8

Fleet Street legend Marje Proops dies

'Dear Marge': gave advice and attacked social taboos

Sue Quinn

MARJORIE Proops, the legendary personal advice columnist and veteran of Fleet Street, died last night.

Ms Proops, better known as Dear Marje, dispensed wisdom and encouragement and attacked social taboos during a career that spanned a moral revolution and more than 44 years on her beloved Daily Mirror.

She was believed to be 85 when she died in hospital after suffering from pneumonia, although she did her best to hide her age.

Labour leader Tony Blair said last night: "She was a legend in journalism and will be sadly missed, not just by the Mirror and its readers, but by the country, who came to appreciate her warmth and generosity."

Her journalistic career began with the Daily Herald in 1945 as fashion editor, but by 1954 she was agony aunt on Woman's Mirror, where she asked readers to send stamped addressed envelopes for special advice on matters deemed improper for publication. By the permissive 1960s her column was openly advising young girls on contraception and abortion, and young men about their sexual inadequacies.

She once proudly boasted that she was the first journalist in Britain to address the issue of masturbation.

Her columns reflected the evolution of social mores, covering issues from battered wives and children to Aids.

She was devoted to the Daily Mirror, which she steadfastly refused to leave despite lucrative offers from the competition because, she said, it reflected her feelings about society. "It, too, cared about what happened to ordinary folk, to those underdogs I worried about so much."

She had a staff of eight to handle 50,000 letters a year. She logged every one as some correspondents leant on her for regular comfort.

But behind the huge trademark spectacles and long cigarette holder was a woman not at ease in her own life.

An authorised biography released in 1993 revealed a 20-year adulterous love affair during a sexless marriage to Sidney Proops. The marriage, she said, forced her to appreciate the meaning of agony.

Last night fellow agony aunt Claire Rayner said: "She was a remarkable woman. I shall miss her."

Proops philosophy, page 8; Obituary, page 11

1996

Listen, I could do as you ask and give you 20p for a cup of tea, but I'm not going to and I'll tell you why: Because it would do nothing to help solve your long term problems, whilst it would give the government further excuse to distance themselves from their social responsibilities.
But I tell you what I will do. I'll keep up the fight for a welfare state within a socialist society that will ensure health, housing and employment for all it's citizens.
Great! On behalf of homeless people everywhere I'd like to thank you.
You're welcome.

Why not? Because they don't even like me, Brian, and I certainly don't like them. I'm only invited in the ludicrous capacity of your 'partner'...
... I know it's expected, but I'm not living my life according to other people's expectations...
...don't try and guilt-trip me, Brian, I'm not going and that's that!!
SLAM!
Family Xmas?
Father's funeral.

Hello... yes, Megan I am still here. What do you want? Advice on a case? Can't you deal with it yourself? Oh, go on then, since I'll be here all night anyway.
child welfare case... family currently homeless... mother hears voices... mother's partner not the father of the child... Do we know who the father is? Mother says the father is....
WHAT!! How old is the child? One day! Where is the child at the moment?
IN A STABLE!!! Good grief, Megan, get the kid out of there! The Press'll have a field day if they hear about this....
TELEPHONE
TELEPHONE
Harry Venning

1997

Born on May 4, 1979: two children, two stories
Books: Linda Grant on the Pirelli Calendars
The Network Computer dream
online

45p
Thursday
May 1
1997
Published in London
and Manchester

NEWSPAPER OF THE YEAR

The Guardian

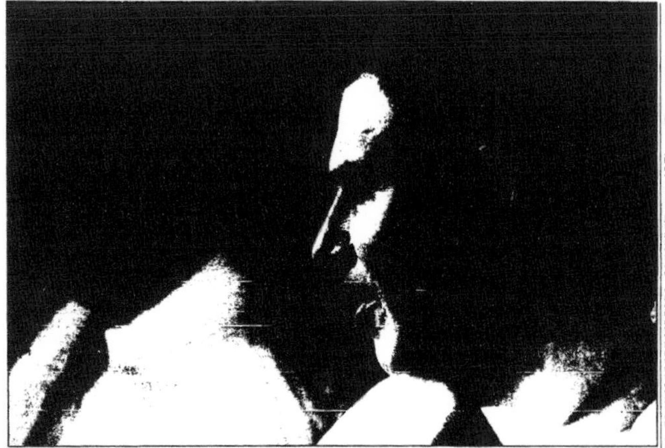

Tony Blair aboard his battlebus yesterday. 'He had the opportunity for a final look at the barred gates of Downing Street. He did not take it' PHOTOGRAPH: MARTIN ARGLES

Looking into the future a mere 24 hours away

Blair was staring with that soulful/purposeful middle distance poster look. He suddenly seemed a long way away from all of this. ***Matthew Engel** on the last day of the campaign*

JUST after eight yesterday morning, Tony Blair's battlebus left Millbank for his final day of campaigning. It swung into Whitehall and gave him the opportunity for a final look at the barred gates of Downing Street. He did not take it. Resolutely, he stared the other way, at the Red Lion over the road, actually.

There was another moment late yesterday when he was in a primary school at Middlesbrough, one of those electioneering stops devised by political impresarios who regard the entire public as props in their stage show. The children were singing Jerusalem, rather beautifully. Cherie Blair joined in lustily. And when we got to the bit about not ceasing from mental fight and the sword not resting in the hand until we have built Jerusalem in our green and pleasant land, she looked at her husband significantly. He did not respond. He was staring with that soulful/purposeful middle-distance poster look. He seemed a long way away from all this.

Tomorrow he will be. Some time after midday he can expect — he does expect, although he has done as much as any human can never to let on — the gates of Downing Street to open for him.

It is just about possible to construct an intermediate scenario in which John Major wins by a seat or two, and everyone hangs on for a few months. But essentially there are only two options.

If Tony Blair loses he will vanish down the biggest political plughole in British history. He will not be Neil Kinnock; he will be ranked alongside Eddie the Eagle. No one will waste time quarrelling over the succession because there will be very little left to lead. The effective leader of the Opposition will be Swampy.

Otherwise he is going to be Prime Minister. At the end of six weeks widely, and fashionably, described as boring, we are approaching one of the defining moments in 20th century British political history.

The calm is almost eerie. The Labour leadership may have wavered in the early weeks of the campaign and concentrated on fearful defence rather than attack, but all the evidence is that the electorate has held on to its resolve. In 1992 the election was won and lost in the last four days; this was won and lost in the last four years.

Mr Blair senses it better than anyone, but will never say it. Yesterday he repeated his phrase about the election not being over until it's over at least three more times. But he also radiated an inner certainty, a sense of destiny even.

He travelled from London to Scotland to Teesside and on to his constituency of Sedgefield, where he was welcomed adoringly in the room at the back of Trimdon Labour Club where he was first selected as a candidate 14 years ago.

He travelled by plane, helicopter, car and battlebus. En route, he hit three winnable marginals. But that was a detail. Having started just after 7am he spent barely an hour in direct contact with the public. On Monday and Tuesday it was half that. Mr Blair leaves London to find set-dressing. He was successful. The last hecklers had vanished. He found friendly, welcoming, photogenic Scots in Dumfries; friendly, welcoming, photogenic shoppers at the market in Stockton-on-Tees; friendly, photogenic kids at the primary school; and a friendly, welcoming cop who had introduced the policy of zero tolerance in Middlesbrough, and, if he wasn't photogenic, the actress Helen Mirren was.

It was all arranged by the party organisation that thinks of everything, except that in the first two weeks of April it forgot to give anyone a reason for voting Labour, and allowed the election to become a choice between the governing party telling the people "you'll get sod all" and an Opposition saying "sorry, you'll get sod all".

Now Mr Blair has found his voice. The message may not amount to much, but it looks and sounds terrific. To the travelling press his stump speech has become an object of ridicule, and it is easy to work out the formula: local reference — joke — soundbite — repetition of message. But when he gets the cadences right it can sound brilliant. "Michael Foot made the same speech everywhere too," said one wise observer. "But he took an hour to do it."

In Stockton he called a half-forgotten figure on to the platform who looked as though he might have been the bus driver or a security man. It turned out to be John Prescott. If this were the Conservative Party, one would think it a coincidence; wandering battlebuses that were bound to collide sooner or later. But it was a vital last-day piece of symbolism; a unified party to go with the kids and the cops and the folks back home in the constituency.

It was intended for the news bulletins, but the people of Stockton — supposedly the props rather than the audience — looked out from the windows above the stores as they do on the old pictures of Gladstone speaking. In modern Britain, I think this is what passes as enthusiasm

Polls put Labour in command

Martin Kettle and Michael White

LABOUR goes into today's general election poised to win only its third working majority of the 20th century, and its first for 31 years, if today's results vindicate overwhelming eve-of-poll evidence that voters have embraced Tony Blair's "time for a change" campaign after 18 years of Conservative rule.

The final Guardian/ICM opinion poll of the campaign gives Labour a 10-point lead over the Conservatives, with four other opinion polls today showing the gap ranging between 11 and 22 points. Today's ICM poll would translate into an 83-seat Labour majority in the Commons, with signs that a stronger-than-average swing to Labour in the Tory-held marginals could boost the majority further, providing a counter to Labour fears of a repetition of the late Tory surge that dished Neil Kinnock's hopes five years ago.

As a dispirited John Major warned against "the false attraction of a well-packaged marketing scam" that would ruin golden prospects for Britain, the Labour leader and his allies refused to take any sort of victory for granted — let alone the landslide which the polls suggest.

But the Guardian/ICM poll contained clear evidence that Labour has fought back strongly in the final week of the campaign, successfully using the pensions issue to halt the Conservatives' earlier Euro-sceptic based recovery. A week after ICM had recorded the lowest Labour lead of the campaign, Labour has hoisted its adjusted lead by five points, narrowed the gap on Europe to a three point Tory lead and heads the Conservatives on pensions by 15 points.

The full adjusted ICM figures show Labour on 43 per cent (up 1 from last week), Conservatives 33 (down 4), Liberal Democrats 18 (up 4) and others 5 (down 1). Since the start of the campaign, Labour is down 3, Conservatives up 1, Liberal Democrats up 1 and others are no change.

ICM's unadjusted survey confirms that Labour has ended the 1997 campaign in a far stronger opinion poll position than it achieved in the ill-fated 1992 camapign. The unadjusted results show Labour on 46 (up 4 from last week), Conservatives 30 (down 6), Liberal Democrats 19 (down 3) and others 5 (no change), giving a Labour unadjusted lead of 16 points.

[illegible] end-of-campaign opinion polls published last night showed a spread of even larger Labour leads over the Conservatives, with one poll putting the gap as big as 22 points but a second hinting at a late, if insufficient, Conservative comeback. All nevertheless pointed to a majority of more than 100 seats for Labour.

NOP for Reuters, with fieldwork on Tuesday, gave the result as Labour 50, Conservative 28 and Liberal Democrats 14, a lead of 22 and a theoretical majority of 223 seats.

turn to page 3, column 1

State of the parties
Adjusted figures

April 9 · 16 · 23 · Now
Labour
Conservative
Lib Democrat
Others 3 · 6 · 6 · 6
Labour lead
Source: ICM

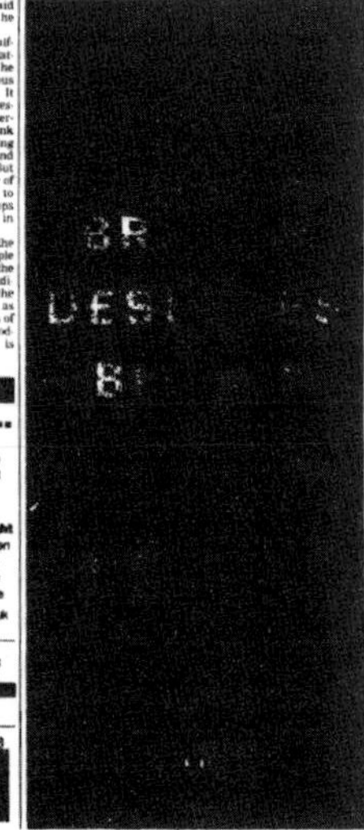

After 46 days, thousands of speeches, hundreds of insults, scores of polls, the election is here at last

"Perhaps it ends like this. There he stood, like a ruler from an earlier age, surrounded and shoved by a mob bent on pushing him from power. 'One more day!' they chanted — and plenty else more foul." **Jonathan Freedland** with the Prime Minister, **page 15**

"Conservative agents were considering whether to return election donations to the multi-millionaire Paul Sykes after the Guardian's disclosure that Euro-sceptics who had taken his cash could be 'gagged' in Parliament from opposing monetary union," **David Hencke and Jamie Wilson** on the candidates who took the anti-Euro cash, **page 11**

"The Conservatives, seizing on a change of emphasis here, an adjusted nuance there, to try and show Blair as a spinelessly shifting reed, spent the election barking up the wrong tree." **Hugo Young** interviews the Prime-Minister-in-waiting, [illegible]

"Across the dispatch boxes, Mr Hague is quick on his pins. He will be witty at the expense of Mr Blair and his pieties. But not nasty; for Mr Hague has another advantage. He is good-humoured, and seems to be good-natured." **Frank Johnson** runs the rule over the Conservative leadership contenders, **page 18**

"Those who had been at the same press conference in 1992 said the body language told the whole story. This time the polls are telling them it's time for a long holiday. Somebody said: 'You've lost it, haven't you?'" **Simon Hoggart** at John Major's final briefing, **page 13**

Don't vote...

Until you've tried the Guardian vote-o-meter, the radical democratic tool that will break the tyranny of sound-bite politics.

Plus: The Long Goodnight All the results as they happen and the big election stories throughout the night on the Guardian's Election website http://election.guardian.co.uk

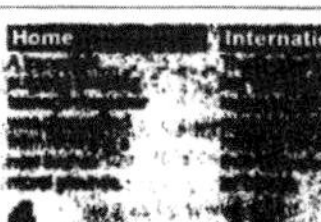
Home

International

Finance
Sport

18
9 770261 307347

1997

The thing about New Year's Resolutions is that one mustn't be too ambitious. Otherwise you set yourself up to fail, and this colours the following twelve months.
So instead of the usual blitz on cigs, booze and chocs I have selected a goal which is both appropriate to my lifestyle and eminently achievable.
Really. What are you giving up this year?
Hope.

97
VICTORY!
92
7
CHAMPAGNE
CHAMPAGNE
SALE OR RETURN
SALE OR RETURN

One more time
Go on, just once more.
Please! Again!
Alright. But this is definitely the last time. I don't want to wear out the tape
Again
Again
Again!
MICHAEL DENZIL XAVIER PORTILLO, CONSERVATIVE, 19,137 VOTES...
Freeze Frame!!

Sport97

The unique sports magazine
David Davies reports on the Ryder Cup wild cards. Plus, Sheringham cracks ribs

Review

Ms Stone to you: Why Sharon has stopped being a man-eating sexpot

45p
Friday
September 5
1997
Published in London and Manchester

NEWSPAPER OF THE YEAR

The Guardian

'The Royal Family have been hurt by suggestions that they are indifferent to the country's sorrow . . .'

Queen to deliver address on TV

Kamal Ahmed and John Arlidge

THE ROYAL Family threw tradition away yesterday when it was announced that the Queen would give an unprecedented television address to the nation about the family's grief at the death of Diana, Princess of Wales.

Stung by criticism that the monarchy had appeared aloof following the princess's death, the announcement was one of a series made by Buckingham Palace which revealed a fundamental break with the defence that protocol dictated how the Royal Family should act.

Bowing to public pressure for a more appropriate response, the palace said that along with the address, which will be shown shortly before 6pm, it had also been agreed that for the first time the Union flag will be flown at half mast over the palace on the day of the funeral.

The moves are a break with tradition and have been described by royal commentators as "cataclysmic".

The palace also announced at a unique on the record press conference that the Queen, accompanied by the Duke of Edinburgh, the Queen Mother and Princess Margaret, will now fly to London early this afternoon from Balmoral in Scotland, rather than arriving tomorrow morning by train as first planned.

More controversially, it was also revealed that no member of the Royal Family will read a lesson at tomorrow's funeral.

Last night they attended a hastily convened special service at Crathie Kirk on Royal Deeside, the family's first public appearance since Sunday.

Lieutenant Colonel Malcolm Ross, comptroller of the Lord Chamberlain's office which has been co-ordinating palace input into the funeral arrangements, said a decision had been taken to break with convention because of the nature of the "unique day for a unique person".

There was a welcome for the astonishing changes from many quarters.

"You have to admire her courage in circumstances that are very painful and difficult," said Lord Blake, the constitutional historian.

Lord St John of Fawsley, the constitutional expert, called on the public not to be curmudgeonly and to respond positively.

Yesterday's unprecedented church service at Crathie was another break with the original timetable. The Queen, the Duke of Edinburgh, Prince Charles and the young princes emerged from Balmoral and joined Prince Charles and Peter Phillips, son of the Princess Royal, after the Queen requested the service yesterday morning.

The family spent several minutes at the gates of Balmoral looking at the flowers and reading condolence cards. Prince Harry gripped his father's hands as he closely read many of the tributes.

Outside Balmoral, Prince Charles' press secretary, Sandy Henney, denied that the family's appearance was to answer criticism. "This is a family going to church for prayer in view of what's happened. It was something that seemed appropriate."

Earlier the first signs that the Royal Family had been moved by concerns that they were not responding adequately to the national mood came when Geoffrey Crawford, the Queen's press secretary, made a public statement.

"The Royal Family have been hurt by suggestions that they are indifferent to the country's sorrow at the tragic death of the Princess of Wales," Mr Crawford said in a move described by royal commentators as highly unusual.

"The princess was a much loved national figure, but she was also a mother whose sons miss her deeply. Prince William and Prince Harry themselves want to be with their father and grandparents at this time in the quiet haven of Balmoral.

"As their grandmother, the Queen is helping the princes to come to terms with their loss as they prepare themselves for the public ordeal of mourning their mother with the nation on Saturday."

The palace said the decision to make the television address was not connected to a number of front page headlines yesterday which accused the Queen of sticking too closely to protocol.

As well as the fact that the Queen had not spoken since a two-line statement was released on Sunday, criticism also focused on Buckingham Palace where the flagpole has been bare all week. Members of the public who had queued for hours to sign the books of condolence asked why a flag was not flying at half mast.

The palace succumbed to the pressure yesterday and said that when the Queen leaves for the funeral by car tomorrow morning the Royal Standard, flown at full mast whenever the Queen is in residence, will be lowered and the Union flag flown at half-mast instead, where it will remain until midnight.

The Duke of York and Prince Edward were yesterday the first members of the family to sign the book of condolence at St James's Palace.

The palace said that the books would be closed at 6pm tonight until 2pm on Saturday, when they will be left available for signing 24 hours a day for a further week.

A Downing Street spokesman said the new arrangements were a further sign that the Royal Family was responding positively and imaginatively to the extraordinary outpouring of grief.

Death of Diana, pages 2-5; Leader comment, page 16; Simon Hoggart, page 17

Prince Harry grips the hand of his father, Prince Charles, as the Royal Family examine floral tributes to Diana outside the gates of Balmoral last night

The Day

- The Queen is to make an unprecedented broadcast to the nation this afternoon following complaints the Royal Family appeared aloof from the outpouring of grief.
- A statement issued through her press secretary said the Queen was hurt at suggestions she was indifferent to the country's sorrow.
- In a break with protocol, the Royal Standard will be lowered at Buckingham Palace tomorrow when the Queen leaves for the funeral, to be replaced by a Union flag at half-mast.
- The Queen, Prince Charles and Princes William and Harry inspected flowers laid at the gates of Balmoral after attending church.
- Princes Andrew and Edward mingled with mourners in The Mall.
- Funeral invitations to editors of six tabloid newspapers were withdrawn at the request of Earl Spencer.
- A credit card hotline with 10,000 lines was installed to cope with donations to the memorial fund. It was estimated more than £100 million had been raised.
- Elton John will sing a special version of Candle in the Wind, and Tony Blair will read a lesson at the funeral. None of the Royal Family will take part.
- 27,000 police officers will be on duty at the funeral as concerns were raised over extreme congestion.
- Three photographers who were at the scene of the crash gave themselves up to police in Paris.

New scandal engulfs Winnie Mandela

Gunman claims she promised 20,000 rand for doctor's murder

David Beresford and Wally Mbhele in Johannesburg

THE Winnie Mandela scandal is about to erupt again with new allegations that she ordered the murder of a Soweto doctor and was involved in a previous killing of a teenager.

One of two gunmen convicted of Dr Abu-Baker Asvat's murder on January 27 1989 now claims he was contracted to do it by Mrs Mandela.

At a Durban prison, Nicholas Dlamini said: "Mrs Mandela promised us R20,000 (£2,600) to murder Dr Asvat."

The Guardian has obtained a copy of an affidavit sworn by a missing witness in Mrs Mandela's 1991 trial, Katiza Cebekhulu, in which he claims that, on the instructions of Mrs Mandela, he pointed out Asvat's surgery to two men hours before the murder.

Mrs Mandela is expected to be questioned by the Truth and Reconciliation Commission on September 25.

Stompie Seipei, aged 14, died after he and four youths were kidnapped from a Methodist place of safety in Soweto by members of the "Mandela Football Club" — a gang of thugs around Mrs Mandela.

At the subsequent trial, she claimed the minister running the home had sexually abused the boys and she denied assault and kidnapping.

Stompie was badly beaten at Mrs Mandela's home, on suspicion that he was an informer. Asvat is believed to have been called in by Mrs Mandela to examine Stompie, whom he found to be dying. She is alleged to have tried to persuade him to back up her abuse story. He refused.

She was brought to trial on charges of kidnapping and assault in 1991. Witnesses who provided an alibi have since retracted. She got a suspended sentence for kidnap.

The football club leader, Jerry Richardson, received life for Stompie's murder.

Mr Cebekhulu joined members of the football club in assaulting his four friends. But he failed to testify and it transpired that he had been spirited out of South Africa by the ANC, landing up in prison in Zambia. He was taken to Britain by MP Emma Nicholson.

In a sworn affidavit taken by a South African officer in London in 1995, Mr Cebekhulu claimed Mrs Mandela took part in the Stompie assault.

"Dr Asvat came and said Stompie could die at any time and must go to hospital immediately. The doctor left . . . Late that night and after the household had gone to bed, I heard steps, looked out and saw Mrs Mandela carrying something in her hand which she lifted high and plunged down into a body that I identified as being Stompie."

He said that later two men came to the house. "Mrs Mandela had called me and instructed me to drive with them and show them where Dr Asvat's surgery was."

His account ties in with that given by Dlamini this week. Although he could not recall the date, Dlamini said that he and Cyril Mbatha — convicted with him for the Asvat murder — were introduced to Mrs Mandela by an intermediary known as Shwala Botha.

He said they went to Mrs Mandela's house. "Mrs Mandela came and greeted us before Botha introduced us. Botha said we are the people who can help in connection with that matter.

"She asked how much would we want. Cyril said R20,000. She said we should first carry out the attack and Katiza will show us Asvat's place."

Dlamini said he had disclosed Mrs Mandela's alleged involvement to police in 1989.

Crisis returns, pages 14 and 15; Leader comment, page 16

Seven die in Israel blast

THREE Hamas bombers created carnage yesterday in a packed pedestrian precinct in Jerusalem, killing themselves, four others and injuring at least 192.

The US secretary of state, Madeleine Albright, last night vowed to go ahead with her planned trip to the Middle East on Tuesday, saying she would not give in to terror.

A senior official of Yasser Arafat's Palestinian Authority pledged "full co-operation" with Israel. But the Israeli Prime Minister, Binyamin Netanyahu, said the peace process could not go on unless Arafat crushed Hamas.

Early today Lebanese security sources claimed five Israeli soldiers were killed during an Israeli commando raid in southern Lebanon.

Report, page 13

Inside

Home — Campaigners for home rule are becoming uneasy over growing opposition to plans proposing limited tax-raising powers **6**

International — A Malaysian judge jailed a Canadian journalist for . . . **13**

Finance — Bruce Gyngell, chief executive of Yorkshire Television and scourge of TV violence, quit with £1 million-plus compensation **20**

Sport — Seve Ballesteros selected Jesper Parnevik and Nick Faldo as his wild card selections for the Ryder Cup **Sport 97** **2**

1997

Listen, Ben, as an impressionable student you must beware of being judgmental. For example, a casual observor passing through this estate will see only poverty, neglect and deprivation.
But spend some time amongst the people here and you will discover a vibrant, diverse, mutually supportive community whose indomitable spirit has been forged in the furnace of adversity.
I know, I live here.
Really? God, you poor thing.

Hurry up Brian, we're already late!
Alright!!
Forgive me for not rushing, Clare, but dinner at your parents' isn't exactly my idea of fun. The same thing happens every time we go: Two glasses of wine and your Dad's off on his favourite rant against 'young People These days'.
Just ignore him, like I do.
Kids these days, don't know they're born! Call themselves druggies, they wouldn't have lasted twenty minutes back in the sixties. I took so many pills I rattled. Can't remember 1968 at all, can we, love.
No, dear.
HARRY VENNING

Donatellos?
No!
Thai Spices?
No!
Andrews?
No!
The Duke of Cambridge?
No!
Noodletown?
No!
Top Nosh?
No!
The Pelican?
No!
Bayleaf?
No!
Karin's Kitchen?
No!
OK, Clare. So where do you think we should go for lunch?
FOR CRYING OUT LOUD, BRIAN! MUST YOU ALWAYS LEAVE IT TO ME TO MAKE THE DECISIONS IN THIS RELATIONSHIP?!!

GUARDIAN
PICASSO'S SOCIAL WORKER

Analysis: is the battle for gay rights over?
Out and equal
Plus: eight pages of books in G2

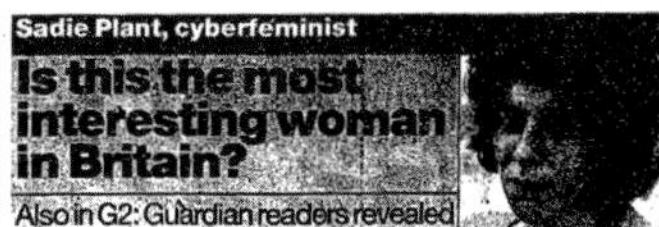

Sadie Plant, cyberfeminist
Is this the most interesting woman in Britain?
Also in G2: Guardian readers revealed

Dip into hypertext fiction
online
The best place for IT jobs
online

45p
Thursday
October 9
1997
Published in London and Manchester

NEWSPAPER OF THE YEAR
The Guardian

Charles Bronson: the most disruptive man in prison has spent 21 of the past 25 years in solitary. Yesterday he got another seven

Duncan Campbell
Crime Correspondent

HE WAS described as the most disruptive person in the British penal system. He holds the national record for push-ups with a man sitting on his back. He has spent 21 of the last 25 years in solitary confinement. His cartoons have appeared in the national press. He once proposed marriage to his medicine ball as the only person he could really trust.

Yesterday Charles Bronson was jailed for seven years for taking three hostages in prison and threatening to kill them if he was not given a jet to take him to political asylum in Libya.

Bronson, aged 44, who was known as Michael Gordon Peterson before he changed his name by deed poll, pleaded guilty to charges of blackmail and threatening to kill when he appeared at the Old Bailey. With shaven head, ZZ Top beard and dark glasses, he arrived in the dock with six officers and a further five placed around the courtroom.

Asked if he was guilty of taking two Iraqis and another prisoner hostage on September 7 last year, he stood up straight in the dock and announced: "Guilty — as guilty as O J Simpson . . . Guilty — as guilty as Adolf Hitler."

Before he was sentenced, Bronson told Judge Brian Watling: "I was on a mission of madness, but now I am on a mission of peace and all I want to do now is get home and have a pint with my son." He had just received a letter from his son whom he had not seen since 1975.

The judge told him he was clearly two people: one a frightening person with a capacity for violence, the other a warm individual who was a pleasure to deal with. But his offence had been a serious one and a jail sentence was inevitable.

Prosecuting counsel Jeremy Donne told the court that Bronson was regarded as the "most disruptive prisoner" in the prison system. He was immensely strong, he said, able to bend cell doors with his bare hands, but he was also an intelligent man who had spent around 21 of the last 25 years in solitary confinement and had had only two short periods of liberty.

Originally jailed for seven years for robbery and aggravated burglary in 1974, most of his subsequent time inside had been a result of taking hostages in prison or wounding fellow inmates.

Bronson was being slowly rehabilitated by volunteer officers in Belmarsh prison in south-east London and seemed to be making good progress, when the incident which brought him to the Old Bailey took place. He had been learning computer skills and had the run of five cells which no one entered without his permission. His main visitor was a fellow inmate called Jason Greasley who played Scrabble with him.

On the morning of September 7, Bronson had been brushing the floor outside the cell of an Iraqi charged with the hijacking of a Sudanese airline when he asked his friend Greasley to bring another Iraqi, also charged with the hijacking, to the cell. He then pushed all three men inside, tied them up with shoelaces and torn bedding and barricaded himself inside.

"If my demands aren't met within an hour, you'll need four body bags," he warned. He told prison officers he was

turn to page 3, column 1

Mad, bad and dangerous to know . . . Charles Bronson, now embarking on a mission of peace inside Wakefield prison

Clarke opens old wounds

Michael White
Political Editor

KENNETH Clarke last night fired a warning shot across William Hague's bows when he reminded the new Conservative leader that he still wants to be prime minister and could challenge him for the Tory leadership.

The timing chosen by the former chancellor astonished senior colleagues battling at their Blackpool conference yesterday against an angry grassroots rebellion over Tory 'activists' share of the proposed electoral college for choosing future party leaders.

Asked in a newspaper interview if he would stand for the job again, 57-year-old Mr Clarke replied: "I have no idea. I have no intention of standing against the present one. At the present time."

Mr Clarke's comments meant, in effect, that the old cabinet's big hitter was saying openly what many Tory MPs privately predict: that if Mr Hague's lacklustre performance this summer does not improve and the Tories are humiliated in the 1999 Euro-elections, then he might face a coup before he ever faces Mr Blair for No. 10.

The fragility of Mr Hague's grip on the party was underlined when it emerged that three shadow cabinet members had threatened to resign rather than let the leader rule out membership of the EU's single currency for 10 years.

Mr Clarke, whom 36-year-old Mr Hague defeated in the second ballot last July, has never hidden his ambition and colleagues last night acknowledged his instinct for what some called "mischief". But such an experienced politician — a minister for 18 years — must have known the likely impact of his words on Mr Hague as he struggles to assert his authority over his party.

In angry protests from the conference floor, egged on by Lord Archer, a former deputy chairman, activists blamed undisciplined Tory MPs for

Austin

OATH OF LOYALTY TO MY LEADER

USE BY MAY '99

Labour's historic 179-vote Commons majority and demanded equality with MPs in the electoral college: a 50-50 split instead of the token 15-to-20 per cent likely to be offered. A formula must be agreed by next spring.

Mr Clarke, who declined Mr Hague's offer to become his deputy, has expressed reservations about the new shadow cabinet formula to oppose euro membership "for the foreseeable future".

His interview came as it emerged that three left-leaning shadow cabinet members — Sir George Young, David Curry and Stephen Dorrell — had forced Mr Hague to back down on the shadow team's position on the single currency — until further discussion.

As a result yesterday's foreign affairs debate forced Michael Howard, the Euro-sceptic shadow foreign secretary, to stick to the formula which rules it out for "the foreseeable future". One europhile former minister said: "What Michael said is the line everyone can live with." Another said: "The foreseeable future is about 10 minutes."

The issue will be discussed again only when the whole shadow cabinet is present. "We can survive if we don't talk much about Europe," one member said, as colleagues predicted that Mr Curry might still quit if the "foreseeable future" formula is abandoned and that Iain Duncan-Smith, the Euro-sceptic social security spokesman, may go if it is not.

In his interview with the London Evening Standard, Mr Clarke again complained about his party's obsession with "the precise position we were adopting on the European currency" during last summer's leadership fight.

He said: "I didn't think I could win the leadership in the parliamentary party and I came a damn sight closer than I thought I would."

Given the overwhelming preference for Mr Clarke expressed by the Tory grassroots, peers and MEPs — as well as by most opinion polls — his reference to being rejected by the parliamentary party implies that he thinks he would do better with the wider franchise being haggled over in Blackpool this week.

The Tories like a winner and the man who presided over the Treasury during the post-Lamont recovery looks reassuring to many. Mr Hague knows he still has to earn their affection and respect as he prepares for tomorrow's big speech.

Conservatives in Blackpool, pages 8 and 9; Leader comment, page 18; Hugo Young, page 19

British team discovers the Internet's holy grail

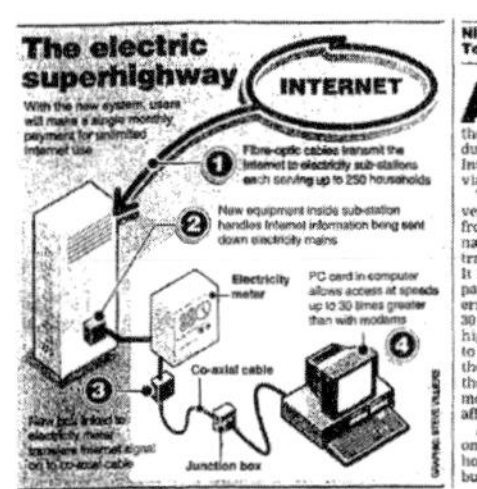

The electric superhighway
INTERNET
With the new system, users will make a single monthly payment for unlimited Internet use
1 Fibre-optic cables transmit the Internet to electricity sub-stations each serving up to 250 households
2 New equipment inside sub-station handles Internet information being sent down electricity mains
Electricity meter
PC card in computer allows access at speeds up to 30 times greater than with modems
4
3
Co-axial cable
Junction box

Nicholas Bannister
Technology Editor

A 100-STRONG team in Essex has discovered one of the holy grails of the telecommunications industry — a way to deliver Internet services to the home via the electricity mains.

The new technology prevents the electrical current from distorting Internet signals and other computer data transmitted over the mains. It will enable electricity companies to offer their customers Internet access at speeds 30 times greater than today's high-speed modems attached to telephone lines, and open the way to mass marketing of the Internet at prices which most families will be able to afford.

At present the system relies on a special feed from the household electricity meter, but the developers, working in Harlow, Essex, are confident that within a few years personal computer owners will just have to plug them into the nearest household electricity point to link up to the Internet.

Norweb Communications, part of the United Utilities water and electricity group, has developed the technology with Nortel, a Canadian electronics group specialising in telecommunications.

The Internet information is lifted from a small box linked to the electricity meter. It is then carried round the house along co-axial cables similar to those used to link televisions to aerial sockets. The cable is linked to the computer using a PC card costing under £200.

Norweb Communications plans to offer the service to its 2 million customers after a six-month marketing trial which will start in the first quarter of next year.

Mark Ballett, the company's managing director, is considering bundling Internet access with the group's water and electricity services in the North-west, and with new information and home management services, including remote meter reading. Customers would pay a fixed monthly fee, yet to be decided, for unlimited usage.

Ian Vance, Nortel Europe's chief scientist, said the link could be used for conventional PCs and network computers — slimmed down versions designed just for accessing the Internet. There was the potential to be permanently on-line, downloading video clips and compact disc quality sound, or joining in high speed computer games or video conferencing.

He said the team was working further on the technology so it would be suitable for telephone calls, but "it is a couple of years before it becomes a serious volume business".

At present the system has to use conventional telecommunications networks to link the electricity sub-stations to the Internet. But the research team hopes to be able to squeeze the telecom companies out by using the country's high-voltage national grid instead.

The developers have been testing the technology for 18 months, not least to ensure the Internet signals do not affect domestic appliances.

Energis, one of the newer telecom companies, is working with Nortel and others on developing similar technology to take its advanced telecom services into businesses via the local electricity network. This technology, which has higher capacity than that announced today, is unlikely to be available for 18 months.

Leader comment, page 18

41
9 770261 307347

1997

Aaaah! Beautiful!
Gorgeous!
Sweet little thing!
You must be very proud.
Yes, I am. But that's enough fuss over my new State-Of-The-Art laptop, come and have a look at the baby.

I'm just off on a home visit to see Mr. Hobbs.
He's my third age client. He's been having problems around anger management for some time, but he's recently started self-medicating with alcohol and I'm concerned he may present challenging behaviour.
Would you like me to come with you?
Yes please. You know what the stroppy old bastard is like when he's ratarsed.

So, Clare, what happens when a client phones up at half past five with a difficult, time consuming problem?
Good question, Laura.
A social work office has a well established proceedure to cover every eventuality. In this case we would simply refer the client on to the 'out of Hours' team.
And if the client phones at half past four?
Again, one follows well established proceedure...
.... and get them to call back in an hour.

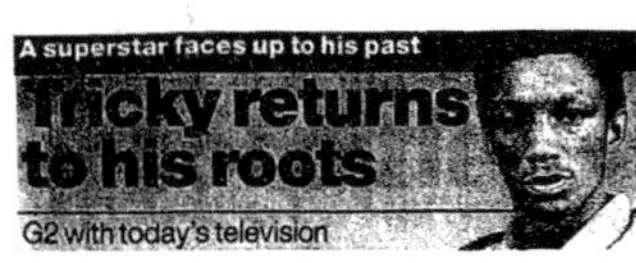

A superstar faces up to his past
Tricky returns to his roots
G2 with today's television

Three women's stories
Why women are worse off under Labour
Plus: Six pages of Books in G2

50 years of the transistor
online
The best place for IT jobs

45p
Thursday
December 4
1997
Published in London
and Manchester

NEWSPAPER OF THE YEAR

The Guardian

Beef: a crisis out of control

Marrow link to BSE brings new bans

Ewan MacAskill, James Meikle and Stephen Bates

A DEVASTATING new disclosure about BSE in British beef yesterday killed off any lingering hope of an early lifting of the European embargo and dealt a blow to consumer confidence and the domestic market's fragile recovery.

The Government, after evidence that BSE had been detected in bone marrow, was forced to extend its ban to cover T-bone steaks, ribsteaks and oxtails, which account for about 5 per cent of the British market.

Butchers will have to debone the meat before selling it on to restaurants and shops. Foreign meat will receive the same treatment. Tesco and Sainsbury's last night withdrew beef-on-the-bone products from shelves. The Consumers' Association advised people who wanted to avoid all risk to avoid eating meat altogether and said consumers may have been given false assurances in the past.

The Government was caught on the hop after a leak forced it to rush its announcement. There was initial confusion over the range of products affected by the ban. Makers of Bovril, for example, insisted its beef ingredients came from abroad and were unlikely to be affected.

Fresh oxtail is banned but makers of oxtail soup said most was produced with meat that had been deboned. The Government confirmed it did not see any significant problem for canned oxtail soup.

A spokeswoman for the Ministry of Agriculture, Fisheries and Food said commercial stocks and cubes could be affected by the latest regulations. "Bones would not be allowed to be used to create soup or stock," she said.

The Government also insisted that gelatin — a beef product made from beef bones used in a range of foods, from sweets to biscuits and Oxo cubes — could only be used if it had been "satisfactorily demonstrated it was BSE free".

The new risk

1: T-bone steaks: 3,000 tonnes sold in Britain for domestic consumption, worth £40 million a year

2: Rib steaks: 25,000 tonnes, worth £110 million

3: Oxtails: less than 1,000 tonnes

Other products

Oxtail soup?
No cooking at home on the bone. Tinned soup will depend on how it is made.

Beef stocks and drinks?
Safe if made with beef products from a country where a BSE case has never been proved, eg New Zealand.

Other products with gelatin such as biscuits, sweets and fizzy drinks?
Thought to be safe, although confusion over full range affected.

The new research shows a possible contamination of "dorsal root ganglions", peanut-sized nerve packets which are encased within the vertebral column. When meat is deboned, the ganglions are removed, but experts fear when meat is sold on the bone, there is a chance they may remain

Yesterday's disclosure came only two weeks before the European Union was due to discuss a partial lifting of its export ban. Northern Ireland and Scotland, which keep better records of their herds, had been in line for possible exemption from the boycott. But the first signals from Europe yesterday indicated that was now unlikely.

Tony Blair told the Commons: "I do understand the plight the beef farmers face at the moment and how great a blow this must be to them, but when we receive scientific advice and the chief medical officer gives us recommendations we feel that we are under an obligation to follow them. We will, however, do everything we can to mitigate the problems." He gave no indication whether beef farmers would receive increased compensation.

The new ban will hit beef prices and force many farmers out of business. The National Farmers Union described it as "a body blow".

The domestic market had staged a partial recovery since the link with BSE was established in March last year. The Meat and Livestock Commission put consumption in Britain in 1995 at 901,000 tonnes before slumping to 739,000 tonnes last year, and, until yesterday, had predicted a partial recovery this year to 839,000 tonnes. The commission said Oxo and other beef stocks were not affected because they were made from Australian beef. The ban will not apply to dog food.

The Minister of Agriculture, Jack Cunningham, insisted in a Commons statement that there was only a "very small risk" from beef on the bone. "British beef is as safe as any in Europe and safer than most," he said.

Labour in opposition blamed Conservative hostility towards Europe for failure to get the export ban lifted. Michael Jack, the shadow agriculture spokesman, said yesterday Mr Cunningham had been long on rhetoric and short on action.

In Brussels, although the European Commission response to Mr Cunningham's announcement was that it would have no effect on the speed of lifting the beef ban, there was private concern at the likely political response from member states to the news that a new risk had been discovered in British beef.

A Commission official said: "Bone and bone marrow have always been considered to be low-risk materials. So long as Britain is just acting in connection with its own meat for its own consumers we would see no reason to intervene."

BSE remains a highly sensitive issue on the Continent, where beef consumption is still down and where Belgium and Luxembourg have both recently reported their first recorded cases of the disease in local cattle. Other member states remain suspicious of the effectiveness of British attempts to tackle the crisis.

The ban on cuts of beef on the bone was one of three options from the Government's Spongiform Encephalopathy Advisory Committee. The others were simply to publish the information or to debone cattle aged between 24 and 30 months in specially licensed plants. Professor John Pattison, the committee's chairman, said: "We are dealing with something that is very small indeed ... we are getting to the stage where BSE in cattle is no longer an issue for human health with all the restrictions we have in place."

The new ban follows evidence from government-sponsored tests that infection from sensory branches of the nerves near the spinal cord of infected cattle was transferred to mice. The spinal cord is already removed from food for human consumption but these other tissues, dorsal root ganglia, would be left with the bone when meat was cut off the spine. Bone marrow was also infected in one test.

Just when you thought it was safe, pages 4 and 5

A blow to the ribs . . . a York butcher cuts into a rib of beef. Butchers will have to debone meat before selling it on to restaurants and shops

'I understand the plight the beef farmers face at the moment and how great a blow this must be to them, but when we receive scientific advice and the chief medical officer gives us recommendations we feel that we are under an obligation to follow them. We will, however, do everything we can to mitigate the problems'

Tony Blair

'British beef is as safe as any in Europe and safer than most'

Jack Cunningham

Royal Opera chiefs defy MPs who say they must go

Dan Glaister
Arts Correspondent

THE Royal Opera House was last night fighting a rearguard action in the face of an unprecedented attack by a committee of MPs demanding the resignation of the entire board.

A report yesterday from the Culture, Media and Sport committee called for a government-appointed administrator to run the company. If the board refused to go, it said, the ROH's £15 million annual subsidy should be withdrawn. Another option considered by the report was to privatise the ROH.

The sternest criticism was levelled at the chief executive, Mary Allen, who in her previous job as secretary general of the Arts Council had overseen the award of £78.5 million lottery money to the ROH and the granting of an annual subsidy of £15 million. The report said: "Ms Allen's conduct fell seriously below the standards to be expected of the principal officer of a public body." It called for her immediate resignation. But as Ms Allen stood firm, Chris Smith, the Culture Secretary, stressed the need for "planned change".

In an unusually prompt response to the findings of a select committee, Mr Smith wrote to its chairman, Gerald Kaufman, to say: "I am concerned that overnight and precipitate change either in the management of the Royal Opera House or by an instant withdrawal by the Arts Council of financial support for the Royal Opera House would in fact endanger your and my underlying objectives."

The move was welcomed by Mr Kaufman and reduced the likelihood of a clash between him and Mr Smith.

Michael Fabricant, a Conservative member of the committee, said: "If there were now precipitate action we believe a disastrous situation would be made even worse."

Determined to fend off demands for such radical reform, the ROH last night launched a counter-offensive. Ms Allen said: "I entirely reject the criticisms in the committee's report." If she made a mistake at the time of her appointment by the ROH, she said in a statement, "it was an honest one". The report said her account of the appointment was "entirely unconvincing".

Any significant changes are likely to be put on hold until Sir Richard Eyre has completed his report into the provision of lyric theatre in London. His working group, which includes Ms Allen, as well as nominees from the English National Opera, the Arts Council and independent figures, is due to report in May. But most observers believe it is only a matter of time before the ROH is subject to far-reaching reform.

Damned, blamed, accused, scorned, pages 8 and 9; Leader comment, page 22; David Mellor, page 23

Modern warfare: now you see us, now you don't

Tim Radford
Science Editor

DEFENCE scientists in the United States are working on the ultimate smokescreen. They have developed an artificial fog that will keep the enemy in the dark but not the soldiers advancing under its cover.

The new stealth camouflage, called Magic Vision, will not just confuse the gunners on the other side, it will also baffle their infrared detectors.

The details of the technology — developed by the Defence Advanced Research Projects Agency (Darpa) at Arlington, Virginia — are hazy. According to New Scientist today, it is still in early development and scientists are reluctant to discuss it. But the idea is that the smoke cover will absorb or scatter radiation in the visible and short wavelength infrared. The smoke generator will be light enough for one person to carry, along with 19 litres of fuel. It will have to generate a cloud big enough to mask a small group of soldiers, who will be equipped with smokescreen-penetrating goggles. And it must hang around as long as possible to cloak their activities.

"Perhaps most difficult of all, Darpa wants to make the smoke non-toxic and environmentally friendly," says New Scientist.

The research adds a new twist to the old art of military camouflage.

A naval development called Sea Wraith, unveiled earlier this year, envelops an entire ship with a fine spray of water from thousands of tiny nozzles. The idea is that the droplets will mask the ship from prying eyes in the visible and infrared wavelengths, but let the ship's radar beam out.

Most of the great military stealth effort, however, has gone into making planes covered with a paint that absorbs radar beams, so that they are not reflected back to detectors.

Earlier this year scientists announced a catch: the paint washes off in the rain.

How the enemy will see it

49
9 770261 307347

1997

What would I do without you, Ross The Dog? When it comes to sharing a problem you're the best listener I know. If you ever want to discuss your love life and relationships, I'll be there for you....
Well thanks a bunch, but aren't we forgetting something? You had my knackers removed when I was a puppy. I don't have a love life or relationships.
It's the drink and drugs talking, right?
By all means think that if it makes you feel better....

...by which time, of course, I'd found out that she didn't even live in the borough and there was nothing I could do to help her. It was so frustrating.
There I go again, talking about work. I just find it so hard to cut off at the end of the day. Thanks for listening, Brian. The team are so envious that I've got such a supportive partner, and I really appreciate it...
...but you must promise me one thing: You'll let me know if I'm boring you.
BRIAN!
Nguh, Ugh, Ngh!...what? ....er, she was refused benefit, right? Then what happened?....
HARRY VENNING

Brian!! You haven't heard a word I've been saying, have you.
Pete isn't pulling his weight in the team but gets away with it because Miriam lets him, but everyone else in the office resents it and looks to you to sort it out.
That's typical of you, Brian. You deliberately listened out of spite because you knew I'd ask.
HARRY VENNING

Inside today's four-section Guardian with the unmissable new magazine
space
interiors/property/design
Review
Lady Chablis: black, beautiful and male
98
Golf's finest hit heavy weather
A league of it's own
www.football.guardian.co.uk

45p
Friday
April 10
1998
Published in London and Manchester

NEWSPAPER OF THE YEAR

The Guardian

Sinn Fein anger as Blair backs Unionist plan to delay north-south body

The moment of truth

David Trimble yesterday PHOTOGRAPH PETER MACDIARMID

2am: Trimble last minute move to dilute Dublin role pushes Adams to brink

Protesters outside the Ulster Unionists' headquarters in Belfast yesterday afternoon as David Trimble left for Stormont PHOTOGRAPH JUSTIN KERNOGHAN

John Mullin and Stuart Millar in Belfast

TONY BLAIR and Bertie Ahern, the Irish prime minister, early today endorsed a novel plan to unlock the deadlock at the Northern Ireland talks, apparently paving the way for a historic political settlement after the midnight deadline passed with negotiations still in full swing.

Ulster Unionists appeared to have won significant concessions on the controversial issue of cross-border bodies amid growing indications that a deal was close.

But Sinn Fein, which saw the move as diluting talks chairman George Mitchell's draft settlement, looked to have severe difficulty in agreeing. There were rumours, later denied, that Sinn Fein was planning to walk out of Stormont.

David Trimble, the Ulster Unionist leader, who had earlier won a standing ovation from his party executive, forwarded a proposal that would delay the setting up of north-south implementation bodies until the Northern Ireland assembly had been up and running for several months. In return, it was conceded that there should be a power-sharing executive.

The plan was acceptable to the British and Irish governments. The SDLP was also reluctantly compromising. But Sinn Fein, which had been close to endorsing Mr Mitchell's document, was furious. Under the sufficiency of consensus rules, the other parties could agree a deal without Sinn Fein.

The prime ministers were desperate to keep Sinn Fein on board. Mr Blair spent 90 minutes with Gerry Adams, president, and Martin McGuinness, chief negotiator, trying to placate them.

Mr McGuinness said: "Unionists are trying to change important aspects of Senator Mitchell's paper. We told the British prime minister to avoid going to the Unionist position."

Mr Trimble's plan is a cunning fudge. It delays until later in the year one of the key battles that the parties were meant to settle last night, and raises the prospect of the deal collapsing then. After assembly elections on June 25, a power-sharing executive would be set up. The "shadow" assembly would not formally start operations until it helped to set up the north-south implementation bodies, dealing with areas such as economic development, tourism and transport, along with the Irish government. Each would begin operations at the same time, probably next February.

Unionists like the plan because it means that the implementation bodies are set up after the assembly, and they can therefore claim they are less important.

Nationalists can buy it because both bodies would begin their work at the same time, and they have also won their key demand of cabinet-style government.

Unionists have also conceded that the cross-border bodies will be enshrined in legislation at Westminister and the Dail, making them interdependent. One talks source said: "If either the assembly or the Council of Ministers falls, so does the other. Neither side can scupper the other. That is the safeguard."

Mr Blair was taking a central role. The Northern Ireland Office was said to be being bypassed in most of the negotiations.

Several matters remained to be sorted out early today. Policing and the issue of paramilitary prisoners were still to be settled. But all parties, with the exception of Sinn Fein, were saying a deal was close.

There were angry confrontations at Castle Buildings when Ian Paisley, leader of the Democratic Unionist Party, which walked out of the talks when Sinn Fein was admitted, descended on Stormont with 300 supporters to reinforce his determination to beat any settlement at the simultaneous referendums in Northern Ireland and the Irish Republic on May 22.

Heckled by supporters of loyalist fringe parties, he told reporters: "If they sell us out as it looks likely they are go to do, then we are going to have a great victory."

Earlier, Sinn Fein was thought to be considering an historic move by taking up seats in any Northern Ireland assembly and ditching its decades-old policy of refusing to participate in the government of Northern Ireland.

Although the party has filled its one seat in the Irish parliament, it has always viewed any Northern Ireland body as representing British colonialism and Unionist dominance. Sinn Fein takes a different view of local councils, where its elected members play an active part.

Early today Mr Adams' party was negotiating hard on cross-border bodies and the make-up of the assembly, backing the SDLP's preferred option of a power-sharing executive. That would mean Mr Adams and Mr Paisley being asked to form part of the same cabinet.

A Sinn Fein spokesman reiterated party policy to boycott an assembly. But asked whether he could envisage any situation in which Sinn Fein would take up its seats after standing in an election, Mr McGuinness said: "We would need to sit down for half an hour on that one."

Roller-coaster ride, page 2

And the groom wore a green anorak

Michael White Political Editor

THE Foreign Secretary, Robin Cook, and his fiancee, Gaynor Regan, yesterday made New Labour history when they sacrificed a sure-fire Fleet Street photo-opportunity in favour of Old Labour privacy by staging a dawn raid on Tunbridge Wells register office.

Instead of tying the knot, in what was a second marriage for both Mr Cook and his diary secretary, in their grand country house at Chevening, near Sevenoaks, Mr and Mrs Cook opted for the register office and what aides called "a private event free from media intrusion" — 10 days earlier than planned.

To make sure they would evade the Fleet Street paparazzi, they also arranged at the last minute not to be married at 5pm yesterday, but before normal matrimonial opening hours, at 8.30am. Building works and a skip outside the door helped spoil any lurking photo-opportunity.

But, while the Foreign Secretary outflanked the media, he was unable to escape the prying eyes of the construction community. Builder Robert Harman saw the party arrive. "It was just the two of them and two men. I think the men were witnesses, although one of them who was wearing a kilt looked like a minder. Mr Cook was wearing a green anorak-type coat and she was wearing a dark suit."

His colleague, painter Allan Oakeshott, said: "When they came out, he [Mr Cook] punched the air." Air, incidentally, that remained confetti-free.

"Robin and Gaynor are delighted to be man and wife. I hope they will be left alone to enjoy the short break they deserve together," said Mr Cook's

constituency agent, Jim Devine, understood to be "the man in the kilt".

The wedding party then repaired to Chevening, set in 3,000 prime acres, to celebrate. Mr Cook let it be known he would be paying for the food and drink out of his own pocket.

His wife of 28 years, the Edinburgh hospital consultant Margaret Cook, told Channel 5 News: "No comment, but I suppose I wish them well." Since her dramatic separation on the eve of a family holiday, when the News of the World broke news of Mr Cook's liaison, she has given waspish media interviews about the hopeless immaturity of middle-aged men — and threatened to do more in the weeks ahead.

The new Mrs Cook, aged 41, and her husband have also been hurt by media attention, including the dubious accolade of a Private Eye cover.

Conspiracy theorists at Westminster could not decide whether the Cooks were attempting to upstage the Northern Ireland peace process or, on balance more likely, to marry while media attention was focused on Belfast.

Leader comment, page 19

Karadzic 'set to surrender'

Richard Norton-Taylor and Jon Henley in Paris

RADOVAN Karadzic, the increasingly isolated former Bosnian Serb leader indicted for genocide and crimes against humanity, is preparing to give himself up to the International War Crimes Tribunal in The Hague, according to Western intelligence and diplomatic sources.

Mr Karadzic, the most wanted Bosnian Serb, was reported last night to have signalled his willingness to surrender to the Hague tribunal subject to conditions, including guarantees about legal representation.

He has been in indirect contact with the tribunal, which was yesterday holding two Bosnian Serbs, Miroslav Kvocka and Mladen Radic, who were arrested on Wednesday by British soldiers understood to be members of the SAS.

The two men face 33 indictments relating to the infamous Omarska death camp, where Serb forces killed, raped, sexually assaulted and beat Muslim and Croat prisoners. They were seized by British special forces in Prijedor, near the former camp in north-west Bosnia.

The French newspaper *Le Monde* said yesterday that Mr Karadzic had left his mountain hideout in the Bosnian Serb capital of Pale last November and was in an unidentified eastern European country, possibly Belarus.

French intelligence sources told the paper that Mr Karadzic had contacted two American lawyers, who are investigating the conditions under

turn to page 3, column 6

Leader comment, page 19

15
9 770261 307354

1998

You are the limit, Brian. We were mature enough to acknowledge that our relationship was in crisis and honest enough to realise that we needed help...

We discussed going to couple counselling and agreed that it would be the most appropriate forum to address our difficulties.

But every week it's the same! Counselling comes round and you go into this big baby strop, and you have to be bullied and cajoled into going. What is your problem?

I want you to come with me.
Yeah, and make me miss my Badminton night. That's so typical of you, Brian....

Welcome aboard, Ben. You'll soon find out that I'm not the sort of practice teacher who just lets her student sit back and observe. You will be expected to make a full and active contribution to the team.
Great!

But before you can do that it's essential that you learn a few ground rules.
Shall I make notes?
By all means, if it helps.

Ready?
Ready.

Right. I'm an Earl Grey, Megan's a PG Tips, Helen's a chocolate Option and Ray's a herbal infusion. Everyone's also a coffee except Ray, who's a Barleycup. NEVER get the two confused! OK, 11 O'clock cakes....

This is the real Crete. Magnificent, majestic, rugged, unspoilt.

Far from the lurid sea front bars, far from the high-rise hotels and apartment blocks....

...far from the teeming hordes of tourists with their football tops and T-shirt tans....
...and far from the nearest phone. Honestly, Brian, if you'd worn your proper shoes like I told you...

1998

The final Test, live online
www.cricket98.co.uk

Glad to be glam — the return of rock's hairiest moments
Review

England's batsmen slump at Headingley
Sport98

45p
Friday
August 7
1998
Published in London and Manchester

NEWSPAPER OF THE YEAR
The Guardian

Do these markings mean that the legend of King Arthur is now fact?

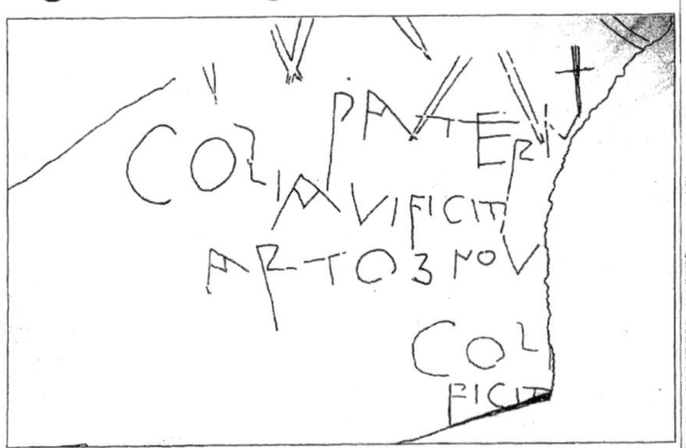

The newly discovered slate which points to Arthur as a warlord of the Dark Ages and (below) a traditional image of King Arthur PHOTOGRAPHS: SAM MORGAN MOORE

Maev Kennedy on a piece of Cornish slate archaeologists say is the 'find of a lifetime'

A SMALL piece of slate inscribed with the word "Artognov" has been found at Tintagel in Cornwall, the traditional birthplace of King Arthur. The stone — described by archaeologists as "the find of a lifetime" — is the first scrap of solid evidence discovered linking the legendary Arthur with a real man.

The chief archaeologist of English Heritage, Geoffrey Wainwright, described the link between the stone, the legend and Arthur as "inescapable".

The stone has been dated to the sixth century by the style of the inscription and the broken pottery and glass found with it. The archaeologists believe it was originally built into the wall of a house that collapsed, before being re-used as a drain cover.

The rocky island site of the castle is one of the most romantic in Britain and it was on the edge of the cliff overlooking a tavern traditionally known as Merlin's Cave that the stone was found. Archaeologists have spent much of this century demolishing links between Arthur and the site as mythical. But what has now been found is evidence of a real historical figure on which the legend was built.

Dr Wainwright said yesterday: "There are two Arthurs. King Arthur the myth — Malory, Tennyson, Excalibur, Guinevere, Lancelot — I'm afraid is fiction. But the warlord who lived in the Dark Ages, named as Arthur in later texts, who fought and won battles, was real.

"What we have here is the right time and the right site and the actual name of Artognov — the coincidence is quite remarkable."

The stone was found on July 4 by a team from Glasgow University led by Chris Morris. It was cleaned and studied at Glasgow before being returned to the site yesterday. One inscription is strongly incised but broken and indecipherable. The other faintly scratched into the stone is mainly in Latin but in post-Roman sixth century script. It reads Pater Coliavificit Artognov, which Charles Thomas, an expert on Tintagel and inscriptions of

turn to page 2, column 8

Leader comment, page 15

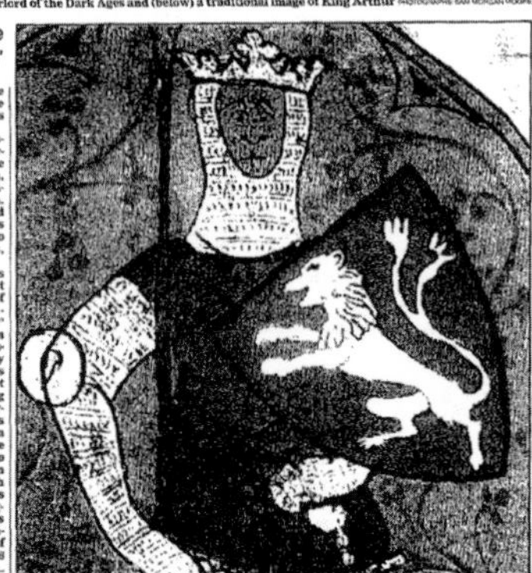

Gag on BBC over MI6 death plot

Richard Norton-Taylor

A BBC television Panorama special was blocked by the Government last night, hours before it planned to reveal further details of an alleged plot by MI6 officers to assassinate the Libyan leader, Colonel Muammar Gadafy.

In the latest twist in the growing international row surrounding attempts to gag former MI5 and MI6 officers, government lawyers served the BBC with an injunction preventing it from making new disclosures about the allegations.

The injunction — which the BBC is expected to challenge in the High Court today — followed the breakdown of protracted talks between the corporation's top executives and government officials.

It is understood the investigation by a BBC journalist, Mark Urban, sheds new light on the circumstances surrounding the alleged plot against Col Gadafy.

The Guardian yesterday published allegations made by David Shayler, the MI5 renegade now locked up in a Paris jail, of an attempt to assassinate the Libyan leader two years ago.

According to Mr Shayler, the failed plot led to the deaths of several bystanders after agents placed the bomb under the wrong car in Col Gadafy's cavalcade. The agent in charge of the 1996 assassination attempt was alleged to have ties with a rightwing group in Libya and was paid $160,000, Mr Shayler says.

The allegations were first published in the New York Times on Tuesday.

The BBC said in a statement last night that it had been investigating for many months suggestions of a plot to murder Col Gadafy. It said: "Some of the detail of the allegations was covered by an injunction which only the Government or the courts have the power to lift."

The statement added: "On Wednesday in the light of foreign press disclosure of an assassination attempt, the BBC asked the Government to lift the injunction so that the whole story could be told."

The BBC said it was particularly anxious to establish that nothing it proposed to broadcast would threaten the safety of security personnel. It said it was urgently considering the next step "in the belief that the public interest now requires full examination of the allegations made by Mr Shayler".

The Government earlier moved quickly to rubbish Mr Shayler's allegations, although ministers were careful not to deny an unauthorised operation.

Lord Williams, the Home Office minister, denied on BBC Radio 4's Today programme there was an "official plot" to kill Col Gadafy. "The matter that really matters to the public, in my opinion, is was there a plot, officially sanctioned, to kill Gadafy?" he said. "That's not true." Questioned by journalists later, Lord Williams said: "In the nature of things, what on earth would be my knowledge of unofficially sanctioned plots?"

The Foreign Office, meanwhile, said: "The central claim that there was an official plot to kill Gadafy is untrue."

A spokesman added: "It is inconceivable in normal peacetime circumstances that authority for the secret intelligence services to conduct assassination attempts would be granted."

Officers from MI5 and its sister service, MI6 — the foreign intelligence agency — were said to have been locked in a frantic damage-limitation exercise.

They are deeply concerned about the seepage of further revelations from both Mr Shayler and Richard Tomlinson, a former MI6 officer, who this week was served with a gagging injunction in New Zealand.

The Government seems particularly anxious to stop the Panorama programme delving into claims that MI6 officers were involved in an operation against Col Gadafy.

Mr Shayler was arrested in Paris late on Saturday night on an extradition warrant pending prosecution in Britain under the Official Secrets Act.

Mr Tomlinson — who was released from prison this year after being convicted for disclosing secrets — was arrested in Paris the previous day at the request of the police Special Branch. He was later released.

In an interview on New Zealand television last night, he accused MI6 of acting illegally and of being poorly managed. He said he was determined to write a book. The broadcaster has also been served with an injunction which it says it will fight.

Letters, page 15

I had sex with Clinton, says Lewinsky

Gary Younge in Washington

A GRIM-faced Monica Lewinsky, whose testimony has the power to alter the course of Bill Clinton's presidency, emerged from the federal grand jury in Washington yesterday after eight hours of interrogation about exactly what took place between them.

After seven months of rumours, leaks and allegations, Ms Lewinsky admitted that she did have sex with the president and that he had encouraged her to keep quiet about it, legal sources said.

One report claimed she had confessed to 10 sexual encounters with Mr Clinton over the course of a year.

She reportedly testified that their relationship had started in November 1995 and that she had sex with him in the Oval Office. The kind of sex they had was not deemed by the president to constitute a sexual relationship.

She gave the evidence to the grand jury in return for full immunity for herself, her mother, and, it emerged, her father. But she insisted that the president had never asked her to lie under oath.

"Monica and her family are relieved that this ordeal finally appears to be coming to an end," said Judy Smith, representing Ms Lewinsky. "She answered each question truthfully, completely and honestly that was posed to her by the Office of Independent Counsel and also questions that were posed to her by members of the grand jury."

It was not immediately clear whether she would have to return to answer more questions. Linda Tripp, Ms Lewinsky's former friend who handed over tapes of their private conversations, was interviewed for eight days by the same panel.

Wearing a navy blue suit, a visibly nervous Ms Lewinsky, the 25-year-old former White House intern, had been ushered into a side entrance of the courthouse. She was hugged by one of her lawyers before disappearing into a lift usually reserved for judges.

Only a few streets away President Clinton, looking uncharacteristically flustered, stumbled over a speech at an anti-crime event in the White House's Rose Garden.

In public the president's legal team said they hoped Ms Lewinsky's testimony would mark the beginning of the end of a scandal that has engulfed the presidency. "The view here is that we're hopeful that this means a four-year investigation that has cost upwards of $40 million [£25 million] is finally coming to a conclusion," said the White House deputy press secretary, Barry Toiv.

But privately they are anxious to learn precisely how convincing Ms Lewinsky's testimony is, and how much of it can be backed up. They are particularly keen to know the results of the FBI forensic examination of a dress, handed over to the independent prosecutor Kenneth Starr by Ms Lewinsky as part of her immunity agreement.

Mr Starr is also believed to have procured presents the president gave to Ms Lewinsky, taped messages from him on her answering machine, and a signed picture.

Last December, Ms Lewinsky signed a written affidavit in the Paula Jones sexual harassment case, claiming she did not have a sexual relationship with the president.

Mr Clinton, who has denied having a sexual relationship with her under oath and in public, is to appear on August 17 before the grand jury, in a live video link-up from the White House.

Lifetime chained to scandal, page 10; Guardian website: http://reports.guardian.co.uk/clinton/clinton.html

Inside

Home Official figures reveal a marked resurgence in hardcore football-related violence at English league matches. **6**

International Hanan Ashrawi resigned from Yasser Arafat's cabinet, accusing him of failing to curb corruption in public life. **11**

Analysis Are Britain's top clubs really going to defect to a European Super League and is it a serious proposal or just a poker game? **13**

Finance Boom has turned to bust in the semi-conductor business, bringing a potential jobs crisis to Tyneside and South Wales. **18**

Weather 13; Obituaries 16
Comment 14; Crossword 22
Friday Review
Quick Crossword 28
Television 26; Radio 27

32
9 770261 307354

1998

So, Clare, what exactly is your policy towards giving money to beggars?
It's quite clear, Megan: DON'T!
It's disempowering, patronising and ultimately self-defeating, a futile gesture that helps perpetuate the problem, not alleviate it, a sop to guilty liberal conscience rather than genuine concern.
If you want to help street people then fight to change the system. In the meantime all requests for loose change should be met with a firm, polite but unequivocal 'No!'
But you just gave that chap 20p!
Yeah, well, he had a puppy.

You'd arsing well think.... that the stupid bastard publishers... would sodding well realise.... that if they made it so bloody small.... people would lose the sodding, arsing, bloody bastard thing.....
Honestly, Clare, don't worry. I can always get my own copy of 'The Little Book of Calm'.

I know you're in a difficult position, Megan. But people have to be allowed to make mistakes and learn from them. You can't just barge into their lives, like some god of the ancients, and take control.
I know, Clare, but to sit by and do nothing, it's killing me!! Intervention isn't necessarily control. To share information is surely an act of empowerment. What do you think?
I think that next time we should go to a pub without a quiz on.
Gary Cooper, Gary Cooper, It's Gary Sodding Cooper, you morons.
High Noon? That's John Wayne, isn't it?
Definitely.
I agree.
Who's John Wayne?

What is he playing at?

G2 with today's television

Why self-help books are no help at all

Women, G2 page 4

45p

Thursday
September 10
1998
Published in London
and Manchester

NEWSPAPER OF THE YEAR

The Guardian

Benefit payments in chaos

Computer collapse wipes out records

David Brindle, Social Services Correspondent

THE main computer register of the national insurance records of everybody in Britain has collapsed, throwing the social security system into turmoil and forcing benefit offices to make payments to claimants without knowing if they are eligible.

The Department of Social Security has been trying to play down the crisis, believed already to have hit at least 80,000 claims for jobseekers' allowances and incapacity benefits, but last night admitted it was in difficulties.

While stressing that a fall-back system was coping with the vast majority of problems caused by the collapse, a department spokesman said: "For some claims it may not always be possible to finalise entitlement to a number of benefits. To protect these customers, contingency measures were put in place and interim payments have been made."

The department has set up a telephone helpline for people hitting problems with benefit claims or with new state pensions, payment of which is being delayed in a growing number of cases.

The collapse of the national insurance register, known as NIRS, has occurred during the transfer of its records to a new computer under the biggest and most complex information technology project in Europe. The £170 million project is being spearheaded under the private finance initiative by contractor Andersen Consulting.

The ill-fated project has already been severely delayed, with Andersen's contract having been renegotiated in 1996 and the company having paid compensation for its failure to deliver on time.

Although the DSS has been reluctant to admit NIRS has ceased functioning, it has issued a circular to local authorities — responsible for payment of housing and council tax benefits — on what to do in light of the system's "closure". One reason for the department's coyness is likely to be fear of encouraging fraud. Local authorities are being told to make benefit payments on account, assessing the claimant's eligibility as best they can, and to make corrections later when the computer comes back on line.

The Contributions Agency, which handles national insurance records, says it can establish most claimants' eligibility to jobseeker's allowance (JSA) by checking an alternative source, its central index. However, the agency says that in a "small number" of cases — which it cannot quantify — it is unable to do this. In these cases claimants are being asked to produce former employers' P60 forms and wage slips. If these are unavailable or inadequate, they are being awarded interim payments of benefit which are not JSA, have no such standing in law and therefore cannot be used to determine entitlement to other benefits.

One local government benefits expert described the impact on councils as "quite drastic" and said there was anger that the DSS had sought to keep quiet about the problem, believed to have started in June, until the circular was issued last Friday.

A spokeswoman for the National Association of Citizen's Advice Bureaux said the association had been told nothing about the problem, but bureaux including those in Leeds and Stoke-on-Trent had started to report complaints and delays.

David Rendel, social security spokesman for the Liberal Democrats, described the position as "a complete mess". He feared widespread overpayment of benefits, with no clarity as to who would be responsible.

"The main concern, though, has to be the potential for very considerable fraud. They cannot be sure of getting it right even where they are using people's wage slips," Mr Rendel said.

Benefit officials are braced for the NIRS system to be out of action until at least the end of October, although Andersen's is understood to think it is close to solving the problem.

All interim and "on-account" payments will be reviewed once the computer becomes operational, with the DSS expected to underwrite losses incurred through overpayment and fraud. No claimant is expected to be asked to repay money.

A spokesman said: "In these circumstances, ministers have asked that we are sensitive in the way that we go about applying the legislation on recovery of overpaid benefit."

Clinton affair at crisis point

Martin Kettle and Mark Tran in Washington

THE key to the fate of Bill Clinton's threatened presidency finally arrived at the United States Congress last night in a 500-page report by the independent counsel, Kenneth Starr, accompanied by 36 boxes of evidence.

In the climax of a fast-moving day in Washington, Mr Starr delivered his long-awaited report on the Monica Lewinsky affair in two vans under FBI guard. The report with its accompanying documents and tapes was immediately transferred to a specially prepared secure room on the ground floor of the House of Representatives on Capitol Hill.

The arrival of the vans at 4pm local time touched off the next and potentially most critical phase of the Lewinsky crisis, as Mr Clinton battles to avoid becoming the first US president to be successfully impeached by Congress.

Mr Starr's spokesman, Charles Bakaly, told reporters the report contained "substantial and credible information that may constitute grounds for impeaching the president of the United States" — the phrase specified in the constitution. Mr Bakaly said Mr Starr's office had "fulfilled its duty" and the matter now rested with Congress.

The White House immediately denied the report threatened Mr Clinton's presidency. "The president has apologised for his relationship with Ms Lewinsky and has asked for forgiveness," Mr Clinton's lawyer, David Kendall, said.

He said the documents "represent only the prosecutor's allegations, allegations that we have been denied a chance to review. But we do know this: there is no basis for impeachment."

The House Speaker, Newt Gingrich, who has initial custody of the report, said he expected the report and its accompanying materials would not be inspected until the House passes a procedural resolution tomorrow.

Initial reports said approximately 280 pages of the report concerned the Lewinsky case.

Mr Gingrich said a resolution on Congress's handling of the report would be agreed by the House rules committee today and would reach the House tomorrow. "None of us would have access to that room until after we passed that resolution on the House floor."

The report eclipsed a day in which Mr Clinton was forced by senior Democrats to issue his most fulsome apology for his affair with Ms Lewinsky.

He told a Democratic fund-raising event in Florida: "I let you down. I let my family down. I let this country down. I'm trying to make it right. I'm determined to never let anything like that happen again."

Mr Clinton said a young boy had said to him earlier in the day that when he grew up he wanted to be president. "I want to be able to conduct my life and my presidency so that all the parents of the country can feel good if their children were able to say that again."

He asked his audience to "tell your friends and neighbours that I'm grateful and I'm determined to redeem the trust of all the American people".

His comments came as a direct response to an ultimatum from fellow Democrats yesterday to mend his ways and grovel publicly to the American people if he is to save his embattled presidency.

In what was described as "a very, very emotional" White House confrontation with senior members of his own party, senior House Democrats told Mr Clinton to show more contrition "on a continual basis" for the affair.

Amid reliable reports that the president's marriage is still seriously under pressure, Mr Clinton's advisers pressed for First Lady Hillary Clinton to break her silence and make a statement of forgiveness to her husband for lying about his affair with the former White House intern. A spokeswoman for Mrs Clinton said she had no plans to do so.

With few if any public figures willing to stand up for the errant president's response to the crisis, there was speculation that the former senator George Mitchell would shortly be appointed as the key liaison between the White House and Capitol Hill.

The House Democratic whip, David Bonior, warned: "The president needs to make it clear to the American people in the way that he did to us today, his contrition, his sorrow for his actions and he needs to do that not just once. He needs to understand that this is a process that will be ongoing."

The drumbeat of Democratic disapproval continued yesterday, with the veteran Senator Richard Byrd of West Virginia accusing Mr Clinton of making "many of the mistakes" in the Lewinsky scandal that Richard Nixon made over Watergate. Senator Fritz Hollings of South Carolina said: "We're fed up. The behaviour, the dishonesty of the president is unacceptable."

There is a growing belief that the Democrats will lose Senate contests in California, Illinois, Kentucky, Nevada and South Carolina on November 3, giving the Republicans a 60-40 Senate majority.

Mr Gingrich faced the press yesterday to pledge a bipartisan approach to the handling of the report, flanked by fellow Republicans Dick Armey, House majority leader, and Henry Hyde, judiciary committee chairman, and by their Democratic equivalents, Dick Gephardt and John Conyers.

"We have made a good start at making this a non-partisan effort," Mr Gephardt said.

"This is a lousy job, but somebody has to do it," said Mr Hyde, whose committee will be the first to weigh Mr Starr's report. "No one looks forward to this traumatic journey."

President under siege, page 13

President Clinton boards Air Force One yesterday to fly to Florida as Starr delivered his report PHOTOGRAPH: WIN McNAMEE

'I let this country down. I'm trying to make it right. I'm determined to never let anything like that happen again'
President Clinton

'The report contains substantial and credible information that may constitute grounds for impeaching the president'
Kenneth Starr's spokesman

Royal Opera to close for year in rescue deal

Nick Hopkins

THE Royal Opera House was in a precarious limbo yesterday following the announcement of a rescue package which could either save the company or see it slide into oblivion.

After 48 hours of frantic negotiations between ministers from the Department of Culture, Media and Sport and the Arts Council, chairman Sir Colin Southgate revealed that the opera house would close next year to save money.

However, to the astonishment and anger of many in the arts, Sir Colin said the company, a model of financial incompetence in recent years, had been promised extra funds to bring its spiralling debt under control in time for a grand reopening in December 1999.

There is a catch: the money is dependent on the company honouring firm commitments to continue to cut its costs, become less elitist and reduce ticket prices.

Crucially, the agreement hinges on whether the company's 600 staff agree to give up their restrictive working practices, and accept redundancies. Negotiations between management and the unions will start shortly and

turn to page 2, column 4

Opera crisis, page 5; Hugo Young, page 18; Leader comment, page 19

Inside

37
9 770261 307347

1998

Megan, I've made a decision. I'm going to talk to Brian. I'm going to say to him:
'Brian, we just don't communicate any more and as a result we've become emotionally distant. For the sake of our relationship I think it's vitally important that we put aside the next couple of hours and simply talk about our hopes, our fears, our dreams... our future'.
Good for you, Clare! You can't put these things off.
Who says? I'm planning on doing it Sunday night as the World Cup final's about to start.
HARRY VENNING

So, Julie, your course is nearly over and the big bad world is out there taunting you to come and have a go if you think you're hard enough....
I hope that the six weeks you've been here on placement have given you an insight into the life stretching ahead of you as a social worker.
Come on Julie, at least open your present.

In any group situation there is always a danger that the most socially inadequate or personality challenged member is singled out by the others and used as a focus for discontent...
...and as a team I think we should acknowledge firstly that we have established such a scapegoat, secondly that it is a group dynamic that we are all responsible for, and thirdly...
...she's coming this way.

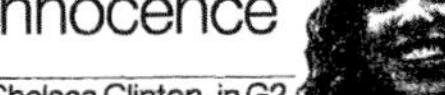

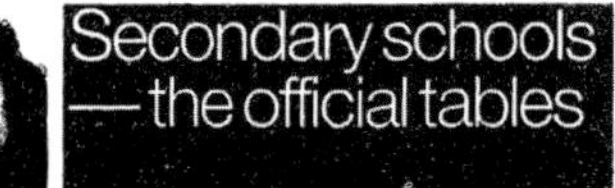

Join our
Christmas
appeal

This section, p8

45p
Tuesday
December 1
1998
Published in London
and Manchester

The Guardian

City crisis as 5,000 jobs lost

Jill Treanor

THE pace of job losses in the City surged yesterday with the news that up to 5,000 workers face the sack as a result of Deutsche Bank's purchase of Bankers Trust of America for $10 billion. The deal will create the world's largest financial services company.

The job cuts will weigh heavily on the City, where many financial firms have already cut up to 5 per cent of traders and financial staff as a result of losses during the recent global stock market upheavals.

Banking sources also fear the worst is to come as other financial groups chase merger partners to increase their presence in the world financial markets.

Deutsche Bank, announcing the record-breaking deal in Frankfurt, said that in a move to cut costs as a result of the acquisition, it would slash 5,500 jobs in London and New York. City sources said last night that at least 3,000 would be felt in London, where Deutsche and Bankers Trust have considerable overlap in some business areas.

"Next year it's going to happen more because other organisations are going to go through the same merger process," said Nick Marsh, marketing director of MSL, an executive search company.

The fact that two non-British owned financial firms can inflict such damage on the City is a sign of the changing structure of ownership of the City's main employers.

Deutsche Bank helped set the pace in 1989 when it swallowed Morgan Grenfell, one of the oldest City firms. German rival Dresdner bought Kleinwort Benson, another City firm, while a Swiss bank gobbled up Phillips & Drew.

The big three
World's biggest banks

Deutsche Bank
Takes over Bankers Trust
- Assets: **$800bn**
- Employees: **96,442**

Citicorp
Citigroup and Travelers merger in April 1998
- Assets: **$700bn**
- Employees: **162,000**

UBS
UBS* and Swiss Bank Corporation merger in December 1997
- Assets: **$600bn**
- Employees: **56,000**

*Union Bank of Switzerland

American banks have also jumped in, including Merrill Lynch, which bought British stock broker Smith New Court, while earlier this year Bankers Trust bought part of NatWest's investment banking business. Earlier this month Merrill Lynch announced that 450 jobs would be cut in London.

Few of the main players in the financial markets are now British-owned, with the exception of investment banks Schroders and Rothschild.

The City feels the pain of many mergers and cut-backs because it has one of the largest concentrations of financial services jobs in the world. A recent report by the Corporation of London calculated that more than 250,000 people are employed by financial services in London.

London jostles with New York and Tokyo to claim the title of the world's largest financial centre and dwarfs Frankfurt, even though the German city is home to the new European central bank.

"London as a financial centre is not losing out," said Matthew Czepliewicz, banking analyst at Salomon Smith Barney, the US investment bank.

The London International Financial Futures and Options Exchange (LIFFE), the City's derivatives exchange, is also cutting 600 positions to reduce costs. Its first step towards phasing out its colourful trading floor for the sedate world of electronic trading began yesterday and that move is also being blamed for job losses in the financial markets.

It was unclear last night which parts of the Deutsche and Bankers Trust operations in London would feel most of the cuts, which will be phased in over a year. Deutsche is the bigger employer in London, with more than 6,200 staff, while Bankers Trust, which employs 1,000 people in Edinburgh, has a total of 3,500 employees in Britain.

Deutsche Bank said yesterday that it is setting aside $400 million (about £240 million) to persuade key staff not to leave Bankers Trust as a result of the deal. Insiders described the atmosphere in Bankers Trust's London office as subdued yesterday.

The employees heard the news of the merger, first rumoured last month, over live television links to the Frankfurt news conference. City sources also said that Deutsche Bank employees were feeling uncertain.

The prospects are bleak for some of those who will lose their jobs. City career management firm Meridian Consulting estimated that the time it was taking to find employment in the City had reached nearly 19 weeks, against 14 weeks a year ago.

"There are lot more people on the streets," said Linda Jackson, principal consultant at Meridian Consulting. "Up to 40 per cent [of those who are losing their jobs] are leaving the City anyway," she said.

The acquisition trail, and City Notebook, page 23

The general gets his orders: stop moaning and get out

A sticker on the fence of Grovelands Priory Hospital in London suggests a solution to the dilemma posed by its unwelcome inmate PHOTOGRAPH: ADAM BUTLER

Nick Hopkins and Richard Norton-Taylor

CHILEAN officials were trying desperately to find accommodation for General Augusto Pinochet last night after the private clinic where he is staying said it would consider suing him unless he leaves immediately.

The Grovelands Priory Hospital in Southgate, north London, has been urging Gen Pinochet to go for a fortnight.

Doctors treating the former Chilean dictator say there is nothing wrong with him, and staff are tired of the disruption his presence is causing. "Grovelands is not a hotel and it is not a secure unit either," said a source.

There have also been murmurings that Gen Pinochet, who is used to staying in five-star hotels on his travels abroad, has been a difficult and fussy patient who "enjoys a good moan". The hospital's frustration came to a head yesterday afternoon when executives, led by Grovelands' director, David Cole, issued an ultimatum.

In a terse meeting, the general's aides were told that he had outstayed his welcome and that other patients needed his bed. The hospital, which charges up to £330 a day, indicated it would take "whatever means necessary" to evict him.

Afterwards, the hospital said it was preparing to "discharge Gen Pinochet from its care". The statement continued: "It was stated in open court over two weeks ago that Gen Pinochet was fit enough to appear at an initial bail hearing.

"He no longer requires the specialist medical and nursing care provided at Grovelands Priory. The management has reminded his advisers of this and it is hoped that Gen Pinochet will find alternative accommodation as quickly as possible."

Mr Cole made it plain he will instruct lawyers if there is any prevarication. One option is to sue the general for trespass. "That is a possibility," said a source. "The hospital is considering several legal alternatives."

The Grovelands hospital first mooted that Gen Pinochet should leave two weeks ago, when an in-house psychiatrist, Geoffrey Lloyd, concluded that the 83-year-old was not suffering from any psychological problems.

Reports last week that the general, who was admitted on October 29, shortly after surgery on his back, might be suffering from a stress-related disorder amazed his carers. "He could have left weeks ago," said a source.

"We have been told, time and again, that his people are looking for another place for him to stay, but nothing has happened."

The Chilean embassy is looking at properties in Weybridge and Virginia Water, upmarket areas of Surrey.

Diplomats were caught out by last week's law lords decision that Gen Pinochet was not immune from prosecution, and are trying to hire a

turn to page 3, column 1

Letters, page 21

Green fairy fires spirits after long absinthe

Absinthe makes the art . . . detail from Degas' L'Absinthe

Stuart Millar

MANET, Degas and Picasso painted it, Toulouse Lautrec drank it from a hollow walking stick, and Hemingway did knife tricks on it. This week, absinthe, a 70 per cent proof, hallucinogenic concoction hailed as the ultimate in *fin de siècle* decadence, will be legally available again in Britain after an 80-year absence.

Twice the strengh of most other spirits, the emerald green tipple of choice for 19th century artists and intellectuals has been banned in France, Belgium, Switzerland and the US since the first world war.

Now, to the horror of alcohol awareness campaigners, a British company has secured an importation contract with a tiny Czech distillery after discovering that the drink was never formally prohibited in this country.

Green Bohemia — set up by the Idler magazine, a drinks importer and a former member of the indie rock group Jesus and Mary Chain — plans to market absinthe as an exclusive and extremely potent way of celebrating the new millennium for those desperately seeking a new kick. It will retail at £40 a bottle — reflecting the sizeable alcohol duty taxes involved — via mail order and the Internet under the slogan The Spirit of Freedom.

The drink's revival has provoked astonishment among campaigners who accuse Green Bohemia of giving young people the ammunition to drink to dangerous excess.

"We can understand people wanting to party to celebrate the millennium, but we would suggest that they didn't necessarily have to be comatose to do so," said Caroline Bradley of Alcohol Concern.

Imported from Switzerland to France in 1797 by Henri Louis Pernod, the aniseed-flavoured drink is made by soaking dried wormwood in ethanol alcohol along with other herbs such as hyssop and lemon balm. Its active ingredient, thujone, has a similar molecular structure to cannabis. The accepted method of consumption has guaranteed that the drink is likened more to narcotics than to other alcoholic substances. It involves filling a spoon with sugar which is then soaked in absinthe, set alight and dripped into a glass of absinthe, which also catches fire.

At this point water should be added, but such is the potency of the drink that it can be difficult to put out the flames: when the Pernod factory in Pontarlier was struck by lightning in 1901, it burned for four days.

The precursor to the French staple pastis — literally, a pastiche of its more potent cousin — absinthe rose to popularity alongside cocaine fortified wines last century after successive failures of the grape harvest caused the price of wine to soar.

By the late 1800s, La Fée Verte — the Green Fairy — was being consumed with such fervour by the Parisian artistic and literary set that cocktail hour was renamed L'Heure Verte.

Among its devotees were Oscar Wilde, Ernest Dowson and Charles Baudelaire. Van Gogh's ear-cutting incident is popularly attributed to absinthe intoxication.

Absinthe: hallucinogenic

Inside

Home
The president of one of the medical royal colleges criticised them as cosy clubs, which discreetly promote the interests of doctors, not patients.
Page 5

Analysis
Should farmers become agri-businesses or environmental custodians? James Meikle reports on the growing crisis down on Britain's farms.
Page 19

Sport
Australia need just one more Test victory to retain the Ashes after their comprehensive three-day demolition of England in Perth.
Page 28

International 14–18
Weather 19; Comment 20
Letters 21; Finance 23–25
Prices 28; Crossword 30
Quick Crossword 18
Radio 19; Television 20

1998

Your compassion does you credit, Ben. Which of us hasn't looked at one of the poor wretches and thought: 'There but for the grace of God go I'? But never feel sorry for them, whatever you do. They can sense pity a mile off, and they'll hate you for it.
Besides, they get stacks more holidays than we do.

I'm so glad you could make it tonight, Clare. I think I'd have gone crazy and exploded if I hadn't talked to you and got it out of my system.
Honestly, we men are so scared of making ourselves vulnerable by expressing our feelings, sharing our fears, discussing our problems...
...but with you I really feel I can talk about anything deeply personal that's bothering me, safe in the knowledge....
...that you're not listening to a word I'm saying.
The pool table's free. Fancy a game?

Clare, what do the team clerks do?
The team clerks?
The team clerks, Ben, are a behind-the-scenes army of colourful characters without whose dedication, effort and commitment no social work office could ever hope to function.
But what do they do?
Who cares?
HARRY VENNING

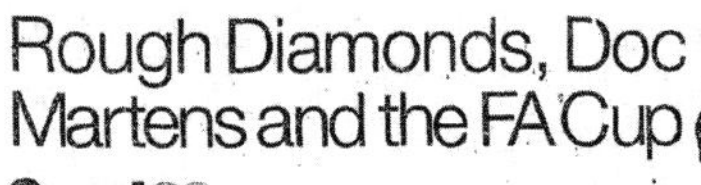

Rough Diamonds, Doc Martens and the FA Cup
Sport99

Did Humphrey Bogart destroy Lauren Bacall?
Friday Review

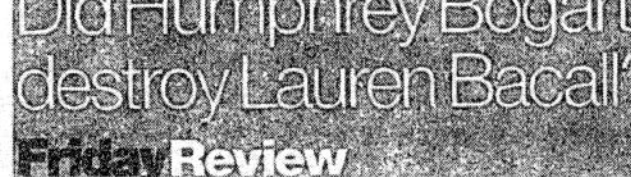

45p
Friday
January 1
1999
Published in London
and Manchester

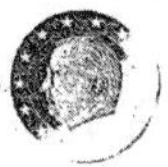

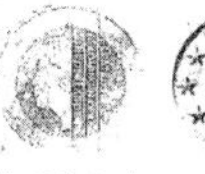

Austria | Belgium | Finland | France | Germany | The Netherlands | Ireland | Italy | Portugal | Spain

Welcome to Euroland

The face of a euro is unveiled in Paris while, above, the euro coins of the participating countries are shown. The coins will not come into use for three years. Belgium and Luxembourg will share the same coin MAIN PHOTOGRAPH MAL LANGSDON

Britain on sidelines as 300m people in 11 states launch single currency

Alex Brummer, Mark Milner and Martin Walker in Brussels

EUROPE today took its boldest step towards integration when 11 states scrapped centuries of history to adopt the euro as their common currency.

Euroland, as the new currency bloc is known, will be one of the world's economic powerhouses, embracing more than 300 million people and responsible for one fifth of the world's output — not far behind the United States.

The arrival of the euro is emblematic of Europe's 50-year drive to bury the ghost of two world wars and usher in a period of harmony and stability based on common economic interests and developing political and defence ties. It grows out of the ideals established by the Treaty of Rome in 1957.

Amid the elan, enthusiasm and balloons which attended the birth at a champagne reception in Brussels yesterday, there were still shadows over the project. Notably absent from the party was the Chancellor, Gordon Brown — Britain remains outside Euroland — and there was bickering about the future leadership of the all-powerful European central bank.

The German chancellor, Gerhard Schröder, was quick to endorse the single currency, in which his country will play the anchor role. "Our future begins on January 1 1999: the euro is Europe's key to the 21st century. The era of solo national fiscal and economic policy is over," he said. His paean to the euro contrasts markedly with his views as recently as March 1998, when he characterised it as a "sickly premature infant", the result of an "overhasty monetary union".

The European Commission president, Jacques Santer, registered the importance of the currency, saying: "The euro is now in your hands. It belongs to you, citizens of Europe. It is in your interests to use it and give it life."

'Our future begins on January 1 1999: the euro is Europe's key to the 21st century. The era of solo national fiscal and economic policy is over'

German chancellor Gerhard Schröder

Wim Duisenberg, president of the new European central bank, commented: "The euro is far more than a medium of exchange ... It is part of the identity of a people. It reflects what they have in common now and in the future."

But even as the euro was launched Mr Duisenberg had to defuse a row with the French government over when he would quit as president of the ECB to make way for France's Jean-Claude Trichet.

The launch of the euro came into effect at midnight last night, after European finance ministers had set the rates at which national currencies are now "locked" into the euro. One euro will initially be worth 70p.

Although notes and coins will not circulate until 2002, and British membership remains in abeyance, UK business instantly adapted to the new regime. From today British Airways passengers flying to and from Europe will be offered the option of paying in euros. Marks & Spencer stores will be fully equipped to accept euros, and building societies and banks are offering euro savings accounts and mortgages.

When financial markets reopen for full-scale trading on January 4, after the New Year holiday, some 9,851 financial institutions from Helsinki to Rome and from Dublin to Vienna will be engaged in a spider's web of transactions, using the euro. The first foreign exchange trades in the euro will take place in Australasia on Sunday night.

The City of London, the world's biggest foreign exchange market, will start to trade in euros in the early hours of Monday morning. Shares in leading European companies, government bonds and sophisticated financial instruments will be quoted in euros.

Many corporations, including some British firms like ICI, will be invoicing in the currency. Some 60 per cent of shares traded in London are in foreign companies, many of them European.

Some 30,000 City staff will be at work today as the financial community begins the task of switching its systems from trading in the 11 member currencies to the euro.

City restaurants and wine bars will be open, tons of freshly made sandwiches are being shipped into the Square Mile, and London Underground will open the special line which moves thousands of commuters from Waterloo to Bank station, in the heart of the City. Some 3,500 free parking spaces are being allocated, and banks have block-booked hotel rooms.

More than one-third of the world's foreign exchange transactions are conducted by the British banks and the 500 foreign institutions across the City — six times more than in Frankfurt, the home of the European central bank.

The 11 Euroland countries — Germany, France, Italy, Spain, Portugal, Belgium, the Netherlands, Luxembourg, Austria, Ireland and Finland — come together at a fortuitous juncture. Inflation across the 11 slipped below 1 per cent in November, down from 1.7 per cent a year earlier. The gap between the highest and the lowest inflation countries has narrowed considerably, which may make it easier for investors to accept the euro as a serious rival to the dollar.

There is a general expectation that when full-scale trading starts the euro could initially rise against the dollar, the yen and the pound.

Birth of euro, page 3; Paul Lashmar, page 14; Letters and Leader comment, page 15; Notebook, page 16; London weighs risks, page 17

EMERGENCY Winter Appeal
What way is this to start the New Year?

Cold, homeless and alone

Hundreds of young people, from across the UK, will come to us over the next few weeks – the coldest of the winter. Christmas – a time of 'family togetherness' – is also when many young people are thrown out of home. Without immediate help homelessness can soon become a way of life – and cause of death.

Alone in London runs a unique service to help young lives shattered by family breakdown. Right now our Crisis Counselling and Family Mediating Teams are working flat out to ensure these young people do not become permanently homeless. Starting with a hot meal and help for emergency accommodation we take practical steps to reconcile young people with their families or support them in starting a life away from home - secure from the cold and danger of the streets of London.

❄ **£30 could help 1 young person**
❄ **£270 could help 9 young people**

I will give ☐ £30 ☐ £270 ☐ £1000 My choice £_____ to save young people from homelessness (Cheque to Alone in London).

Mr/Mrs/Miss/Ms _____
Address _____
_____ Postcode _____
I will pay by Access/Visa/AmEx/CAF Card
No. _____
Signature _____ Date _____

Return to: Depute Quinn (QE1) Director, Liverpool, Winter Appeal, Alone in London, Unit 5 BELLPORT LONDON, LONDON WC1H 9HB. Registered Charity No 280425

Help put shattered lives back together

MM minus I bugs Roman scholars

Julian Borger in Washington

WHILE the pundits have been wringing their hands over Y2K — the prospect of a computer meltdown in 2000 — they have somehow allowed another quandary, brewing since Roman times, to creep up. Is this the first day of MCMXCIX, MDCCCCLXXXXVIIII, or just MIM?

There seems to be no consensus on how to write 1999 in Roman numerals, leaving architects, librarians, Olympic organisers and the people who do the rolling credits at the end of movies stuck for a definitive answer.

Even the US National Institute of Standards and Technology, the arbiter of most time-oriented problems with all its scientists and nuclear clocks, admits it is baffled.

A spokesman for the institute, Michael Newman, conceded yesterday: "We got a question about this some time ago and some researchers have been working on it, but there is no one answer.

"Romans did not use subtraction like we do now — IX for 9 for example. So they would have spelt it the long way: MDCCCCLXXXXVIIII. We felt MCMXCIX tends to follow the 20th century tradition."

But what about the modishly compact MIM? Mr Newman said it got the thumbs-down for not being sufficiently posh.

"I don't think MIM will get used all that much. It looks a little dinky. If you're using Roman numerals, you probably want it to look impressive."

Part of the problem is that the Romans never came up with a figure for zero — that was left for Arab mathematicians. But despite its obvious advantages, the Arab system did not supplant Roman numerals until the 16th century. And even four centuries later, the Roman style retains a certain kudos.

The Institute of Standards freely admits to having been blind-sided by the problem, as it had been focusing on the burning issue of when the new millennium really starts — January 1 2000, or a year later. At least, Mr Newman pointed out, the MIM crisis is unlikely to prove as catastrophic as Y2K, or should that be YMM?

Millennium bug could close schools, page 9; End of world very nigh indeed, page 10

How Harold Wilson aimed to ban foreign holidays

HAROLD Wilson's Labour government drew up a secret plan in 1968 to ban foreign holidays and restrict luxury imports in a bid to save the economy, cabinet papers released today reveal.

Under the plan, imports of French wine, Swiss chocolate, avocados and out of season strawberries would have been limited in the event of a "major external cataclysm". Wilson and his colleagues agonised over the inclusion of tinned salmon on the list.

The plan, never implemented, was overseen by the then chancellor, Lord Jenkins. Only the prime minister and a handful of cabinet ministers were aware of it.

The fingerprints of MI5 can be found throughout the documents released today, as Wilson's government struggled with internal splits, leaks and street protests.

MI5 conducted a leak inquiry into Guardian journalist Ian Aitken and Financial Times reporter John Bourne over cabinet split stories. It also provided lurid briefings about the influence of "extremists" in demonstrations, and reported that what had been regarded as spontaneous marches by dockers backing Enoch Powell had been organised by the far right.

Full reports, pages 4-5; Leader comment, page 15

Inside

Home	**International**	**Finance**	**Sport**
The hostages who survived the bloody gun battle in the Yemeni desert began their journey back to Britain.	Muscovites rushed to buy presents, champagne and vodka, despite the expectation of three-figure inflation in 1999.	Eight of Britain's largest building societies face a battle over their future after being targeted by rebel members.	England countered the recall of Shane Warne by summoning Ashley Giles for their 5th Test squad in Sydney. Sport99
7	**12**	**16**	**4**

Weather 11; Obituaries 13
Comment 14; Crossword 16
Friday Review
Television and radio for New Year's Day 18-19

53
9 770261 307354

1999

... and another thing.... oh, excuse me, Mrs Potton...
BBBRING
Hello.... For God's sake, Brian!! How many times have I told you not to phone me at work?!!! I will NOT blur the line between my professional and personal life. Now, if you'll excuse me, I'm with a client! Goodbye!
Was that your boyfriend?
Yes, that's right.
I see what you mean about clingy. No wonder you feel suffocated by his constant need for reassurance and I'm frankly not surprised you've withdrawn from him, both emotionally and sexually...

What's wrong, Clare? You've been staring at that screen for ages.
The rest of the world embraces the future, Megan, leaving me alone in my ignorance. And it's a scary, solitary place.
The 20th Century gives way to the 21st, science fiction becomes science fact, the familiar is suddenly unfamiliar! God, am I the only person frightened by I.T.?
Of course not. It's really scary....
... but everything's OK in the end because Elliot helps him escape on the flying bicycle.
Talking to you, Megan, is strangely comforting.
You're welcome

You have just broken the first rule of social work, Megan...
But honestly, I've never heard anything as ridiculous in all my....
No Ifs or buts, Megan....
It's not our job to tell clients what to do, and certainly not get into an argument with them. Mr. and Mrs. Phipps want to name their baby daughter after the all-time greatest Manchester United XI...
... and it's nobody's business except Mum's, Dad's and little Chloe, Stepney, Crerand, Meredith, Edwards, Stiles, Robson, Giggs, Hughes, Charlton, Best, Cantona's! End of story!!
BUT FOR CRYING OUT LOUD, CLARE, I HAD TO SAY SOMETHING!! MARK HUGHES OVER DENIS LAW, I ASK YOU!!!

The secret life of Redford Jnr

G2 with today's television

When your husband also loves a man

Women, G2 page 6

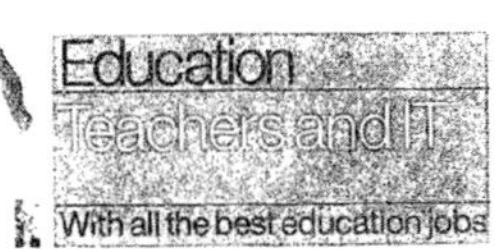

Education Teachers and IT

With all the best education jobs

45p
Tuesday
February 2
1999
Published in London and Manchester

NEWSPAPER OF THE YEAR

The Guardian

Hoddle: my conscience is clear

Nick Hopkins and Martin Thorpe

SENIOR executives of the Football Association were in crisis talks over Glenn Hoddle's future last night as they considered whether they could fire the England coach or issue him with an ultimatum that would force his hand.

Four members of the FA's international committee, which appointed Hoddle and is the only body that can sack him, were poring over the details of his £350,000-a-year contract, in preparation for a meeting with him this morning.

With condemnation coming from all sides — including a surprise intervention from Tony Blair — the FA may find the pressure to sack him for his remarks about disabled people irresistible.

But the FA, which will make a further statement at lunchtime today, is also investigating other options.

One would be to rebuke Hoddle and order him not to talk to the press about anything other than football. That sanction may not prove strong enough to defuse the row.

Many senior figures in the FA have been unhappy with Hoddle's reliance on the faith healer Eileen Drewery, and may use the crisis to demand that he sever all ties with her. If that is suggested, Hoddle may leave of his own accord, albeit with an estimated £500,000 pay-off.

The England manager ruled out resignation yesterday during a round of TV interviews in which he initially denied telling the Times that people born with disabilities were being punished for the sins of their past lives.

"I am not going to resign over this because at the end of the day I didn't say those things ... I let my guard down. I am sorry for the distress it might have caused the disabled," he said.

But in an interview with the Mirror today, he admits that the Times quoted him accurately, and says: "The reporter from the Times did not misquote me but he did misrepresent me. The point I wanted to make was that there has to be some reason why some people suffer in the world and others do not.

"Why some people are poor and starving and others rich and well-fed ... And yes, why some people have the terrible misfortune to be born disabled while others like me are born healthy. There has to be some reason for it all.

"Certainly, I do not believe that disabled people deserve what they get. That would be an obscene thought. They have been wronged as much as I have been wronged."

In an interview yesterday with ITN, Hoddle referred to his work with disabled people, saying: "All the work I have done over the years — 25 or 26 years — is there for everyone to see. There are a lot of things privately that I am not going to get involved in because I don't think it's the right time to bring it up.

"I have never gone on record anywhere saying that disabled and handicapped people ... are being paid back for their sins, are being punished for their sins, that is something I would never dream of ever even thinking of saying."

Hoddle was not entirely convincing. He offered no substantive explanation of his views and appeared to contradict himself.

The interviews were clearly Hoddle's last-ditch attempt to save his job and swing public opinion behind him. But his grip on the England job seemed to loosen throughout the day, as the FA was bombarded with calls from disabled groups and politicians demanded his dismissal.

The FA's acting chief executive, David Davies, said last night that talks over Hoddle's future were well under way, even though he had not been formally interviewed by FA chairman Geoff Thompson.

"Senior members of the FA have held a series of meetings and conversations today in connection with the weekend's events," said Mr Davies.

"These will go on into tomorrow. Our priority throughout this has been fairness to all concerned and also to do what is right for English football and the English team."

Mr Davies said he had had a number of discussions with Hoddle since the weekend and expected an announcement at lunchtime. "Glenn Hoddle has given his version of events in television interviews today. Those matters will be considered by senior FA members. I have my own private thoughts, but I'm not going to say anything that might prejudice events. Our great regret and Hoddle's great regret is any upset caused to disabled people."

Earlier, FA officials said they would have to take outside opinion into account when they considered what to do next — and that could seal Hoddle's fate. Disabled campaigners, church groups and MPs have condemned Hoddle, and yesterday the Prime Minister intervened, saying it would be "very difficult" for Hoddle to stay if he had been quoted correctly in the Times.

"If he said what he is reported to have said in the way he is reported to have said it then I think that was very wrong," Mr Blair said.

Man who seemed to have the world at his feet, page 3;
Leader comment and Letters, page 17;
Sport, pages 24, 26;
G2 cover story

England coach Glenn Hoddle ruled out resignation yesterday and denied saying people born with disabilities were being punished for sins of their past lives PHOTOGRAPH CLIVE BRUNSKILL

'The only reason people are saying I should resign is that they are saying I have come out and said that people disabled and handicapped have been paying for their sins and I have never ever said that. I don't believe that. At this moment in time, if that changes in years to come I don't know'

Glenn Hoddle

New nurses get 12pc rise

Blair's radical £1.5bn public pay deal angers teacher unions

Michael White
Political Editor

THE Government last night received a mixed reception from the public service unions after unveiling a radical £1.5 billion package of incentives and fresh flexibility for the pay structure of the NHS, teaching and the armed forces in the decade ahead.

With Gordon Brown presiding over buoyant Treasury finances, the overall 1999-2000 pay settlement of 4.1 per cent for 1.3 million public sector employees, from judges and Whitehall officials to nurses and soldiers, was generous by recent Tory and Labour standards — and consistent with Bank of England advice.

But the enthusiasm of key groups that stand to do well from Tony Blair's determination to reward performance and responsibility — including primary headteachers, who will get up to 9.5 per cent, and newly qualified nurses, who will get up to 12 per cent — was tempered last night by predictable anger among disappointed teachers.

Nigel de Gruchy, general secretary of the National Association of Schoolmasters Union of Women Teachers, accused the Government of "making a pig's ear" of teachers' pay. "Last year we had staging, this year we have discrimination," he said.

Primary headteachers will get a 6.5 per cent rise, with 9.5 per cent for some in small schools. But for the rank-and-file teacher the increase is 3.5 per cent.

Frank Dobson, the Health Secretary, was last night promoting the pay deal as the best for nurses in real terms for 10 years — and one that would help to restore morale and staff recruitment.

Nurses' leaders and NHS managers united in predicting that the pay award would help to tackle staff shortages, now estimated to be running at as many as 13,000.

Christine Hancock, general secretary of the Royal College of Nursing, said it would "send a very positive signal", although most nurses will get 4.7 per cent.

Stephen Thornton, chief executive of the management NHS Confederation, warned that most NHS trusts had budgeted about 3 per cent for pay and would be about 1 per cent short, even allowing for a £100 million transfusion from the Government's NHS modernisation fund.

Doctors and dentists, who were quick to voice disappointment last night, will receive a 3.5 per cent rise, as will 210,000 members of the armed forces and 438,000 teachers. But what are billed as "restructuring" elements, to reward responsibility, will add to most bills.

The Chancellor called the deal "fair, affordable and right" while Mr Blair stressed "recruitment, retention and motivation" as the key criteria, alongside agreed "output targets for the delivery of services".

Most of this year's deals proposed by the pay review bodies will be paid on April 1 in a single stage, for the first time for up to five years in some cases.

That is bound to raise the hopes of up to 5 million more public sector employees who will settle in the months ahead, knowing that Mr Brown's spending plans have, so far, undershot.

Ministers insist the money turn to page 2, column 3

Details, page 9
Letters, page 17

Main points

- 4.7 per cent increase in basic pay for nurses, with a 12 per cent rise for newly qualified staff taking them to £14,400 a year.
- 3.5 per cent rise for all teachers, an average 6.5 per cent for primary head teachers, with a 9.5 per cent rise for some in small schools.
- 3.5 per cent average rise for military lower ranks, up to brigadier, with the emphasis on rewarding privates and junior commissioned officers.
- GPs should get a 3.5 per cent rise in basic salary, as should salaried dentists in the NHS.
- Top civil servants' pay should rise by an average of 2.8 per cent

'Terror mission to Britain' foiled

Ian Black
Diplomatic Editor

URUGUAYAN security forces have foiled an alleged Islamic terrorist mission to Britain on a tip-off from the CIA, it was reported yesterday.

In a case said to be linked to the shadowy Afghanistan-based terrorist Osama bin Laden, three suspected Muslim extremists were arrested with false passports near Uruguay's border with Brazil on Friday, en route for London.

Reports from Uruguay's capital Montevideo described the three — an Egyptian couple and a Jordanian — as members of the banned Egyptian Gama'at al-Islamiya (Islamic Groups), held responsible for the massacre of 58 Western tourists, including eight Britons, at Luxor in December 1997.

Egypt has requested the extradition of the Egyptian man, the Uruguayan foreign minister, Guillermo Stirling, said yesterday, after a judge charged Said Hazan al Mohammed with travelling with false documents.

Reports said the CIA suspected the man of links with Bin Laden.

The Egyptian woman and the Jordanian were released on Sunday, but an international search was reported to be under way for two other men travelling with them.

Foreign Office officials said they were checking the story, which comes amid fears of attacks on United States and British targets after the bombing of two US embassies in east Africa last summer.

British security worries have been heightened by its participation as Washington's only military partner in December's Operation Desert Fox air strikes against Iraq.

The CIA was said to have congratulated Uruguayan intelligence on foiling what they dubbed "the London mission".

The US has offered a $5 million (£3 million) reward for information leading to Bin Laden's arrest or conviction for the embassy attacks, in which 260 people died.

His Al-Qaida group became a top priority for British security last summer. Whitehall sources say they are aware of the danger of links between Bin Laden and British-based Muslim radicals, and that Abu Hamza al-Masri, the London cleric implicated in the Yemeni hostage case, has been under surveillance.

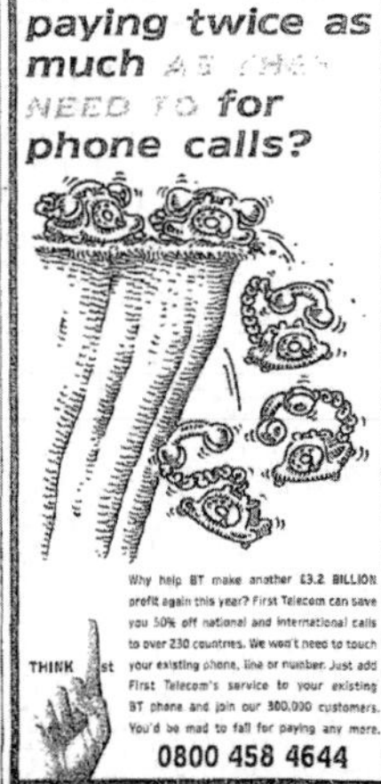

Inside

Home Marksmen with rifles and shotguns will try to blast Britain's 3,000 ruddy ducks out of existence over the next three years. 5

International Ian Traynor assesses the performance of Gerhard Schröder's government as it celebrates 100 days in office. 13

Analysis Chimpanzees have developed an immune system that can fight Aids – but how close are scientists to finding a human vaccine? 15

Finance Predators were circling publishing group Portsmouth & Sunderland Newspapers after a family split. 21

Weather 15; Obituaries 18
Comment 16; Crossword 20
G2
Quick Crossword 18
Radio 19; Television 20

9 770261 307323 05

1999

What are you drinking, Helen?
Just a Slimline Bitter Lemon, please Clare. I'm watching my weight.
Oh, for goodness sake, Helen!!!
Don't you realise that dieting is just another form of male oppression, a means of undermining womens' confidence by forcing us to aspire to a ludicrous stereotype of beauty which is unattainable....
You don't want to diet! You want to search within yourself and discover the self-esteem to be proud of your appearance.....
... and maybe also stop wearing those stripey dresses, they make you look huge....

Well, quite a lot, since you ask. There's guilt. Guilt that I'm abandoning my clients. Guilt that I'm putting my own needs before theirs.
I suppose I use my work as a way of convincing myself I'm a worthwhile person. Take it away and I'm really insecure.
I define myself by my profession. Without it I don't know who I am! I don't know how to act, to behave....
Er, I think I had better rephrase the question: What non-emotional baggage are you bringing with you?
FLIGHT 2875
Oh. Right. Just a suitcase.
AIRHOLS

Dos cervezas.
Two beers
Why didn't you ask him in English? Everyone speaks english.
Yes, Brian, they do. Because economic and cultural Imperialism forces them to speak a foreign language in their own country.
So, as a mark of respect for his homeland, and to show that some Brits are prepared to make an effort, however small, I ordered without using English.
Dos cervezas? But we're in Turkey.
I know we're in Turkey, thank you Brian, but I'm hardly going to learn Turkish just for a crappy week.

Bless you, Carewoman. How can we ever thank you?
No need for thanks, Citizen. I was just doing my job.

Results, reports, analysis

The gospel according to Holyfield

10 years of freedom
1989-1999 in G2

45p
Monday
March 8 1999
Published in London and Manchester
www.guardianunlimited.co.uk

The Guardian

Blair's revolution for learning

Plan for huge rise in university numbers

John Carvel
Education Editor

TONY Blair is planning a huge expansion of universities over the next eight years to ensure that at least 50 per cent of young people under 30 participate in higher education.

He is expected to make that goal one of the key pledges in Labour's next election manifesto. It would form part of a second-term strategy to turn Britain into a high-skill society competing in the global economy by virtue of brainpower and innovation rather than low wages and traditional manufacturing.

The Prime Minister has instructed his officials to start work on how best to provide hundreds of thousands of extra university and college places, mostly for students in their twenties.

The students would be encouraged to secure academic qualifications through short courses combined with longer periods of part-time study undertaken without interrupting their careers or family responsibilities.

At present 33 per cent of school leavers in England go straight to university before the age of 21 and another 7 per cent enter higher education between 21 and 25.

The Government does not yet have reliable data about how many additional students qualify by the age of 30 and the figures are further confused by students who drop out and then re-enter education when they are older.

But ministers are assuming that student numbers would have to increase by about a quarter if the goal of a 50 per cent participation rate is to be achieved by the end of a second Labour term.

Mr Blair has asked David Blunkett, the Education Secretary, to work out how that target could be reached without exposing the Government to criticism that it was devaluing the quality of undergraduate degrees.

The universities have grown at a breakneck pace since the early 1960s when only 5 per cent got any form of higher education. An influential committee under Lord Robbins then recommended expansion to give everyone the opportunity to obtain a degree.

From 1970 to 1988 the proportion entering higher education hovered around 15 per cent until a further phase of expansion was ordered by the Conservative education secretary, Kenneth Baker. He proposed a doubling of student places over the next 25 years, but Mr Baker's goal was achieved within six years, thanks partly to rapid growth of the polytechnics which converted to university status in 1992.

Mr Blair's proposals will not necessarily require a further substantial increase in the number of universities. Existing institutions will be asked to develop more flexible courses to handle larger numbers of students.

Mr Blunkett has embarked on the first stage of this expansion by setting a target of 35 per cent of 18- to 21-year-olds in higher education by 2001/2. The Treasury's comprehensive spending review last year provided resources to do this by creating 40,000 extra full-time places and 60,000 for part-timers.

Under current published plans, student numbers in England will increase to 1,416,000 by 2001/2. More than a third will be part-timers.

Under the Downing Street plan, there would be only modest further growth in full-time student numbers. Mr Blair and Mr Blunkett are exploring a range of career-friendly modular courses that could attract hundreds of thousands of extra part-timers.

These could include a basic two-year diploma programme with a practical vocational element, followed by further modules of part-time study to secure a full honours degree.

Mr Blunkett has asked his officials to take a "genuinely futuristic look" at new patterns of learning that would give students more flexibility and more experience of the skills they would need in their chosen fields of employment.

Although the Treasury is understood to be keen to make all degrees employment-related, the Department for Education and Employment is reluctant to abandon the traditional view that students can be stretched by theoretical courses that have no immediate economic application.

The Government's introduction of tuition fees for full-time undergraduates and the phasing out of the maintenance grant has paved the way for the expansion of higher education. This is expected to free about £1.5 billion over the next 15 years, allowing resources to be redeployed to universities.

Leader comment, page 17

Stop and search leaps by 20pc

Duncan Campbell
Crime Correspondent

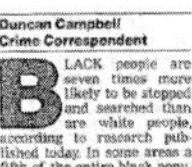

BLACK people are seven times more likely to be stopped and searched than are white people, according to research published today. In some areas a fifth of the entire black population aged over 10 has been arrested in the past year.

Merseyside police had one of the highest rates, with nearly one in three black people aged over 10 arrested, according to the figures. The number of black people sentenced to prison terms was between four and seven times greater than that of white people in 10 selected police forces.

The figures, compiled by the independent research bulletin Statewatch, come in the midst of the argument about the policing of ethnic minority communities. The bulletin suggests that "institutionalised racism pervades the criminal justice system".

Among the survey's findings are that in 90 per cent of cases where white people have been murdered, suspects have been identified. The figure for murders of black people is only 60 per cent.

Stop and search, which has increased by 21 per cent in the past year and ninefold since 1986, also points up differences. Black people are 7.5 times more likely to be stopped and searched, and four times more likely to be arrested, than white people.

Of the 43 police forces in England and Wales, 15 arrested the equivalent of one in five of the black population over the age of 10.

The use of stop and search in general varies widely. Dorset, with four stops per 1,000 population, and Essex, with six, are at one end of the scale. In Cleveland, home of "zero tolerance", the figure is one in 10.

The rate for white people in general was 19 per 1,000, for black people 142 and for Asians 45. Cleveland stopped and searched 418 out of every 1,000 black people. Merseyside was the next highest – three in 10 of the black population, according to the report.

In 1997-98 there were 1,954,686 arrests in England and Wales, a rate of 43 per 1,000 of the population over the age of 10. Cleveland and Merseyside (70 per 1,000) have the highest arrest rates, and Surrey (24 per 1,000) and Cornwall (19 per 1,000) the lowest.

Norfolk had the highest arrest rate of black people relative to their numbers, arresting 857 of an estimated black population of 1,400 – a rate of 612 per 1,000 – although Statewatch caution that the figures could have been distorted by an event attracting black people from outside the area.

In Norfolk a black person is 18 times more likely to be arrested than a white person.

The next highest area was Merseyside (298 per 1,000), followed by Staffordshire (291 per 1,000). The lowest rates were Cumbria (38 per 1,000) and Humberside (75 per 1,000).

The proportion of arrests arising from stop and search has fallen from 17 per cent in 1986 to 10 per cent in 1997-98. At least 900,000 people in England and Wales were stopped and searched last year and allowed to go on their way. Of those arrested, 30 per cent were subject to no further action.

"One of the most significant statistics, in light of the Stephen Lawrence inquiry, is the huge differential in the proportion of black and white homicides in which someone had been identified as a suspect," says the report, compiled from figures from the Home Office, Audit Commission, Office of National Statistics and Her Majesty's Inspectorate of Constabulary.

There was no suspect in 10 per cent of cases with white murder victims, but the same applied to 40 per cent of cases with black murder victims.

Cautioning was used less frequently for black people than for other ethnic groups, the survey found. Black people also serve longer prison terms on average, with 47 per cent of white prisoners serving more than four years compared with 61 per cent of black prisoners.

Tony Bunyan, editor of Statewatch, said the report indicated a collective failure to tackle racism within the criminal justice system since the Scarman report of 1981.

Malcolm McDowell in Stanley Kubrick's 1971 film version of A Clockwork Orange, one of several landmark films which earned his reputation as one of the greatest ever directors

Kubrick, controversial maker of 2001 and A Clockwork Orange, dies at 70

Amelia Gentleman

STANLEY Kubrick, one of the century's great film directors, died yesterday, aged 70. News of his sudden death at his home in Hertfordshire, where he lived as a virtual recluse, shocked the film world; it was not clear whether the director had been suffering from any illness.

Actors, fellow directors and critics last night paid tribute to his achievements.

Kubrick used his savings to finance his first film at the age of 25 and went on to make more than a dozen landmark films, including A Clockwork Orange, 2001: A Space Odyssey, Lolita, The Shining, and Full Metal Jacket.

Hollywood actors Tom Cruise and Nicole Kidman, who star in his latest film, Eyes Wide Shut, made in great secrecy over more than two years and due to be released in July, said: "He was like family to us and we are in shock and devastated."

Kubrick's family would not give details of the cause of death. Hertfordshire police said they were called to his home yesterday to record the death, but there had been no suspicious circumstances.

Stanley Kubrick: 'Films had terrific power and originality'

Hailed as one of the most innovative post-war American film makers, Kubrick abandoned the US in the early 1960s to spend the rest of his life in this country, where he led a secluded life at Childwickbury Manor, his sprawling estate, near St Albans.

He is survived by his widow Christiane, and daughters Katharina, Anya and Vivian.

A spokesman for the British Film Institute said: "This is a huge loss. He was one of the landmark directors of the century who helped to define cinema."

Film director Stephen Frears said: "His films had terrific power, originality and very high intelligence. Because he was so obsessed with technology he would always find very innovative solutions to problems.

"He has left a fantastic body of work – very idiosyncratic but very intelligent. He brought power to his films through photography and performance and great detail."

Despite Kubrick's reputation as a demanding director, there were few actors who would not jump at the chance to work with him. Jack Nicholson, star of The Shining, said: "He gives new meaning to the word meticulous."

The French critic Michel Ciment described him as "one of the most demanding, most original and most visionary film-makers of our time."

Barry Norman, film critic for Sky television, said: "This has come as a real shock. He was just an extraordinary man and film-maker. He made some very remarkable movies."

Derek Malcolm, page 3; Obituary, page 15

SEE INSIDE

10
9 770261 307316

1999

Ok, the resolution is carried unanimously – since everyone has had a quiet week on the emotional front, nobody has any burning issues around their masculinity to discuss, and we are all feeling reasonably comfortable in our sexuality, The Mens' Group can talk about the cricket.

Well, this is pleasant. This country really has improved immeasurably over the last few years. Not long ago you would have had to travel to the continent if you wanted to enjoy a glass of pinot and a salad nicoise in the setting of an intimate pavement cafe...

N.U.F.C.

Have you had a chance to read my report on the Tinsley Family?
I have, Maureen. I found it well written, forcefully argued and meticulously researched.
But I'm afraid that I won't be acting on any of your recommendations.
No? And why is that?
Because of office politics? Because you're scared of the media reaction? Or because you haven't got the guts to take the bull by the horns and deal with the problem?
No, Maureen...
Because you're the cleaner.
Scum o' the earth, those Tinsleys. Ask anyone round our way...

CARING
LIBERAL*
AGAINST
RIGHT WING
ESTABLISHMENT
* Small L

guidewednesday Eight pages of the best daily TV, cinema and entertainment listings in G2

45p
Wednesday
June 9 1999
Published in London
and Manchester
www.guardian.co.uk
Newspaper of the Year

The Guardian

Thrills that can kill In G2

Annie Proulx on inspiration In G2

Charles Jennings on parent-rage In G2

and in society 78 pages of jobs

Former cabinet minister Aitken gets 18 months for 'weaving a web of deceit'

Prison, the final disgrace

David Pallister and **Jamie Wilson**

More than five years after he started lying about a modest hotel bill in Paris, Jonathan Aitken yesterday sunk to the nadir of his professional and personal life when he became the first former cabinet minister this century to be sent to prison for perjury and perverting the course of justice.

He stood impassively in the dock of No 1 court at the Old Bailey to be told by Mr Justice Scott Baker that he would have to serve nine months of an 18-month sentence for "calculated perjury pursued over a long period of time" and the "gross and inexcusable breach of trust" in getting his 16-year-old daughter, Victoria, to sign a false witness statement.

As he turned to walk down to the cells Aitken allowed himself a brief smile as he blew two kisses to his family who had turned up in strength for the hearing.

With tears in their eyes, his three daughters, 14-year-old son, mother and sister, the actress Maria Aitken, were driven away from the court without commenting.

Last night Aitken was taken to Belmarsh, London's most modern local as well as high security prison, where he will be processed before being transferred.

The judge delivered a stern rebuke. "Jonathan Aitken," he said, "for nearly four years you wove a web of deceit in which you entangled yourself and from which there was no way out unless you were prepared to come clean and tell the truth. Unfortunately you were not.

"You hoped that by committing perjury and perverting the course of justice the truth of who paid the bill for that weekend at the Ritz in Paris 1993 would never see the light of day.

"No one whatever his position or status is entitled dishonestly to manipulate the evidence to his advantage."

Mr Justice Scott Baker said that perjury struck at justice itself. "The message has to go out loud and clear that condign punishment is likely to be imposed on those who are caught."

Sir John Nutting, Aitken's counsel, spent two hours on an impassioned mitigation. "In a real and fundamental sense this defendant had brought about his real destruction," he said.

"Not since the days of Oscar Wilde has a public figure who told lies in a libel case suffered such humiliation and public vilification and personal vindictiveness at the hands of some members of the press.

"The fall from grace has been complete, his marriage has broken down, he has lost his home, he is one of only three people this century forced to resign from the privy council, he is bankrupt and his health has suffered. His public humiliation has been absolute. These are real and considerable punishments."

The judge did accept in mitigation that Aitken had pleaded guilty and had shown "very considerable" remorse. Adopting Sir John's submissions, and the glowing testimony from the only witness, former defence secretary Malcolm Rifkind, the judge said Aitken had been a successful minister who had contributed significantly to the interests of the country.

Dozens of friends and colleagues had written to the judge praising him.

Aitken faced his judgment day two years after the collapse of his libel action against the Guardian and Granada TV's World in Action, which had revealed his long financial relationship with the Saudi royal family and other Arab businessmen. But at the centre of the allegations was the charge that he had lied when he claimed his wife had paid his 8,010 franc bill at the Paris Ritz in September 1993.

The Guardian and Granada were able to prove, 17 days into the trial, that Mrs Aitken had not been in Paris and that the bill was paid by Aitken's former Saudi business partner, Said Ayas, on behalf of Prince Mohammed, a son of the Saudi king.

After he was arrested and charged last year, Aitken said in a statement to the police: "I deeply regret the lies I told and decisions I took to mislead a large number of people. This is a burden I will have to bear for the rest of my life. I am very ashamed of all my actions."

Although it was not aired in court, the Guardian established after the collapse of the libel trial that Mr Ayas, Aitken and Prince Mohammed had discussed arrangements during the Ritz weekend which involved British arms firms paying millions of pounds in commission to a secret Swiss bank account. While Aitken publicly promoted the deals as minister for defence procurement, Ayas privately agreed commissions with the firms which in one deal alone would have been worth up to £50m.

One plank of Aitken's anticipated mitigation – that he acted as a secret agent between Britain and Saudi Arabia – did not emerge, but Sir Malcolm did confirm that Aitken had taken a report about Iranian submarine threats to King Fahd in December 1993.

But Aitken's principal explanation, as set out by Sir John, was that he told the first lie to the Guardian about the hotel bill in order to put the newspaper off the scent. The Saudis also insisted on keeping his contacts with them a secret. It was at the height of sleaze allegations against the Tories and Aitken wanted to keep his reputation clean. It was not clear that allowing the prince to pay was a breach of ministerial guidelines, given the "generous" hospitality between Aitken and his friends.

But when the Guardian and Granada made further serious allegations of corruption and arranging prostitutes for Arab friends in April 1995, Aitken was faced with a dilemma.

Sir John said: "To say nothing and allow very serious allegations, the falsity of which he believed he could prove, to go unchallenged – or to fight them and risk that in the Ritz bill he would have to tell a lie." But he had already lied about this to both the cabinet secretary and the then prime minister, John Major. To admit the truth at that stage would have left him with no credibility.

Days into the libel trial, when he realised his case had a serious weak point, he then enlisted the help of his daughter. Sir John said he now felt deep remorse and shame.

Jonathan Aitken arriving at the Old Bailey yesterday: 'No one, whatever his position or status, is entitled dishonestly to manipulate the evidence,' the judge said Photograph: Sean Smith

> "It is undoubtedly a tragedy for him and for his family. But if his sentence teaches others the risks of abusing the democratic bargain which underpins all our liberties, then Mr Aitken may unwittingly have served the cause of free speech once more"
>
> **Leader comment, page 21**

● **Fall of Aitken, pages 2 - 5**
● **David Leigh, page 19**
● **Read all the original documents and correspondence on the Aitken affair on the Guardian network at www.newsunlimited.co.uk**

End to bombing imminent as Serbs waver

Ian Black in London, **Stuart Millar** in Kumanovo and **Martin Walker** in Brussels

Serbian generals returned to Macedonia last night for talks with Nato commanders amid renewed speculation that they were close to signing orders for a withdrawal from Kosovo.

The late-night session inside a camouflaged tent at Kumanovo military base began as President Slobodan Milosevic came under unprecedented international pressure to pull his troops out of the province in return for a halt to Nato's bombing. Earlier in the day Nato and Russia finally closed ranks to achieve a diplomatic breakthrough that could bring the Yugoslav war to an end within 48 hours.

Senior Nato officers were taken by surprise by the Serbs' moves towards signing the military agreement. Lieutenant-General Sir Mike Jackson, commander of the Nato implementation force in Macedonia, received a call at his headquarters in Skopje from a senior member of the Serb delegation.

The Yugoslav general asked for another meeting and was told by Gen Jackson it would only take place if the Serbs were willing to sign the agreement. That assurance was given and senior Nato sources predicted that the signing was little more than a formality.

But it soon became clear that progress was not as smooth as expected. Nato spokesmen were briefing journalists in the mud outside the tent with a more cautious line, warning them that a resolution was still some way away.

After midnight the ▶ **Page 2**

War in Europe, pages 6 – 7
Harold Evans, page 20
Leader comment, page 21
Kosovo latest on the Guardian network at www.newsunlimited.co.uk

The day the sword of truth struck home

Matthew Engel

With an extraordinary symbolic coincidence, the end linked back to the beginning. Right at the outset, Jonathan Aitken said he was going to fight "the cancer of bent and twisted journalism" with "the simple sword of truth".

And, straight in front of him, all day yesterday, was the sword. The Sword of Justice, to be precise, forged by a master cutler in 1563, and always placed at the Old Bailey behind the highest ranking judge on duty. When Mr Justice Scott Baker sentenced him to nine months' imprisonment, Aitken had nowhere else to stare.

He faced that ordeal impassively, indeed impressively. He had not had to say anything all day except admit who he was, and his expression gave no clues. But at moments of stress – when someone said something really horrid – he would begin blinking furiously. The last such moment came when the judge ended any smidgen of doubt about jail, and used that splendid judicial phrase "condign punishment".

When sentence was passed, there was just a nudge from the warder (privatised, from Securicor, a little reminder to the prisoner of the government in which he served). Then he bowed deeply to the judge, blew two kisses to his family and was led away from the wood-panelled courtroom down stairs with white-tiled walls to the white-tiled world where he will remain, on present projections, until March 2000.

There never was any serious doubt. Murders, kidnaps and rapes come and go. As far as judges are concerned, they happen to other people. But perjury is a crime against the judicial system itself. It is a crime against judges. It is never, ever, treated leniently.

In a curious way, though, it was Aitken's day. The prosecuting counsel, David Waters, dealt simply with the two charges, to which Aitken had already pleaded guilty. The defence adopted a different tack. Sir John Nutting's speech often sounded more like spin than mitigation. Since the Guardian, in the nature of things, was unrepresented, he was able to make an array of statements that in other circumstances would have been challenged.

He painted a picture of a man entirely broken by his misfortunes. Aitken was "bankrupt", "a single parent", "severely disabled" (by asthma), and "vulnerable". He had lost everything, even his watch and his books. He was a man of "religious faith" suffering "regret and mortification" that were "heartfelt and genuine". And they were, he implied again and again, only a couple of teeny-weeny fibble-wibbles. The rest of his life was exemplary. Sir John even praised his "openness" and "candour", contrasted with the "vindictiveness" and "slimy red herrings" of the media. He put a deadly emphasis on the first syllable of the word "Guardian", managing to make it sound truly frightening.

It would have been a sensational speech to a jury, particularly if Sir John were less verbose and repetitive. There was no jury. There was only the judge, who seemed to be having trouble concealing his irritation. One fancied that he might be adding to the sentence at a tariff of about one day for every minute Sir John hanged on.

His interventions were infrequent but telling. His first remark attached the adjective "grave" to the use of Aitken's teenage daughter Victoria in furtherance of the lies. He then listened for some time to an account of the birth pangs of the lie about the Paris Ritz, then announced that it was irrelevant. "Could he not at the time of the libel action have told the truth?"

Much of the day was taken up with testimonials to Aitken, solicited or otherwise. Sir Malcolm Rifkind, the former foreign secretary, was the only witness, and he praised to the skies his contribution when they worked together as defence ministers.

We heard of a vast array of letters from other ministers (though there was nothing from John Major), from seven clergymen, and from many of his constituents from the seat he held from 1974 to 1997. These included the editor of the Thanet Gazette, who described Mr Aitken as "the best MP Thanet has had for at least 50 years". Since his rivals for this title included a man known to everyone at Westminster as "the one-armed bandit", this may have been fairly faint praise.

As Sir John said, it was hard to reconcile all this with the "greedy, amoral, dishonest and selfish man" portrayed by the media beyond Thanet. But that is the essential, fascinating, paradox of Jonathan Aitken. The court's geography ensured his family supporters were mostly out of sight. If he looked ahead Aitken could see only the judge and the sword. To his left were the media. To his right, for much of the morning, sat Lord Longford, a visit from whom is regarded by criminals as the worst punishment of all.

He may fear that. Broken, though? This was not a man who looked breakable. The next nine months will test that proposition. But as he faces that awful reality, it is impossible to withhold – amid all the emotions felt on this newspaper – just a tinge of admiration for that.

23
9 770261 307330

1999

What's up, Clare? You're very quiet.
That home visit. It's so easy to forget that so many people's lives are a relentless round of disadvantage and despair.
Megan, can I ask you a serious question? Do you ever worry that constant exposure to the kind of human suffering we've just witnessed might someday desensitize you to it completely?
That is a serious question, Clare. But before I answer it may I ask you one first?
By all means.
What do you fancy for lunch? I'm a bit sick of sandwiches.

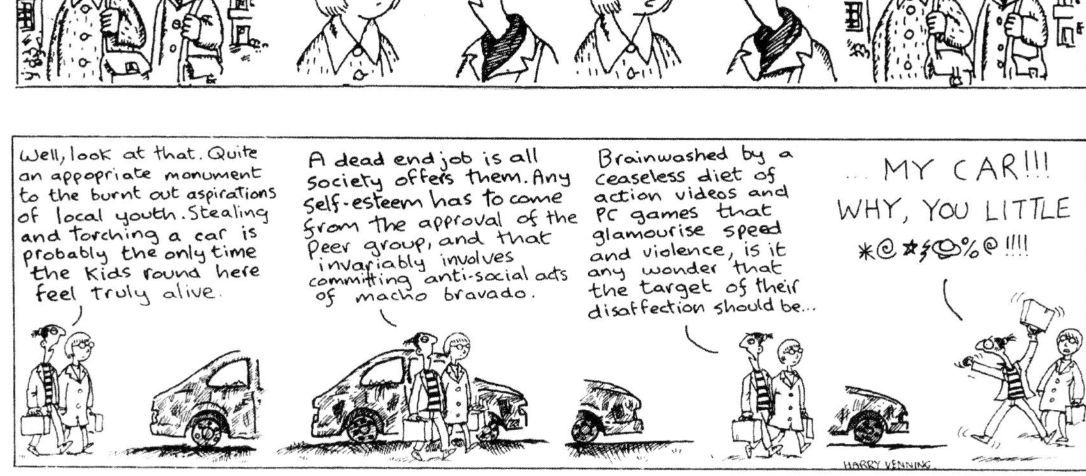
Well, look at that. Quite an appropriate monument to the burnt out aspirations of local youth. Stealing and torching a car is probably the only time the kids round here feel truly alive.
A dead end job is all society offers them. Any self-esteem has to come from the approval of the peer group, and that invariably involves committing anti-social acts of macho bravado.
Brainwashed by a ceaseless diet of action videos and PC games that glamourise speed and violence, is it any wonder that the target of their disaffection should be...
... MY CAR!!! WHY, YOU LITTLE *@*$@%@!!!!
HARRY VENNING

Contradiction? Not at all. As feminists we must give total support to our sisters in their struggle for equality...
...campaigning for a woman's right to pursue the sport of her choice....
...until every woman and girl has the opportunity to participate in boxing on exactly the same footing as men.
And then?
Then we ban it.

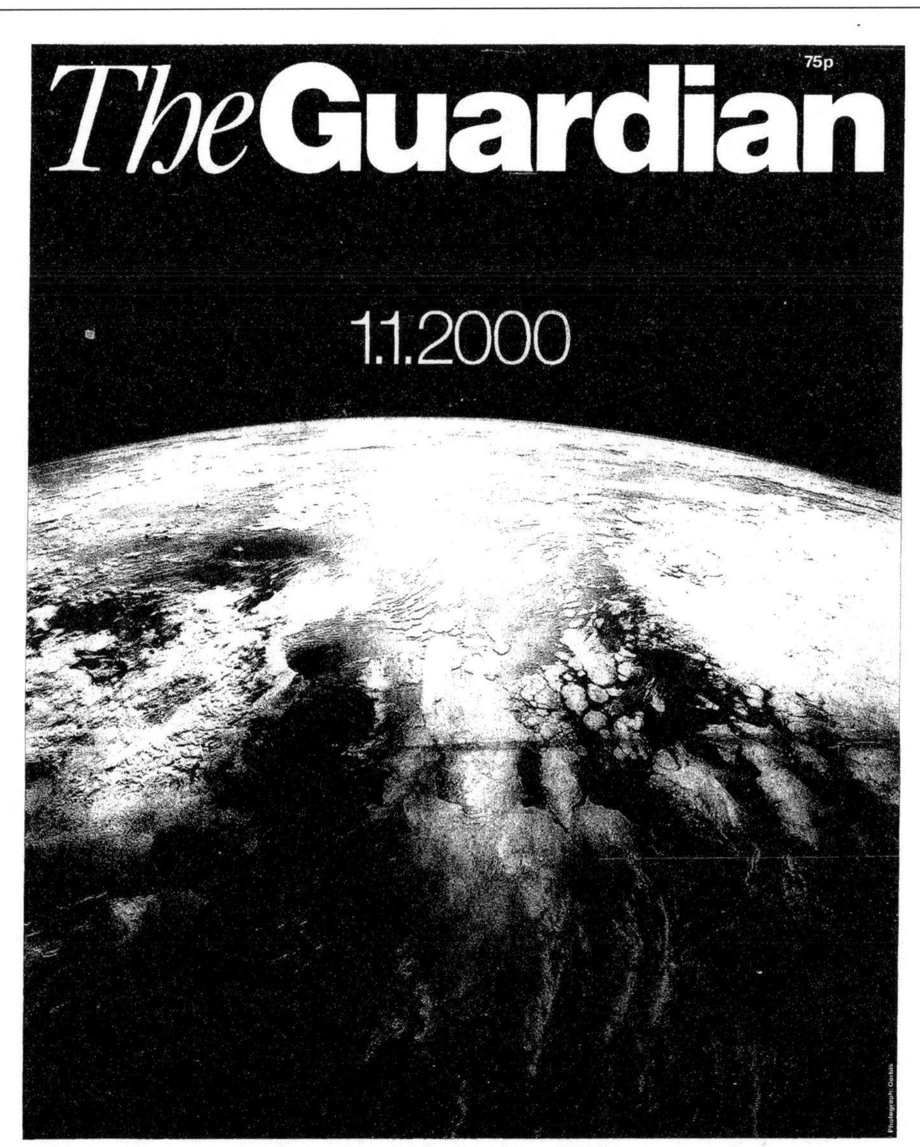

Dawn of a new millennium

There have been billions of dawns since earth was first formed. But, according to the calendar most of us share, with today's dawn the human race enters the third millennium. We may feel awe and humility, and even surprise. For more than two generations we have survived our power to destroy all life while slowly engineering the planet's asphyxiation. Somehow we have made it.

The sceptics will say that today's date is only a number; the pedants insist it is not even the right one. But for everyone else, just as the dawn marks the start of a new day, and January 1 announces the start of a new year, so today's dawn opens a new chapter in the human story.

We do not wake this morning to a blank slate: there is something deathly in that idea. We wake instead aware of the long past we leave behind.

But the turn of the millennium requires us to pause a moment, turn around, and ready ourselves for the future. What will it be? Can we possibly imagine it? The perspective of the lens in space is denied us. The century just gone is too close to disentangle its miracles from its horrors. Even the still beauty of the image is a lie because its gleaming perfection masks the potential for catastrophe. But a millennium offers renewal. "To make an end is to make a beginning," wrote Eliot. "The end is where we start from." Continued page 19

75p
Saturday
January 1 2000
Published in London
and Manchester
www.guardian.co.uk

2000

I have to tell you, Megan, my Brian has been a star these last few days. Funny to think it takes a flu epidemic to make you really appreciate someone. He did everything I told him to....
...He tucked me in bed to keep warm, brought in the telly so I didn't get bored, slept on the sofa so as not to disturb my sleep, waited on me hand and foot and generally did everything possible to conserve my strength and my energies...
...otherwise, God knows, we'd probably both have gone down with it.
Choo

Working late, Clare?
Yeah. Ironically enough, I can't go home until I've dealt with all these client questionnaires.
Management left them in the waiting room so that service users could feedback as to the effectiveness and efficiency of our work.
Really? what aspects did we do well in?
I don't know, I haven't filled them in yet.
HARRY VENNING + KATE

Honestly, Angus, your wife leaves you and you tell me you're 'fine'. I know you find it difficult to share your emotions, but by denying them completely you'll crack-up.
Of course you don't want to be vulnerable. Of course you fear further rejection. But you must learn to express your feelings. Go on, Angus, take the risk. What's the worst that can happen?
You're right, Clare. I feel scared, lonely, worthless....
Bugger! Eastenders!
Well you've made a start, and that's the most important thing....
HARRY VENNING

2000

What George Walden, John Tusa and Terry Wogan have in common. In G2

45p
Wednesday
September 6 2000
Published in London
and Manchester
www.guardian.co.uk

The Guardian

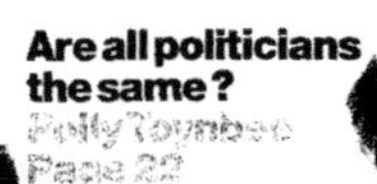

Get set for the designer Olympics In Sport

Are all politicians the same? Polly Toynbee Page 22

Return of a superstar DJ In G2

An extra £47m for the dome – but even that may not be enough

Failed attraction: millennium commissioners now admit that as few as 4.5m visitors will buy tickets for the dome, little more than a third of the 12m originally predicted Photograph: Kieran Doherty

If we can't make this work, we're not much of a government

Deputy prime minister John Prescott in 1998

Kevin Maguire
and Fiachra Gibbons

Dome facts

Monthly attendance figures

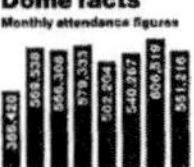

Visitor projections

Cash grants

- **February** £60m when dome chief executive Jennie Page resigned
- **May** £29m when dome chairman Bob Ayling stood down
- **August** £43m advance payment from sale of dome at the end of the year to a consortium backed by Japanese finance group Nomura
- **September** £47m with the arrival of new executive chairman, David James

Saving the dome, trying to save face, page 5

Pension row mars Tory policy launch

Nicholas Watt
Political correspondent

Hague: echoes of 1997 clash

Hague unveils battle plan, page 11
Polly Toynbee, page 22
Leader comment, page 23
Francis Wheen, G2 page 5

Inquiry into leak of former MI5 head's memoirs

Richard Norton-Taylor

2000

...and they all lived happily ever after.
Now be good boys and go to sleep, and tomorrow Auntie Clare will read you another of her case Reports.
HARRY VENNING

Clare, I think you Should come and have a look at this.
Hmmm. I see what you mean. That is quite an astonishing figure. And frankly it confirms what I've suspected all along....
We'll never get any bloody work done in this office whilst everyone's logged on to 'Big Brother'.
Quick! Come back! He's about to get out of the shower!

That was brilliant, absolutely brilliant. It was exactly what a one-day workshop should be all about!
Yeah!
Dynamic, inspiring, educational, imaginative, challenging. In fact it was so good....
...I almost wish I'd gone back in after lunch.
Me too. another pint?

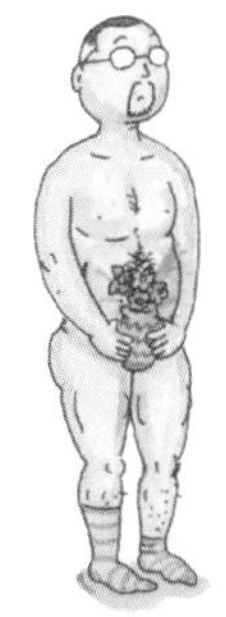

Gas attack Rob Evans explains what really happened to the men at Porton Down. In G2

45p
Wednesday
November 8 2000
Published in London
and Manchester
www.guardian.co.uk

The Guardian

Nick Hornby Autism and my son Danny **In G2**

Amanda Roocroft Still not at ease with stardom **In G2**

Francis Wheen How does MI5 justify this surveillance? **In G2**

Class acts Opera and art calm the mean streets **In Society**

The great dome robbery

The scene inside the dome's money zone after yesterday's raid, with the digger allegedly used to smash into the grounds and building Photograph: Tony Harris

- £350m of diamonds targeted by 12-strong gang
- Thieves use digger, smoke bombs and powerboat
- Armed police disguised as cleaners trap raiders

Nick Hopkins and **Tania Branigan**

Twelve men equipped with a bulldozer, a powerboat and as much audacity as any criminals since the Great Train Robbery almost 40 years ago raided the Millennium Dome yesterday hoping to pull off one of the most daring robberies the country has seen.

Four of them, wearing gasmasks and body armour, crashed through the perimeter fence on a mechanical digger and hurtled towards a display of diamonds worth as much as £350m, lobbing smoke bombs and firing nailguns as visitors, including children, were touring the site.

But instead of escaping with the 203 carat Millennium Star – one of the most valuable stones ever cut – and 11 other "priceless" blue diamonds – they were snared by a police operation every bit as bold as their own.

Officers from Scotland Yard's Flying Squad and armed response units were posing as cleaners, their guns hidden in black binliners. They lay in wait for the robbers outside a 4ft thick concrete vault where the stones were on display.

Police said no shots were fired and the robbers surrendered without a struggle.

In a day of unremitting drama, eight of their alleged accomplices were also arrested. All were British. One, who was seized at a farmhouse in Kent, is aged 62.

The raid had been anticipated for months following a tip-off to the Metropolitan police, thought to have been from a paid informer.

An operation involving 100 officers from London and Kent – codenamed Magician – was set up in total secrecy. The Cabinet Office and senior figures in the New Millennium Experience Company, including Pierre-Yves Gerbeau, and the mining company De Beers, which owns the diamonds, were informed.

The commissioner of the Metropolitan police, Sir John Stevens, was also briefed.

The decision to allow the raid to take place was a risky one, especially as schoolchildren were in the dome when the raid occurred. However, the officer in charge of the investigation, Detective Superintendent Jon Shatford, said it was the only way to gather compelling evidence.

Austin
WHAT DID YOU THINK OF THE DOME, THEN?

Police refused to be drawn last night on whether the attempted heist was the work of sophisticated criminals or "chancers". Some aspects bear striking resemblances to the recent James Bond movie The World Is Not Enough. "It is obvious there was a good degree of planning," a source said.

One suspect was seized in a powerboat which had been moored to the Queen Elizabeth II pier next to the dome.

The Millennium Star, chief prize among the 12 stones

Another was arrested on the north bank of the Thames at Lower Lee Crossings, opposite the dome. This suspect is believed to have been monitoring police messages.

Six other men were arrested at two farm houses in west Kent – at Collier Street and Horsmonden – by the local force's serious crime squad. Police released the ages of five: 32, 34, 38, 58 and 62.

All 12 men were being questioned at stations in London and the south-east last night.

Events unfolded at 9.30am, half an hour after a powerboat glided up to Queen Elizabeth jetty and cut its two engines to avoid drawing attention.

On the other side of the dome site, four men posing as builders revved a bulldozer, preparing, it seemed, for work on a nearby site. To the 64 visitors already touring the dome, the movements yesterday were without significance. To the Flying Squad, they signalled the imminent attempt to pull off the biggest robbery since the Brink's-Mat raid at Heathrow in 1983.

At 9.30, the gang made an audacious and extraordinary move: the digger clattered at full pelt into the wire fence, crushing it flat before startled security guards. It then charged towards the dome's money zone. In the mayhem, ▸ **Page 2**

Special report on the Guardian network at www.guardianunlimited.co.uk/dome

Nailbiting finish as Gore wins key states

Martin Kettle in Washington, **Julian Borger** in Austin and **Duncan Campbell** in Nashville

Al Gore and George W Bush were early today locked in the tightest head-to-head battle for the White House since the Kennedy-Nixon era.

Exit polls showed each making important gains in the vital battleground states as Democrats and Republicans mobilised to capture every available vote. Early this morning the Gore camp took great delight at capturing several key early states including Florida, Illinois, New Jersey and Michigan.

There were whoops of delight in the Gore camp as the Florida and Michigan results were announced. There was also excitement that some states that had appeared to be in Mr Bush's hands were being deemed too close to call.

A Gore aide said that their core vote had held up very well and they were particularly pleased with a turnout of loyal black American voters in urban areas.

Mr Bush had drawn first blood by capturing Indiana, a traditional Republican state, and Kentucky, which voted for Mr Clinton in 1992 and 1996. Kentucky has voted for the winning presidential candidate in every election from 1964 to 1996.

Mr Bush added to his total with wins in Alabama, Georgia, Kansas, Mississippi, Oklahoma, Virginia, North and South Carolina and his own stronghold of Texas. He was ahead in Missouri, Ohio and West Virginia and was also leading in Mr Gore's home state of Tennessee and in Bill Clinton's Arkansas. He was also in front in Wisconsin and Oregon, where votes for the Green candidate, Ralph Nader, threatened to cost the Gore camp.

Mr Gore added Maryland, Connecticut and Vermont to his tally. Most reports had him easily ahead in California, the most important state of all, with 54 electoral college votes. He was also reported to be ahead in Maine and Washington state.

A Fox News exit poll had Mr Gore doing well with voters who had made up their minds in the past three days. They divided two to one in his favour.

Places in the Senate were also up for grabs, with the Democrats ahead in six swing seats, and losing to the Republicans in two others, suggesting that the Republicans may just retain control.

So close was the race for votes during the day that in a dramatic move yesterday afternoon the Gore campaign hastily deployed top vote-getters into Pennsylvania and New Hampshire. Mr Gore sent Jesse Jackson to Philadelphia, the main city in Pennsylvania, and asked Senator Edward Kennedy to deploy more than 100 extra trade union volunteers in New Hampshire.

Hillary set for victory

Hillary Clinton was heading for a historic victory in her battle to capture one of New York's two Senate seats early today. Exit polls put her eight points clear of her opponent, the Republican congressman Rick Lazio.

If she succeeds, the 53-year-old first lady will be the first wife of a sitting president to win elected office.

Mr Lazio was seen as the underdog in the race, but Mrs Clinton had to fight off a series of highly personalised attacks.

The race was one of the costliest Senate campaigns in history, with the candidates spending $78m (£54m) by the middle of last month.

After weeks of not being wanted by the Gore campaign, President Clinton was also called into battle, giving brief interviews on several local radio stations in key areas.

Turnout was reported to be extremely high in several keenly contested areas, with well over 70% voting in Detroit and Miami.

The crucial arena of battle remained the electoral college, the 538-member body where votes for the president are distributed according to the population of the 50 states, and where 270 votes are required for victory. A tie was not being ruled out.

With a long, tense night ahead of him, Mr Bush voted in the late morning at the courthouse in Austin. He then joined his running mate, Dick Cheney, to watch the results on television.

The seemingly indefatigable Mr Gore voted in the local elementary school in his home village of Carthage, Tennessee, at the end of a 30-hour nonstop final campaign swing which began in Iowa in the early hours of Monday morning and ended at the Gore family farm last night.

Race for White House, pages 3–5
Geoffrey Wheatcroft, page 21
All the latest news on the Guardian network at www.guardianunlimited.co.uk/uselection

Atwood takes Booker prize

John Ezard and **Rebecca Allison**

The Canadian novelist Margaret Atwood last night emerged victorious from a closely fought contest for this year's Booker prize.

Atwood won the £21,000 prize for her tenth novel, The Blind Assassin, beating five other shortlisted authors.

Her win came after three previous shortlistings for the Booker. The chairman of judges, Simon Jenkins, hailed her at the award dinner at Guildhall, London, as "three times the bridesmaid – and now the bride".

This year's competition was regarded as unprecedented because there was at first no clear favourite in a strong field including three little-known authors.

Praising her rivals, led by the Japanese-born British novelist Kazuo Ishiguro, as "such good sports", Ms Atwood said: "This is not just about one book. Somewhere out there is another writer who is writing the next Booker. The novel will never be dead wherever there are young writers and readers".

Mr Jenkins said: "The Blind Assassin is a complex book that works on many different levels. Far reaching, dramatic and structurally superb, it demonstrates Atwood's immense emotional range, as well as her poet's eye for both telling detail and psychological truth.

"The book demonstrates the mature pessimism of age and does so brilliantly." It made him believe in the novel as a form.

The novel's narrator is the elderly Iris Chase Griffen reviewing her life and, in particular, her relationship with her sister Laura, whose premature death in the 1940s makes her famous as the author of a scandalous novel.

Full report, page 8
Special report and extensive background on the Booker prize at www.booksunlimited.co.uk/bookerprize2000

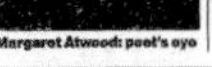

Margaret Atwood: poet's eye

Quick Index

9 770261 307330 45

2000

You can't say that!!
I bloody well CAN say it, Brian, and let my explain why....
Because I have just told you how I feel, Brian. I have claimed my feelings and they are not subject to discussion, debate or negotiation. You cannot argue against them or refute them or contradict them because how I feel is how I feel!
And you feel I'm a useless prat.
Exactly.

Here, Ben, Sweet hot tea. The best thing for shock.
God.... I must seem so feeble...Such a weakling....
CAFE
Of course you don't. Every Social worker reacts like you did, the first time. It's almost like a rites of passage.
Next you'll tell me it gets easier.
No, Ben, It never gets easier. But believe me, in time, you will find ways to cope.
SHE WAS SO RUDE!!
Doctors' Receptionists, Ben. They're part of the job.

...It's just that sometimes I feel overwhelmed by the apparent futility of it all. I mean, do I make any difference?
There I am, day in and day out, daubing away at the weeping sores of society with cotton buds of compassion....
...to what effect? Poverty will never be eradicated. Suffering won't cease. There will always be, by definition, an underclass...
Look. I'm flaming suffocating down here. If you're not going to concentrate...
Sorry.

Richard Williams The day Keegan ran away and England confronted the truth. In Sport

45p
Friday
December 22 2000
Published in London
and Manchester
www.guardian.co.uk

The Guardian

Christmas 2000

Why the Turks want Santa back
In G2

Merope Mills goes undercover in the grotto
In G2

The week's best reads
The pick of the world's media
In the editor

Hamilton protests as he loses the last battle

Neil Hamilton and his wife Christine leave the high court yesterday after the former Tory MP lost his appeal against a jury's libel verdict Photograph: Martin Godwin

Steven Morris

The disgraced former Tory MP Neil Hamilton's six-year battle to clear his name in an English court ended in defeat yesterday when three appeal court judges refused to overturn a libel jury's verdict against him.

Mr Hamilton's only option now is to take his battle to the European court of justice, a move which he said he would consider after calling the latest finding against him "justice in Wonderland".

The former MP for Tatton has now been branded corrupt in the course of two high court cases since the Guardian first reported the cash-for-questions scandal in 1994. He has also been hauled before the Commons committee on members' interests and been heavily criticised in a report by the standards and privileges committee.

Yesterday – a year to the day after losing a desperate libel battle against Mohamed Al Fayed – his attempt to have the verdict set aside was turned down by three appeal court judges, including Lord Phillips, master of the rolls.

Mr Hamilton claimed the trial was unfair because crucial court documents taken from bins outside his barrister's chambers had been bought by Mr Fayed.

The court accepted that the Harrods owner probably had been involved in the plot but decided that it would not have made any difference to the outcome of the case.

Crucially for Mr Hamilton and his wife Christine, the court also lifted "stays" which had been put on costs orders relating to the trial and on the naming of the backers who have bankrolled Mr Hamilton's fight. It is estimated that he could face costs of £2m and the prospect of losing his Cheshire home.

The couple showed little emotion as the judgment was handed down in court. Outside, however, Mr Hamilton said: "This is the most bizarre and unexpected of results.

"For six and a quarter years I have been fighting a billionaire crook. I cannot believe that this is English justice. Outside this court it says 'high court of justice' but I am thinking of going out to buy the letters I and N to add to that."

Mr Hamilton said he would be consulting his lawyers before deciding whether to fight on. Asked if he was bankrupt, he said: "Not as we speak." Mrs Hamilton added quickly: "That is a technical term."

Asked how he would pay his costs, he said: "You can't have less than nothing. I can't pay Fayed anything. I already owe more money to my lawyers than I have."

Mr Hamilton had sued over claims made by Mr Fayed in a Channel 4 Dispatches programme in January 1997 that he corruptly demanded and accepted cash payments, gift vouchers and a free holiday at the Paris Ritz in return for asking parliamentary questions.

Yesterday's judgment recalled how the trial judge, Mr Justice Morland, had crystallised the case in a single question put to the jury: "Are you satisfied on the balance of probabilities that Mr Fayed has established on highly convincing evidence that Mr Hamilton was corrupt in his capacity as a member of parliament?"

Lord Phillips said: "The jury answered 'yes' and found accordingly for Mr Al Fayed ... The single question put to the jury represented the single issue in this case."

The judges did not agree with the claim during this appeal that Mr Hamilton had lost because of separate allegations which surfaced just before the trial that he had corruptly taken money from Mobil for parliamentary services.

Lord Phillips said: "We do not agree ... On the material before the court and in the light of [Judge Morland's] summing-up, the jury may have found against Mr Hamilton on the cash-for-questions issue, the Mobil issue or both."

The judge said that on the balance of probabilities the court believed Mr Hamilton's claims that a character called Benjamin Pell – nicknamed Benji the Binman – did supply documents to the freelance journalist Mark Hollingsworth, who passed them on to Mr Fayed's head of security, John Macnamara, for £10,000.

Furthermore, the court believed that in making the payment Mr Macnamara was acting on behalf of Mr Fayed. Lord Phillips said Mr Fayed, who testified in court that he knew nothing of the documents, was "not an impressive witness". But the judges decided that there was "no reason to believe that they [the documents] will have given any significant procedural advantage to Mr Al Fayed."

Lord Phillips said: "The judge gave the jury as strong a warning against giving credence to Mr Al Fayed's uncorroborated evidence as it is possible to imagine. We do not believe that evidence that he had been party to the purchase of the stolen documents would have done any harm to his credit. He had no credit."

Special report on the case at www.guardianunlimited.co.uk/hamilton

Express owner linked to live sex website

Kevin Maguire, David Teather and Steven Morris

Fresh evidence of the involvement of Richard Desmond, the new owner of the Daily Express and Daily Star, in the selling of hard pornography emerged last night after an investigation of his web of interlinked companies.

Inquiries by the Guardian have revealed that a company wholly owned by Mr Desmond has registered a website which promises live heterosexual sex, live lesbian sex as well as other images portraying women as old as 78, pregnant, and one who calls herself Anal Annie.

A spokesman for Mr Desmond, who was out of the country last night, admitted that the "fantasy" website was part of the businessman's empire, which includes a whole stable of top shelf publications, OK! magazine, and now the Daily and Sunday Express and Daily Star, purchased last month for £125m.

The sale of the newspapers, with a combined circulation of 1.6m, has yet to be referred to the trade secretary, Stephen Byers. The office of fair trading has invited comments on the acquisition and has set a deadline of next Wednesday. A report will then be passed to Mr Byers who, if he chooses, can refer the deal to the competition commission on public interest grounds.

A precedent was set a decade ago when David Sullivan, publisher of the lurid Daily Sport newspaper, was prevented from taking over the Bristol Evening Post by the then monopolies and mergers commission, now the competition commission.

Although there was no reason to block the takeover on competition grounds, the MMC decided that Mr Sullivan's ownership of the newspaper group "could harm the standing of the papers in their community".

If Mr Sullivan had bought the newspapers he "could be expected to influence editorial policy and the character and content of these papers and this would harm both the accurate presentation of news and the free expression of opinion", it added.

The OFT inquiry is purely on competition grounds, but may also reflect any other public

interest comments made by third parties.

Mr Sullivan was referred automatically to the MMC because the combined circulation of his papers and the Bristol Evening Post group breached the rules on newspaper mergers.

The acquisition of Express Newspapers by Mr Desmond has already attracted controversy. An early day motion by Brian Sedgemore and signed by 10 Labour MPs expressed "grave concerns that national newspapers within the Express Group should have fallen under the ownership of a publisher of pornography".

Mr Desmond has set up an advisory board between himself and the newspaper editors to soften criticism that he interferes in the content of the titles, but many staff consider the system to be worthless.

Norman Baker, the Liberal Democrat media spokesman said: "The facts that have been uncovered will cause concern for many longstanding Express readers. If he wants to run sex shows on the sidelines he is happy to do so, but in the public interest, none of that must cross to the newspapers."

Mr Desmond had a 30-minute meeting in Downing Street last week with Tony Blair, who is unlikely to have known the full extent of his involvement in pornography.

On his internet site Mr Desmond charges £9.99 a month to watch "live" sex on webcams, and promotes his magazines.

Desmond empire, pages 4 and 5
Leader comment, page 17

No murder evidence in new Telford inquiry

Vikram Dodd and Nick Hopkins

Detectives investigating the deaths of two black men found hanged within six months of each other in Telford have concluded that there is no evidence they were murdered, the Guardian has learned.

The families of Errol McGowan, 34, and his nephew Jason, 20, had criticised West Mercia police for dismissing both deaths, which followed racial abuse, as suicide. The furore forced a reinvestigation and an apology from the force's chief constable.

In a significant move, West Mercia police say they have sent a file on Errol's death to the coroner and not to the crown prosecution service, where it would be sent if detectives believed there was evidence to support charges.

The decision was made after police found no hard evidence that the two men were hanged by another person or persons.

West Mercia confirmed that their fresh investigation into the death of Errol is no longer "proactive".

The reinvestigation began on February 1, and in an unprecedented move after criticism, hate crime experts from Scotland Yard were called in to give advice.

Police reports will be considered by a coroner who will hold separate inquests next summer which will rule whether the deaths were unlawful, accidental or suicide.

Errol McGowan was found with electrical flex around his neck, hanging from a 5ft-high doorknob in a friend's house on July 2 1999. His family was told he was on a far-right death list after clashing with white youths while working as a doorman in the Shropshire town. Jason McGowan was found hanging by his belt from 5ft-high railings by a roadside last New Year's Day.

The family said neither had any reason to commit suicide, and that Jason had been investigating his uncle's death when he died.

West Mercia police insist the investigation is continuing, though the inquiry has been scaled down.

In a statement West Mercia police said: "We do not submit files to the CPS as a matter of course. We would only do so if there was evidence against a specific individual or individuals. This is not the case in relation to the investigation into the deaths of Errol and Jason McGowan. The file in relation to Errol has been completed and presented to the coroner. A further file in ▸ **Page 2**

Madonna's family show

Madonna and her fiance, Guy Ritchie, after the baptism of their son yesterday. Report, page 7 Photograph: Dan Chung

2000

No, Brian, I am not going to tell my friends. Credit me with some sensitivity.
I appreciate your discomfort. It probably feels like the end of the world to you, but it's nothing to be ashamed of....
Brian, it happens.
Honestly, I know loads of people who've found themselves agreeing with Julie Burchill.

You know, Tim, its OK if you want to cry.
I don't want to cry.
But if you did want to cry it would be OK.
Well I don't, OK?
Crying doesn't make you any less of a man.
I don't want to cry.
Sometimes it takes more courage to cry than not to.
I'm OK!
My boyfriend cries.
Yeah? If I were your boyfriend I'd cry too.

No, I'm afraid we can't 'Put them somewhere else'. They are citizens, the same as you, with the same rights. How would you like it if someone 'put you somewhere else'?
Positive criticism and input from the public is welcomed, however I suggest you make your points without using foul and abusive language.
I'm sorry, but since you refuse to stop swearing and calling me names I have no choice but to terminate this conversation...
.... I'll see you for lunch on Sunday, Mother. Goodbye!

...and now on Radio 4, Clare In The Community...

The Open Montgomerie a match for Lytham as Woods struggles to make a mark. In Sport

60p
Friday
July 20 2001
Published in London
and Manchester
guardian.co.uk

The Guardian

Friday Review

Benjamin Britten Why his music still speaks to us

Cerys Matthews The queen of Britpop is back

Polly Toynbee The outrageous smear campaign against Bob Kiley

Page 23

A liar's moment of truth

● Archer gets four years for perjury at 1987 libel trial ● Police may investigate wife's evidence

Paul Kelso

Jeffrey Archer's spectacular fall from grace reached its nadir last night as the peer and former Conservative deputy chairman began a four-year prison sentence after being convicted at the Old Bailey of one of the most serious cases of perjury in British criminal history.

Archer was convicted on two counts of perjury and two of perverting the course of justice after a seven-week trial that saw the bestselling author exposed as a calculating liar who corrupted his friends and employees to secure victory in his 1987 libel action against the Daily Star, which alleged he had sex with a prostitute.

Following the verdict it emerged that Archer's wife Mary may face a police investigation after the trial judge, Mr Justice Potts, drew attention to the evidence she gave in court in defence of her husband, which was based on a statement given at a late stage of the trial. Detective Chief Superintendent Geoff Hunt said the police would reflect on the judge's comments and take action accordingly.

Archer, who was ordered to pay prosecution costs of £175,000, also faces a writ from the Daily Star, which is attempting to recover £2.2m in costs and damages following the libel action.

The News of the World, which published the original story about Archer and paid £50,000 in an out-of-court settlement, said it was seeking to recover £300,000. Archer also faces calls for his peerage to be stripped from him, and the inland revenue is expected to investigate allegations of tax evasion.

The jury of five men and six women reached unanimous guilty verdicts after 23 hours of deliberation. They found Archer not guilty of a lesser count of perverting the course of justice and acquitted his co-defendant, Ted Francis, on a similar charge.

The crown had alleged that Archer procured a false alibi from Mr Francis to help refute the Star's claim that he paid a prostitute, Monica Coghlan, £70 for perverted sex, and forced his personal assistant, Angela Peppiatt, to forge a diary on which he later relied in court.

Sentencing Archer, Mr Justice Potts said it was "unlikely in the extreme" that he would have won the libel action had his genuine diary been seen in court in 1987 and that the charges against him were among the most serious he had ever encountered.

"I take the view having listened to the evidence over many days that these charges represent as serious an offence of perjury as I have had experience of, and as I have been able to find in the books," he said.

"The fact is that in January 1987 you set out dishonestly to manipulate the proceedings that you had chosen to institute against the Star newspaper.

"You swore an affidavit dishonestly as to documents, and finally and crucially you gave false evidence in court." Mr Justice Potts went on to say that "had the court and jury in July 1987 known the facts, it's unlikely in the extreme that you would have succeeded".

The judge said after that victory, Archer had gone from "strength to strength", resuming his political career, being elevated to the House of Lords, and planning to run for mayor of London.

After sentencing Archer, wearing a dark grey suit and a black tie due to the death of his mother Lola last week, was led down to the cells by two security guards before being taken to Belmarsh high security prison in south London. It is likely that the Home Office will allow him out to attend the funeral. If, as expected, he is given the lowest security rating of category D, he will then be transferred to an open prison, with Ford, near Arundel, West Sussex, his most likely destination.

His solicitor, Tony Morton-Hooper, said Archer and his family were "shocked and disappointed" at the verdict and would be lodging an appeal.

Peter Hill, editor of the Daily Star, was delighted with the verdict. "Archer is a proven liar, a cheat and a chancer, a man so arrogant he thought he was above the law. He has got what he deserved," he said.

The News of the World, which initially published Mr Francis's allegations in November 1999, and paid his legal fees, said the result vindicated its story. Its managing editor, Stuart Kuttner, said: "Our thorough journalism has been fully vindicated by the jury's verdict. We note that Lord Archer was convicted on all the offences that we revealed in the newspaper."

There was little support for Archer from his former political allies.

Lady Thatcher declined to comment on the imprisonment of her former favourite, as did William Hague, the Conservative leader who had endorsed him as a candidate of "probity and integrity" in the London mayoral race.

John Major, the prime minister who awarded Archer his peerage, said: "I am deeply, deeply sorry at the outcome. I hope at this difficult time everyone will also remember the many kind and generous things Jeffrey has done."

Lord Archer going into the Old Bailey yesterday before the jury came back with guilty verdicts on two counts of perjury and two of perverting the course of justice Photograph: Martin Godwin

Inside

Archer faces tax and sex claims

Jeffrey Archer faces an inland revenue inquiry into allegations that he evaded paying tens of thousands of pounds in income tax, writes Kevin Maguire.

Officers in a special compliance unit are expected to investigate accusations made by an ex-aide who claims the author used him to channel cash into Britain from Jersey.

The looming tax inquiry is one of a series of fresh humiliations to be endured by the shamed millionaire, with another prostitute, Dorrette Douglas, last night telling how in 1988 Archer paid her £80 for sex.

The Department of Trade and Industry, however, said the report into the Anglia TV shares scandal, as with similar reports, would not be published.

An inland revenue inquiry is expected after Archer's former friend, Michael Stacpoole, claimed that he brought between £7,000 and £15,000 a month into the country on Archer's behalf from an offshore account on the Channel Island. Archer had boasted that there was more than £1m in the account, he said.

The inland revenue refused to discuss the case yesterday, but a spokesman said even tip-offs from anonymous telephone calls were investigated, making it unlikely that evidence from a close associate would be ignored.

Quick Index
Weather **22**
Cryptic Crossword **36**
Quick Crossword **G2, 19**
Today's TV **G2 back page**

The judge's every word dripped with loathing and contempt

Sketch
Simon Hoggart

In the end it happened with manic suddenness. After the jury had spent four days trawling through mountains of files, papers and diaries, there was a shout of "verdict" and it seemed that everyone in the Old Bailey was running into court number eight, jamming the door, scrambling for the seats, pushing QCs aside.

Jeffrey Archer was almost the last to arrive. He stood in the dock staring glumly and fixedly ahead, as he had for the previous 35 days. Except this time there were two officers to guard him.

He was grinding his teeth, a muscle in his cheek flexed rhythmically as he waited. His wife Mary sat below, to his right, legs together, hands upon her knees. She was in black, with a silver crucifix around her neck. For the first time, her eyes were hooded. Her younger son, William, seemed on the brink of tears.

By this time they must have known. Juries aren't told to find a majority verdict, then come back less than an hour later to acquit.

The British legal system, like the army, provides hours of tedium interspersed with moments of high drama and terror. We waited for the judge and then – it seemed like forever – for the jury to file in. Meanwhile, squads of barristers moved around, smiling and joking. For them this was just another day at the office, and of course they cannot lose; the only fight they face now is to decide who pays their massive fees.

But we were certain of the verdict as soon as the jury arrived. While Archer glowered at them, not one of them even glanced towards him. A basilisk could kill you by looking at you; juries work on the opposite principle.

The foreman, a young black man, was asked by the clerk, a young black woman (Lord Archer can console himself that this has been an ethnically diverse hearing) for a one-word verdict. A pause, and the word "guilty" dropped like a boulder into a duck pond. Some young women in the public gallery had time to yell an ecstatic "Ye...!" before being silenced. Archer didn't flinch.

He did a moment later when the foreman cleared Ted Francis, the man he believes betrayed him. He jerked as if he had been shot, and his lips pushed forward in what looked like unbelieving anger. Then the other verdicts, including one acquittal out of five. His expression had been recomposed in an instant and it didn't change again.

Then the sentence and a speech from the judge which surely smashed into him as hard as the prison term. It must have been like being hosed down with sewage. Every word dripped with loathing and contempt: "As serious an offence of perjury as I have experience of, and as serious as I have been able to find in the books."

The judge spoke of the way he had preyed upon the weak and vulnerable to concoct his alibis; the way he had hurried along the original libel trial to tell his lies and spin his fabrications. It was a short speech, but lethal. Mr Justice Potts was about to take away his liberty, but first he wanted to strip off what shreds were left of his reputation.

He said he took "no pleasure" in sentencing him, though he certainly took a deep draught of satisfaction.

"Lord Archer, will you now stand down, please," he said in a somewhat ▸ Page 2

2001

The thing is, she really loves The Teletubbies. Stick on the video and she's engrossed for an hour. Let's face it, its cheaper than a childminder.
But The Teletubbies talk in gibberish and gurgling. Aren't you concerned that their example might impair the development of her verbal communication skills?
Hey, will you two shut the **** up! I'm trying to watch this.
No, not really.

You've been in that bathroom ages, Brian. I hope you're not doing anything to be ashamed of!
Actually, Clare, I'm masturbating. And no, I'm not ashamed to admit it. Masturbation is a perfectly valid form of sexual expression and nothing to be embarrassed about.
Oh yeah? Well if you're so cool about it why have you got the door locked?

I mean, I don't have to tell you two what I was like: work obsessed! Career was everything to me. My life consisted of chasing promotions, making money, closing deals, cultivating clients and playing office politics.
Well, having a baby has liberated me from all that shallow crap. This little girl has made me completely re-evaluate my...
BRING! BRING!
The office! That could be the office!

Media Guardian How the newspapers and broadcasters covered the terror in New York

50p
Monday
September 17 2001
Published in London
and Manchester
guardian.co.uk

The Guardian

Attack on America Gary Younge, Roy Hattersley, William Shawcross, Martin Woollacott, Richard Sennett, Peter Preston

Nick Leeson 'I've had a great job offer — risk management' **Interview, G2**

Plus Ryder Cup postponed **In Sport**

US tells Taliban to give up Bin Laden or face attack

Pakistan delegation to deliver three-day ultimatum to Afghans

Luke Harding in Islamabad, **Julian Borger** in Washington and **Ewen MacAskill**

Afghanistan will be offered a final chance today to escape a devastating US military onslaught when a delegation from Pakistan delivers an ultimatum to the Taliban leadership to hand over Osama bin Laden, the prime suspect in the New York and Washington attacks, within three days.

With thousands of Afghans already fleeing their homes in anticipation of an assault, the US secretary of state, Colin Powell, said: "They will have to make their choice — whether they want to get rid of this curse within their country or face the full wrath of the United States."

The pressure on the US administration to exact revenge was underlined by a public opinion poll which showed that 84% of Americans supported military retaliation. Two-thirds of them would support it "even if it means many thousands of innocent civilians may be killed".

As call-up plans for at least 35,000 reservists were finalised yesterday, the task of planning the US military response shifted to Tampa, Florida, the headquarters of the Pentagon's central command (Centcom), which is responsible for actions in the Middle East, south and central Asia.

The Centcom commander, General Tommy Franks, has at his disposal a range of special forces and two navy battle groups equipped with 900 Tomahawk cruise missiles.

Maleeha Lodhi, Pakistan's ambassador to the US, sought permission from the United Nations to allow the delegation to go to Afghanistan, which is subject to UN sanctions. The UN will have no hesitation in granting it.

She said: "We will be urging the Taliban leadership to accede to the demand of the international community ... to hand over the person that they are harbouring, Osama bin Laden, so that he is brought to justice."

General Mehmoud Ahmed, the head of Pakistan's intelligence agency, who has just returned from Washington, set off last night for the Taliban's headquarters in Kandahar with the official delegation.

But the US-Pakistan move appears doomed. The Taliban leader, Mohammed Omar, who convened a meeting of his inner-circle to discuss options, vowed he would not hand over Bin Laden for trial in the US.

The Taliban foreign minister, Wakil Ahmad Muttawakil, when asked how the Taliban would react to a US strike, said: "On the issue of Osama bin Laden, there has been no shift in our stand. We maintain our old position. We are responsible for the security of all those living in our country."

Bin Laden has fled Kandahar, the Taliban headquarters, along with his large family and supporters, mainly Arabs, according to Pakistani sources. He issued a further denial of responsibility yesterday. "I stress that I have not carried out this act, which appears to have been carried out by individuals with their own motivation," he said.

The US vice-president, Dick Cheney, expressed his conviction that Bin Laden was behind it: "I have no doubt that he and his organisation played a significant role in this. We are quite confident that he is the prime suspect."

Even if the Taliban was to hand him over, that is unlikely to prevent military action. The best the Taliban could hope for is the US focusing solely on Bin Laden's bases and leaving the Taliban forces alone.

The US president, George Bush, speaking in Washington yesterday said the campaign would not be over soon: "The American people understand that this crusade is going to take some time".

> 'They will have to make their choice — get rid of this curse within their country or face the full wrath of the US'

The prime minister, Tony Blair, speaking in Downing Street last night, echoed these sentiments. "We are absolutely at war with the people who committed this terrible atrocity," he said.

He gave the strongest hint yet that Britain would be involved in military action. Asked whether any military strikes would in effect be an American operation in which Britain was obliged take part, Mr Blair said: "This has been an attack on the whole of the civilised world. There are many British casualties, so we have a direct interest in this."

Whitehall sources did not rule out cruise missile strikes later this week. Officials insisted that the emphasis, as far as the British government was concerned, was on the need for any military action to achieve what they called effective "outcomes", rather than just to demonstrate American power.

Any action would involve what officials described as "close contact" — indicating the deployment of special forces that could be dropped into Afghanistan by helicopter.

The US reliance on Pakistan carries the enormous risk of provoking a civil war that could pit the country's Islamic fundamentalists against the military regime of General Pervez Musharraf. The danger is that if Pakistan collapses into instability, it could result in the world's first Islamic fundamentalist government that is armed with a nuclear weapon.

The Guardian has learned that Gen Musharraf, attempting to maintain a balance between avoiding US punishment and keeping his own Islamist population on his side, has ruled out allowing the Americans to station ground troops inside his country or to use its air bases for a strike against Afghanistan.

He was given a warning last night when Samiul Haq, a powerful Muslim cleric, told a meeting "People will come out on the streets if Pakistan is seen as cooperating with the Americans and the Western powers...it will be devastating for the country and the government". According to senior ministerial sources, Pakistan has agreed to open up its air space to American fighters — a key Washington demand. But the country's senior generals have so far rejected the possible deployment of US soldiers inside Pakistan because of fears of an Islamic backlash.

"The risk for Pakistan would be too great," one of Pakistan's most senior ministers told colleagues.

US officials are now believed to be drawing up plans to replace the Taliban government with a broad-based civilian administration, possibly headed by Zahir Shah, Afghanistan's exiled king. Shah, a "recognised patriarch" according to one diplomatic source, has lived in Rome since his cousin dethroned him in 1974.

Another potential leader is Burhanuddin Rabbini, the country's ousted president, who is still recognised by the UN as Afghanistan's legitimate leader.

A firefighter attending a vigil in Union Square, New York, yesterday Photograph: Jeff Haynes/EPA

Sharon puts Arab support for US at risk

Suzanne Goldenberg in Jerusalem and **Ewen MacAskill**

Ariel Sharon ... placed veto on truce talks

Israel emerged as an early stumbling block to Washington's plans to recruit Arab states to a broad war coalition yesterday as the prime minister, Ariel Sharon, rebuffed US calls for ceasefire talks, and ordered the third invasion of a Palestinian-ruled city in less than a week.

European countries, including Britain, fear that Israel is using the international focus on events in the US as a cover for punitive actions against the Palestinians that contravene international law. Last week the foreign office protested to the Sharon government after the Israeli assault on the West Bank city of Jenin.

Before dawn yesterday seven Israeli tanks entered Ramallah, the capital of Yasser Arafat's administration in the West Bank, and shelled security posts and private homes, wounding five Palestinian protesters and killing a policeman. The Israeli military said one of its soldiers was also killed.

On the political front, too, Mr Sharon has toughened his stance. Yesterday he set new conditions for ceasefire talks that appear practically impossible for the Palestinian leader to meet.

The standoff could jeopardise Washington's efforts to secure the support of Arab and Muslim countries, such as Saudi Arabia and Egypt, for military reprisals for last week's attacks.

It has also triggered one of the most serious crises in Mr Sharon's national unity coalition. His foreign minister, Shimon Peres, threatened to resign after Mr Sharon refused to let him hold truce talks with Mr Arafat, tentatively scheduled for yesterday.

However, Mr Peres is unlikely to get much support for talks even within his own Labour party; a meeting of Labour party ministers last night was expected to rally behind Mr Sharon.

The assault on Ramallah adds to a catalogue of Israeli actions since the attack on America last Tuesday. Israel has:

- announced that it would declare areas in the West Bank adjacent to the Green Line military zones, which means that Palestinians found without passes are liable to be shot;
- sent its armour into the desert town of Jericho, the quietest in the West Bank during the last year of upheaval;
- advanced into Jenin, on whose perimeter troops are now dug in;
- launched missile strikes on Palestinian security posts in Gaza.
- used tanks to shell a suburb of Bethlehem, killing an ambulance driver at the weekend
- tightened the siege of the cities of Tulkaram and Qalqiliya.

At least 15 Palestinians have been killed in these assaults.

The hardening of Israel's stand against ceasefire talks appears driven by Mr Sharon's desire to block the possibility of the Palestinians — and Syria — assuming any role in Washington's coalition, a possibility he views as "very dangerous".

One year into the revolt against Israel's military occupation of the West Bank and Gaza, the fault line in the Middle East remains the conflict between the Palestinians and the Jewish state, and intensified violence would make it difficult to get the Arab states on side.

In a measure of the importance Washington attaches to recruiting Arab allies for its cause, President Bush telephoned Mr Sharon on Friday to urge him to allow Mr Peres to attend the truce talks.

The secretary of state, Colin Powell, also spoke to Mr Sharon, and held two conversations with Mr Arafat.

Mr Sharon refused to let the talks go ahead, and at a special session of Israel's parliament, the Knesset, yesterday, the Israeli prime minister hardened still further his opposition to a Peres-Arafat meeting, which has been delayed for weeks.

"If there will be complete quiet for 48 consecutive hours, the foreign minister will meet Arafat in order to advance the process of the ceasefire," Mr Sharon said.

The new conditions were denounced by the Palestinians. "These demands are a pretext to delay attempts to hold a political meeting between Mr Arafat and Mr Peres, and a recipe for a further escalation," said Nabil Abu Rudeineh, an adviser to the Palestinian leader.

Mr Arafat said he remained committed to talks. "We are committed to the ▸ Page 2

Attack on America

'New York's Union Square is decked with peace symbols from the Vietnam era, as well as hand-scrawled signs demanding war. One of the largest signs reads 'An Eye for an Eye = Blindness.'"
Richard Sennett Page 17

"The response of some of the BBC Question Time audience shows the awful truth that these days there is just one racism that is tolerated — anti-Americanism'
William Shawcross Page 17

'Those who believe that America got what it deserved lack any humanism. But those eager to stifle any understanding as to why these attacks happened lack the faculties to imagine how to make the world a safer place."
Gary Younge Page 18

'There is no final defence against a faith-filled lad standing in a queue outside the Houses of Parliament or on the steps of Congress or in your local pizza parlour. Repeat: no defence."
Peter Preston Page 17

On other pages

On Guardian Unlimited

All the latest breaking news from the US, hear and read key speeches, details of security measures in the UK, plus audio and video footage
guardian.co.uk/usterrorism

Quick Index

38
9 770261 307712
CE ABFPRST

2001

It says here that some emotionally repressed people, frustrated at their inability to express their affection through intimacy, channel it into outburst of irritability and bad temper. What do you think?
I think you should put a sock in it during 'Eastenders'! I don't talk during your programmes. And get that flaming dog off the sofa!

...and then, having been so careful to ask me directly if I take sugar, she says to my husband, 'How many does she want?'!!!
Hahaha!
Hahaha!
I guess some people just can't help behaving differently towards me because I'm in a wheelchair.
Ha! Ha! Ha!
Ha! Ha! Ha! Ha!
Ha! Ha! Ha! Ha! Ha! Ha! Ha! Ha! Ha! Ha! Ha! Ha! Ha!
HA! HA! HA! HA! HA! HA!
"HOW MANY DOES SHE WANT?" THAT IS SO FUNNY......!

I don't know, Clare... You seem to find fault with everything I do these days. You can't resist any opportunity to ruthlessly criticise me.
Oh, Brian, that's not true.
Nor is it grammatically correct. "To ruthlessly criticise" is splitting an infinitive....

THE GUARDIAN
SHOCK INCREASE IN GRATUITOUSLY OFFENSIVE HEADLINES
YOU ARSE

Your complete weekend paper with the Guide, the Editor, Weekend and the best jobs

£1
Saturday
December 1 2001
Published in London
and Manchester
guardian.co.uk
* * * *

The Guardian

Harry Woolf
A judge in the radical tradition
Saturday Review

Jon Ronson
Inside the mind of Jonathan King
Weekend

Billy Bob Thornton
The charm of a power-player
Weekend

Robbie Fowler
Why I walked out of Liverpool
Sport

George Harrison 1943-2001

Beatle loses fight against cancer. Richard Williams writes

George Harrison was the youngest and prettiest of the Beatles and, although it may sound improbable now, thinking of latter-day images of a crusty, grey-haired chap supervising an army of gardeners behind the electrified fence guarding a vast estate near Henley-on-Thames, in the beginning he was the one the girls fancied and the boys instinctively wanted to become.

At first sight, Paul McCartney displayed a hint of puppy fat and an ingratiating air, while John Lennon seemed curiously and inappropriately grown-up: there was no innocence in that thin, sarcastic grin. Ringo Starr alone presented himself as exactly the man he would turn out to be. George was only 19 but he was born with the kind of lost-angel looks – hooded eyes, good cheekbones – that all rock stars should have. And he had the best hair, which was supremely important just then: he had the first perfect Beatle cut.

So for a while – between, say, Love Me Do in late 1962 and From Me To You the following spring – he gave the impression of being the face of the Beatles, possibly even the leader. And he was, after all, the lead guitarist, a role which has its own glamour.

It took a while to work out that what made the Beatles different from everything that had preceded them was coming from the puppyish one and the sarcastic one. After all, beat groups had not contained their own songwriters before. As that recognition sharpened the outlines of their characters, so the young guitarist receded into a supporting role, greatly to his frustration.

It would be some years before the true George Harrison emerged – if, indeed, he ever did, at least in public. He was, it turned out, the shy one. And then, after a further interval, the prickly one. No doubt these characteristics were connected to each other, the product of the eternal resentment of the youngest child. For so long he had been overshadowed by the enormous public acclaim for Lennon and McCartney, whose first group, the Quarry Men, had been going for almost a year when he joined them in March 1958 as a skiffle-crazed 15-year-old.

And now he has become the second member of the group to die. With John, the world lost the Beatle who engineered the death of deference, taking a certain tendency within English humour and turning it into a weapons-grade wit that was sometimes delicately sardonic – "the rest of you can rattle your jewellery" – and at others cruelly sarcastic.

George's demise removes the impressionable enthusiast whose inquisitive nature guided the Beatles beyond the frontiers which had hitherto constrained the attitudes and behaviour of four-piece beat groups from the industrial cities of the north. He may not have written the songs for which they will be remembered, but without his gift for discovery the group might have taken quite a different course and possibly a much less interesting and productive one.

It was George who, in Paris in the early weeks of 1964, during a 19-night season at the Olympia music hall, bought the copy of Bob Dylan's Freewheelin' that was to change the way the Beatles thought about songwriting. Brought up on the work of Chuck Berry and professional songwriters such as Carole King and Gerry Goffin, their horizons limited by pop song conventions inherited from Tin Pan Alley, they seized on Dylan's example to help them make the giant leap, in both content and form, from She Loves You and I Want To Hold Your Hand to Norwegian Wood and Strawberry Fields Forever.

If Harrison's enthusiasm had generated the breakthrough, his colleagues were the immediate ▸ Page 3

"We'll miss him for love, music and laughter", pages 2-5
Mark Lawson, page 22
Obituary, page 24

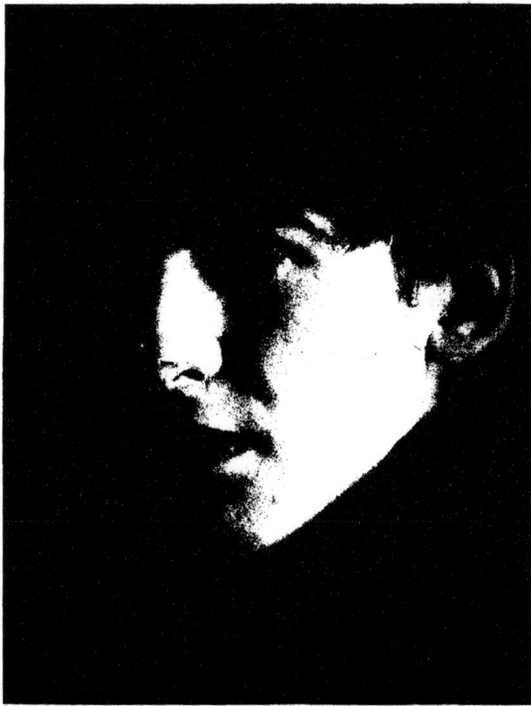

George Harrison in the early 60s. In the beginning he was the one the girls fancied and the boys instinctively wanted to become Photograph: Astrid Kirchherr

Christmas ☆ charity appeal

Which is worse: to be left an orphan with HIV in Africa with four brothers and sisters to look after; or to be stranded, as an asylum seeker, on a bleak British housing estate with your family subject to constant harassment and racist attacks? Both share common characteristics: isolation, deprivation and frequently, desperate social exclusion.

These two groups have been selected as beneficiaries of this year's Christmas charity appeal.

For the next five weeks the Guardian – along with our sister organisations, the Observer, Guardian Unlimited and Guardian Weekly – will be reporting from Africa and refugee centres across Britain about not just their plight but also about schemes which are offering them new hope.

Today is World Aids Day. Three quarters of the world's 36m people living with HIV/Aids are in sub-Saharan Africa. Of all the victims of this grim plague, none is more pitiable than the orphans left behind.

Chris McGreal, our Africa correspondent, begins our series today with an account of one dying mother's plans for her eight-year-old daughter. All the money raised will be forwarded to either Action Aid, which runs projects in 11 African states, or Refugee Action, which works in nine cities across Britain, helping asylum seekers and their families **Pages 18-19**

Errors revealed in siege of Afghan fort

Luke Harding in Mazar-i-Sharif, **Nicholas Watt,** and **Ewen Macaskill**

A series of catastrophic errors lay behind this week's prison siege at Mazar-i-Sharif in northern Afghanistan, where up to 400 Taliban troops died, a Guardian investigation reveals today.

As Amnesty International attacked the government for rejecting an inquiry into the killings, it emerged in Mazar-i-Sharif last night that the captured troops were never meant to be incarcerated in the Qala-i-Jhangi fortress.

Amir Jan, a former Taliban commander who negotiated the troops' surrender, said they were only taken to the fortress after American forces vetoed a plan to take them to an airfield outside the town.

Mr Jan said the first mistake was made early last Saturday after the downfall of the Taliban in Kunduz. The foreign fighters were meant to surrender at Erganak, 12 miles west of the town. Instead, they travelled to Mazar.

At this point another mistake was made by Mullah Fahzel, the Taliban commander at Kunduz. He had instructed the fighters to give up their weapons, but had failed to tell them they would be taken into custody.

After three to four hours of negotiation the Taliban fighters agreed to surrender. They were disarmed by alliance forces loyal to the alliance warlord General Rashid Dostam.

The Taliban forces were put on trucks and taken to his fortress – but only three of the five trucks were searched for concealed weapons.

This allowed a Taliban soldier to detonate a hidden grenade at the fortress late on Saturday afternoon, blowing himself up and killing Gen Dostam's police chief.

On Sunday the riot erupted when Taliban soldiers thought they were about to be shot as they were tied up. The soldiers believed that two television crews from Reuters and the German ARD station were soldiers who had come to film their execution. Alarmed also by the presence of two CIA officers, the soldiers attacked one of the guards and grabbed his gun.

The riot led to the deaths of up to 400 prisoners over three days from a combination of alliance forces and American warplanes.

The row came as the talks on the future of Afghanistan stalled in Bonn. They are expected to resume in Kabul next week.

War in Afghanistan, pages 14-17
Special report at guardian.co.uk/afghanistan

48
9 770261 3074[illegible]
CE ABFFRST

2001

Hi, clare!
Can't stop to chat, Megan, I've got a meeting with Derek.
MANAGER
I have to say, my enthusiasm for the job has been rekindled since Derek became manager. He doesn't so much ask for input as demand it!
MANAGER
He wants opinions, He wants criticism! He wants ideas! well lucky for him I've got plenty of all three.
MANAGER
Funny, I could have sworn he said 2·30.

So, Brian, do you like them?
Track suit bottoms. Do I detect a subtext in this gift?
Don't be so sensitive, Brian. I just want to encourage you to be more active and enjoy all the associated benefits: reduced stress, stronger heart, stronger lungs, better circulation, improved concentration...
So, why didn't you buy yourself a pair?
Because I'm not a great galumphing lard-arse.

I hope Brian is OK back home in England.
Clare, relax! Besides, this anxiety isn't about Brian, its about your guilt over going on holiday without him. Worrying about him helps salve your conscience.
You know as well as I do that Brian is a responsible adult, fully capable of taking care of himself. He really doesn't need worrying about, so put him out of your mind.
I guess you're right.
BASTA

Your complete weekend paper with the Guide, the Editor and all of the best jobs

£1
Saturday
December 15 2001
Published in London
and Manchester
guardian.co.uk
* * * *

The Guardian

Jonathan Franzen
My father's Alzheimer's
Weekend

Steven Rose
Profile of a radical scientist
Saturday Review

John Adams
Music, politics and censorship
Saturday Review

Alan Shearer
Why Newcastle means everything to me
Sport

England player gets community service for affray while 'lying' Bowyer is cleared

Leeds United footballer Jonathan Woodgate leaves Hull crown court yesterday after being found guilty of affray. His team-mate Lee Bowyer was acquitted Photograph: Ian Hodgson/Reuters

Woodgate freed over street attack – but handed £1m bill

Martin Wainwright

Leeds United stars Lee Bowyer and Jonathan Woodgate walked free from court yesterday, almost two years after a vicious, drink-fuelled street attack on an Asian student.

Woodgate, 21, an England international, was sentenced to 100 hours' community service for affray – using or threatening serious violence – but was cleared of causing grievous bodily harm to Sarfraz Najeib, 21, who was punched, kicked and bitten after a nightclub row in Leeds. Bowyer, 24, was acquitted of both charges.

Leeds United defied angry criticism, including a furious denunciation by the victim's family, by announcing within two hours that both players would continue to form part of the Premiership team's squad.

But Woodgate faces expensive disciplinary action and the footballers are each more than £1m poorer after Mr Justice Henriques refused costs.

The judge brushed aside protests from Bowyer's QC with the comment that the player's statements to police had been "littered with lies".

Just one jail sentence came out of the two trials arising from the assault – the first wrecked by a newspaper article – which cost more than £15m in public funds. Paul Clifford, 22, a former boxer and Woodgate's friend since primary school, whose bite-marks were found on Mr Najeib's cheek, was sentenced to six years.

Woodgate's chauffeur, Neale Caveney, 22, another school-friend from Middlesbrough, was sentenced to 100 hours' community service for affray. All four men were cleared at the first trial of conspiracy to pervert the course of justice, along with their Leeds United colleague Michael Duberry.

A fourth player, Tony Hackworth, was acquitted of grievous bodily harm and affray in the first trial because of a lack of evidence.

Mr Justice Henriques told Woodgate that he had caused terror to law-abiding people but had "suffered agonies through the currency of the trials in a way which is etched in your face".

The sentence, well below the maximum three years' jail for affray, also took into account the £13,000-a-week player's seven-figure costs.

With a career that all but collapsed after the drunken brawl on January 12 2000, Woodgate stood stony-faced as the verdicts were announced and said nothing as he left Hull crown court.

By contrast, Bowyer, a former England under-21, blew out his cheeks with relief in the dock and made a jaunty farewell – in keeping with his combative performance in court and exceptional playing form during his 23-month ordeal.

"I'd like to thank everybody for sticking by me. The people that have – I won't forget that," he said. "The people from the club at Leeds United who have stuck by me for the last two years – the manager, the chairman, all the players and the supporters who helped me get through."

In a church next to the courtroom, the Najeib family held a despairing press conference, denouncing a "failure of justice" and revealing that racist thuggery against them has included tyre-slashing a fortnight ago and two threats to their takeaway business in Sheffield. Mr Najeib's father Muhammed, 47, attacked Leeds United and made it clear that a civil action was likely.

"My son suffered a savage and racist attack by five white men," he said.

"Every time he looks in the mirror those bite marks will remind him of the day he was nearly murdered.

"It has been a living hell for our family. Our lives have been shattered. But this is not the end of the matter. I intend to fight on for justice."

Both Mr Najeib and the family's legal adviser, Suresh Grover, repeated their conviction that the attack was racist – a view partly shared by the head of the police inquiry, Detective Superintendent Eddie Emsley, but emphatically kept out of the prosecution case.

The first trial, which collapsed in April, was largely derailed by the persistent rumours about racism which led one juror to ask the judge why Mr Najeib and his elder brother Shazad – who was with him when the brawl began – had not been prosecuted as well.

The prosecution's attempt to stop the trial as a result failed. But Mr Justice Poole called a halt less than two weeks later after a prejudicial interview with Muhammed Najeib was published by the Sunday Mirror while the jury was considering its verdicts – despite the family's stipulation that the article should not appear until after the jury had delivered its decision.

Inside

Leeds football trial
Pages 4-5

'The celebrity of the two leading defendants affected almost every court exchange'
Martin Wainwright, page 4

Plus in Sport, how the trial has affected Leeds United

● Hear Martin Wainwright report from Hull crown court at **guardian.co.uk/audio**

Bin Laden troops in last stand

Rory McCarthy in Tora Bora and Julian Borger in New York

Hundreds of Afghan mojahedin troops, backed by British and American commandos, last night claimed to have surrounded a mountain cave in eastern Afghanistan where they believe Osama bin Laden and a dwindling force of hardcore al-Qaida fighters are hiding.

US bombers delivered huge raids on the cave, high on a ridge in the mountains at Tora Bora, throughout the day. Huge fireballs and plumes of smoke rose into the sky around a small target area.

"There is one cave surrounded by my forces. I think Osama bin Laden is there," said Hazarat Ali, one of the main Afghan commanders leading the Tora Bora attack.

US military officials have said they have good reason to believe Bin Laden is holed up in Tora Bora. They point to the ferocity of al-Qaida fighters around the redoubt, but also claim to have intelligence reports pointing to the militant Saudi's presence.

US defence secretary Donald Rumsfeld yesterday told reporters in Washington: "The ground forces near Tora Bora have advanced about 2km, which is a heck of a lot in that terrain." He added that about 50 al-Qaida fighters had surrendered to Afghan troops and US special forces.

At a briefing, the commander of Operation Enduring Freedom, General Tommy Franks, said the Tora Bora operation was "dangerous work and we have a lot left to do." Gen Franks said Tora Bora could not be called surrounded, but he claimed al-Qaida fighters there were "contained".

The general said up to 1,000 al-Qaida fighters were trapped in two valleys, some of them scattered on valley floors, others in fortified mountainside caves and in tunnels and more along the high ridges.

President George Bush last night reiterated his indifference as to whether Bin Laden was killed or captured. "I don't care, dead or alive. It doesn't matter to me."

There were reports yesterday that two US special forces soldiers had been wounded in combat around Tora Bora. According to CNN, the two soldiers had been shot, one in the shoulder and one in the leg, while attacking an al-Qaida machine gun nest.

Mojahedin soldiers, who have already overrun the main al-Qaida command centre in Tora Bora, pushed up higher into the mountains and captured caves where they found heavy weapons, including rocket launchers and computerised mortars. Commander Ali said there was evidence that the cave was recently occupied by Bin Laden.

A force of up to 180 Arab fighters is now thought to have retreated to a large cave, near the villages of Wazir and Azam, high in the White Mountains on the Pakistan border.

"We have seen the place," said Mohammad Syed Pahlawan, a commander from another Afghan faction. "The US is bombing the area, but the opening of the cave is safe from bombing. The bombs can't reach it."

For several days mojahedin commanders have reported sightings of Bin ▸ Page 1

Christmas charity appeal

Chris McGreal reports from Kigali in Rwanda on the Aids orphans who care for themselves, **page 17**

Quick Index

Sheikh's daughter escaped family's UK home before 'kidnap'

Stuart Millar and Jamie Wilson

The teenage daughter of the billionaire Crown Prince of Dubai dodged security guards and fled from her father's vast private estate in Surrey in a Range Rover, her friends have told the Guardian.

Sheikha Shamsa al-Maktoum ran away, they say, a few weeks before the claims she was kidnapped by members of her father Sheikh Mohammed al-Maktoum's staff and returned to Dubai.

In a growing controversy over the alleged kidnap of Shamsa, who was 19 at the time, ministers revealed yesterday that her father, who in effect runs the oil-rich Gulf state, tried to intervene with the British government over the ongoing police investigation into the allegations.

In a written parliamentary answer, the Foreign Office minister Ben Bradshaw told the Liberal Democrat home affairs spokesman Norman Baker: "Sheikh Mohammed bin Rashid al-Maktoum's London office have raised this matter with the Foreign Office. We have informed them this is a matter for the police."

Mr Baker had asked what contact there had been between the Foreign Office and Sheikh Mohammed over his daughter's allegations.

The world's top racehorse owner, Sheikh Mohammed has remained silent since the Guardian disclosed the existence of a police investigation into his daughter's claims. Officers are trying to establish whether the events took place as described and whether any offence has been committed.

Cambridgeshire detectives have had difficulty in getting access to members of the Maktoums' Newmarket staff, where the famous Maktoum racing stables are based. A small private plane is alleged to have flown Shamsa out of the UK in late August 2000.

Ex-employees at the Longcross estate in Surrey, where Sheikh Mohammed's family were based in the summer, say they had to sign agreements which silenced them about Shamsa's "escape".

Lucy Stevenson, who became close to Shamsa as her riding instructor, told the Guardian there was chaos on the estate in mid July last year when Shamsa disappeared.

Staff at Longcross were sent out to scour the surrounding area for any sign of her but Surrey police were not called.

Ms Stevenson, 29, had moved to another job. But, she said, she was approached after Shamsa ran away by a member of Sheikh Mohammed's staff and questioned over Shamsa's possible whereabouts.

She says she was later followed by members of the estate's security staff, until she complained to police.

Runaway daughter page 3

2001

...it is a global catastrophe just waiting to happen! Which is why we at Rainforest Alert are hoping that you share our passionate committment to environmental protection...
... and will be prepared to make a monthly donation. This will help provide...
Hang on a second....
Your bib doesn't say Rainforest Alert. It says Target Heart Disease.
Crikey! Is it Thursday already?!
Heart Disease is the silent epidemic we ignore at our peril...
TARGET HEART DISEASE

I hate the way the media demonizes young people. Most kids aren't tearaways. They're like that lad there: thoughtful, sensitive, happy to sit on a rock and watch the ducks, as the world goes by.

I can't face it anymore. I can't handle the grief, the hatred, the despair. I just want to stay here and go to sleep. Why bother getting out of bed?
PAY HERE
Because the store closes in ten minutes and we still haven't bought anything for your Mother or Sister.

Happy New Year

The year ahead – an alternative view
Complete bank holiday TV listings
Plus: the 2002 sporting calendar

50p
Tuesday
January 1 2002
Published in London
and Manchester
guardian.co.uk
* * * *

The **Guardian**

The arrival of the euro: their money, our future?

300m Europeans grapple with 6bn banknotes and 37bn coins as leaders welcome an historic new currency

Ian Black European editor

Three hundred million Europeans wake this morning to a new year and an extraordinary new reality that constitutes the boldest experiment ever attempted to bind people together by the money they use.

Heralded from the Arctic Circle to the Cote d'Azur by fireworks, champagne and the strains of Beethoven's Ode to Joy, E-day dawns after years of meticulous planning for the biggest ever currency change and decades of bitter debate — still unresolved in Britain — about how far the continent's nations should integrate.

"The euro is your money, it is our money. It's our future. It is a little piece of Europe in our hands," European commission president, Romano Prodi, declared in Brussels.

Amid worries over price rises and counterfeiting, there was no mistaking the richness of the rhetoric or the thrill of the moment after midnight when cash machines began slipping out crisp new euro notes, the first of more than 45bn to be entering circulation.

Helsinki and Athens, an hour ahead of the rest of the 12-member eurozone, were the first to issue the money, which will have the widest circulation in Europe since the denarius of the Roman empire and is already second only to the US dollar as a global reserve currency.

The mood was uniformly upbeat at parties, pageants and ceremonies bidding farewell to once-treasured marks, francs, pesetas and lire.

"Our countdown is leading towards a new era," Wim Duisenberg, the Dutch president of the European Central Bank (ECB), declared in Frankfurt. "By using euros, we will give a clear signal of the confidence and hope we have in tomorrow's Europe."

On a day of highs, Gerhard Schröder, the German chancellor, hit the highest note. "We are witnessing the dawn of an age that the people of Europe have dreamed of for centuries: borderless travel and payment in a common currency," he said in a new year message.

Mr Prodi marked the change by buying flowers in euros, not schillings, on a visit to Vienna. And in remarks that will alarm a British government watching uncomfortably from the sidelines, the former Italian

€1 = 61.07p

prime minister pledged that the arrival of the euro in people's pockets would lead "ineluctably" to more economic coordination — the great fear of sceptics.

Brussels was celebrating last night with fireworks and dancing. But an earlier event went embarrassingly wrong when a giant euro symbol failed to rise up the facade of the commission's Charlemagne building, generating sardonic comments about a bad start.

Yet when it finally came, it was a grand and very formal moment, an act of stagey transition, and a rite of passage on a continental scale.

So much has been said about Europe's long-awaited date with destiny that it was hard to sort out the predictable hyperbole from the reality.

For countless ordinary people from Lisbon to Luxembourg, that could mean days or weeks of struggling with unfamiliar sums, queuing at cash dispensers, fears of being ripped off, and being unable to decipher bills or pay slips.

But it will also be the first time the EU, seen by so many as a faceless bureaucracy, will have tangible meaning. Officials hope the psychological impact of the euro will help humanise remote institutions and breathe life into an unprecedented debate due to begin in March about the constitutional future of the union.

Troubling questions loom, however, about the state of the eurozone economies: the largest, Germany, is already in a slowdown and dangerously close to breaching the budgetary restrictions laid down by the ECB, whose one-size-fits-all interest rate may be tested in tougher times.

Love it or hate it — and it is a safe prediction for 2002 that Britain's simmering passions will be brought closer to boiling point — the euro is a giant step for European integration.

Under rules laid down by the Maastricht treaty in 1991, the euro began life on January 1 1999 when 11 countries, followed by Greece, surrendered their right to devalue the currency or alter lending rates.

The 12 old currencies will spend up to eight weeks in dual circulation before they are replaced by euro notes embodying generic features of European architecture and culture. The coins retain national images on one side — from Ireland's celtic harp to Germany's double-headed eagle — and will bear the monarch's head if Britain ever joins.

The euro's origins go back to post-war visions of European unity, but the grand bargain — a reunified Germany for the surrender of the mighty mark — was sealed by François Mitterrand, Helmut Kohl and Jacques Delors, then the commission president, after the Berlin Wall came down.

Sweden and Denmark are the other EU members yet to decide on the euro. But with up to 10 more countries set to join the EU in the next few years, 500m people could be using the euro by the end of the decade.

Not everyone liked yesterday's rhetoric. Italy's economy minister, Giulio Tremonti, told La Stampa: "I find the idea that the euro will bring peace and end wars particularly odd. Wars end when consumerism triumphs over romanticism."

As the countdown neared its end last night, 6bn banknotes and 37bn coins worth €144bn had already been distributed.

Launching Europe's single currency is, all in all, a highly ambitious and wellprepared leap in the dark. But it will be judged in the end by whether it meets the test of that simplest of old adages: nothing succeeds like success.

"We are witnessing the dawn of an age that the people of Europe have dreamed of for centuries: borderless travel and payment in a common currency
Gerhard Schröder, German chancellor

Arrival of the euro, pages 4-5
Hugo Young, page 14
Leader comment, page 15
Special report on the euro at guardian.co.uk/euro

Heath was urged to share Ulster with Dublin

Owen Bowcott

Edward Heath's influential Downing Street thinktank examined the possibility of evicting Northern Ireland from the United Kingdom, repartitioning its six counties and inviting in Irish troops to regain the trust of the alienated Roman Catholic minority.

While paramilitary violence grew after the imposition of internment, the Central Policy Review Staff presented the prime minister with a confidential report which described "defeating the IRA" as a "negative aim", according to documents released to the Public Record Office.

A covering memorandum from the cabinet secretary Sir Burke Trend, dated September 3 1971, proposed the Irish Republic be involved in a power sharing deal in Ulster. Written as the Troubles slipped into the carnage of no-warning bomb attacks and daily gun battles between the IRA and British soldiers, the report and memorandum anticipate many features of the peace process which eventually began 20 years later.

The CPRS document would have outraged the Unionist government at Stormont. "The fact that Northern Ireland is constitutionally part of the United Kingdom is no more or less relevant in terms of political realism than the fact that Algeria was part of metropolitan France," it said. "If the six counties ceased to be British ... the net saving to public expenditure would be considerable."

The report noted policy options did not include simply "defeating the IRA and restoring law and order". Such an action was a "negative aim, however desirable" because it "has no positive content unless it masks a hopeless desire to return to the status quo ante". The report concluded: "In a choice of evils, some form of deal with the Irish Republic seems the best option available".

The memorandum by Sir Burke Trend, cabinet secretary from 1963 to 1973, accepts that "to let Ulster go totally in the sense of expelling it from the UK is, presumably, unthinkable in the current climate. But is it less unrealistic to think in terms of an arrangement which would give Dublin not complete control over Ulster, but at least more effective say in its administration?"

His final comment could almost have been written in the knowledge that more than 3,000 people were still to die in the Troubles. "Sooner or later," he noted, "all the parties will be driven to the negotiating table. It will be both more honourable and more economic to go there sooner rather than later".

Public record office 1971, pages 8,9
Peter Taylor, page 14

US accused of killing over 100 villagers in air strike

Rory Carroll in Kabul

Fresh controversy over American bombing flared last night after Afghans claimed more than 100 people died in an air strike. US officials hotly denied that any civilians died during the attack against what it said was an al-Qaida compound from which surface-to-air missiles had been fired.

Reports from the village of Qalaye Niazi, in Paktia province, which borders Pakistan, yesterday said human remains were scattered among craters. Two days earlier, the Afghan defence minister — a leading Northern Alliance commander who wants minimal foreign military involvement in the country — called for an end to the air strikes.

The question of ongoing bombing by American forces pursuing clusters of al-Qaida and Taliban fighters who have eluded them, is one of many issues confronting the man named yesterday as Washington's special envoy to Afghanistan, Zalmay Khalilzad.

Mr Khalilzad, the national security council's specialist on south-west Asia, the near east and north Africa, is to be President Bush's representative to the Afghan people "as they seek to consolidate a new order [and] reconstruct their country", the US announcement of the appointment said.

Trying to hold the government together will be a key task, and the US air raids are among many issues threatening to split the interim administration.

Paktia, just south-west of the Tora Bora cave complex, is a focus of current bombing because it is a suspected hideout of any fighters, including Osama bin Laden, who may have escaped last month's US pounding.

A Qalaye Niazi villager, Janat Gul, told Reuters he was the sole person from his 24-member family to survive Sunday's pre-dawn attack by helicopters and jets. "There are no al-Qaida or Taliban people here," he insisted. Haji Saifullah, head of the tribal council, invited US forces to ▸ Page 2

Debris at the devastated Afghan village of Qalaye Niazi, which survivors say was targeted by US helicopters and jets

2002

Ollie, Clare. Clare, Ollie. Ollie is a mime artist.
Really? How's business? Quiet at the moment? Ha, ha, ha, ha!
...and we have to struggle under the yoke of public ignorance and prove to people like you that it isn't all white faces and black leotards; its not just performing ludicrous charades in silence. The word doesn't even mean 'silence', it comes from the Greek 'mimeo', to imitate. And I'll tell you something else...
Sorry. Should have warned you.

Clare, may I have a word? I just want to reassure you that I am very comfortable with my status as a single woman.
So your sending me a secret Valentine card was a well intentioned but misplaced gesture.
Point taken, Megan. I'll not do it again.
Oh Nooooooooo! So it WAS you who sent it!

Oh well, I suppose an NGO Turf war had to happen some time.
OPEN
OXFAM
CANCER RESEARCH
OXFAM
CANCER RESEARCH
OXFAM
RES
TTER
harry.venning@lineone.net

Christopher Hitchens Let the mourning be brief **Page 15**

Harmony Cousins Celebrity, drugs and me **G2**

Silvio Berlusconi Is Tony's friend out of control? **Media**

Ken Bates View from the Bridge **Sport**

50p
Monday
April 1 2002
Published in London
and Manchester
guardian.co.uk
• • • •

The **Guardian**

Israel vows to avenge bombings

Graham Usher in Haifa and **Suzanne Goldenberg** in Ramallah

Two decades of hatred between Yasser Arafat and Ariel Sharon reached their apex yesterday as the bitter enemies vowed no surrender on a day when a suicide bombing brought fresh carnage to Haifa, and Israel widened its military offensive to occupy a second West Bank city.

At least 16 Israelis were killed and more than 30 injured in the suicide attack on a roadside cafe. Two hours later, a bomber blew himself up in the West Bank Jewish settlement of Efrat, wounding four.

There have now been five suicide attacks in five days in Israel, and a grim-faced Mr Sharon told Israeli television last night: "The chairman of the Palestinian Authority is the enemy of Israel and the entire free world."

In a five-minute speech, which made 14 mentions of the word "terrorism", he added: "We must fight this terrorism, in an uncompromising war to uproot these savages, to dismantle their infrastructure because there is no compromise with terrorists.

In Ramallah, Mr Arafat was equally adamant, despite the roar of Israeli tanks outside his headquarters for the fourth day.

"I am one of the martyrs of my people," he told anti-globalisation activists who broke the quarantine imposed on the Palestinian leader by Mr Sharon on Thursday night.

Shadi Tobassi, an 18-year-old Palestinian from Jenin refugee camp in the West Bank, walked into Matza restaurant at around 2.40pm. The roadside cafe is owned by Israeli Jews, but run by Palestinian citizens of Israel. It was packed with both.

The blast blew a hole in the restaurant roof and set customers and chairs ablaze.

"I was just about to go into the Matza when I was thrown to the ground by a massive boom," Yuhuda Aigzer, 17, said. "Everything was on fire. I saw one man with his hair on fire. A young boy with his face covered in blood. There was blood and glass everywhere."

The attack was claimed by the military wing of Hamas. Abdel Aziz Rantissi, a leader of the Islamist organisation in the Gaza Strip, said the bombings would continue as long as Israel occupied Ramallah and besieged Mr Arafat.

Two hours later, a suicide bomber blew himself up in a paramedics' station in Efrat, injuring four Israelis in an attack claimed by the Al-Aqsa Martyrs' Brigade, an offshoot of Mr Arafat's Fatah movement.

On the Israel-Lebanon border, Hizbullah guerrillas fired at an Israeli army base yesterday. It was the second such incident in recent days, Israeli radio stations reported, raising the possibility of a new front in the conflict. No one was hurt.

By evening, Israeli tanks were on the move again, thundering into Qalqiliya, on the edges of the West Bank, while maintaining their stranglehold on the Palestinian capital, Ramallah. Other tanks and armoured vehicles massed in the Bethlehem area.

About 100 tanks and armoured vehicles rolled into Qalqiliya from four directions, Palestinian security officials said, amid occasional shelling and machine-gun fire. Electricity to the town was cut.

In Ramallah, Israel stepped up its campaign of arresting – or, as Palestinians claim, summarily executing – Mr Arafat's policemen, and stormed a hospital and private homes in search of armed men.

Tanks and armoured personnel carriers encircled the Arab Care hospital, and troops took over the ground floor. Soldiers also tried to occupy the city's largest hospital, but retreated when doctors sat down in front of the tanks at the entrance to the casualty ward. "We took a decision that if they wanted to come in they would have to kill us all," said Dr Mohammed Batrawi.

Jibril Rajoub, the West Bank security chief, told al-Jazeera television that he had received a radio call from a policeman trapped with 30 comrades in a building seized by Israeli soldiers. The caller said his men were being shot. ▸ **Page 3**

Arafat defies Israel, page 3
Peter Preston, page 16
Special report on the Middle East at guardian.co.uk/israel

Week of national mourning announced ● Parliament to be recalled ● Queen Mother will lie in state for four days

Uncertain farewell reveals a nation divided

Jonathan Freedland

The news came as no surprise. The arrangements had been set for years, if not decades. Everything was in place. And yet when the moment finally came, at teatime on a Bank Holiday weekend, Britain was not quite sure how to react.

Uncertainty, rather than tear-stained grief, seemed to be the public reaction to the death of Queen Elizabeth, the Queen Mother.

The rituals for national mourning began almost immediately, with nine days of official lamentation now under way. But everyone knows these are only the outward signs of bereavement: what emotional content they should carry appears oddly undecided.

The BBC, which prides itself on reflecting the national mood on great state occasions, did so again on Saturday – inadvertently conveying this unexpected sense of ambivalence.

Royal correspondents Nicholas Witchell and Jennie Bond followed the pre-arranged script, wearing grave faces and sombre black. But anchor Peter Sissons stayed with grey suit and burgundy tie, sartorially sending the message: business as usual.

There was no Soviet-style clearing of schedules or martial music, promised in years of leaked accounts of BBC rehearsals. BBC1 and BBC2 joined together, but only briefly: the Easter drama Man and Boy was delayed, but only for half an hour.

It was as if people were not quite sure where to place the Queen Mother's death on the emotional Richter scale.

One commentator described it as "tragic"; a teenage girl was shown sobbing as she laid flowers at Windsor castle.

Yet others could not help but point out that a 101-year-old lady slipping away in her sleep was hardly a cause for collective heartbreak.

And so we did the right thing, but we looked a little like a society going through the motions.

The familiar "crowds" were reported gathering at Buckingham Palace, but they turned out to be thin, consisting chiefly of tourists, curious to witness a big news event. Books of condolence were opened, but the queues to sign them – which snaked for miles following the death of Princess Diana five years ago – were brisk to non-existent.

Parliament has been recalled for Wednesday, another measure doubtless demanded by the rule book. But the murmured reaction is one of surprise and scepticism: why are MPs and peers prepared to stir from their Easter break for this, when Parliament remained shuttered as British planes helped bomb Iraq last year?

It is hard to know where the balance should lie. The nine days of official mourning represent a scaling back from the 13 days reportedly envisaged by the planners of Operation Tay Bridge. Perhaps they anticipated the current mood and worried that the nation's grief would not last a fortnight. But is there any guarantee that nine days won't also come to seem excessive?

A royal ceremonial funeral will take place at Westminster Abbey a week tomorrow. Arch-royalists may feel that is too little; they will lobby for Parliament and Queen to make the same exception for the Queen Mother as they made for Winston Churchill in 1965, extending the honour of a full state funeral.

But others might even wonder if a set-piece royal funeral, like Diana's in 1997, is inappropriate for the opposite reason, overestimating the loss felt by the public.

These same doubters will have similar questions about the decision, also announced yesterday, for the Queen Mother's coffin to lie in state for four days at Westminster Hall: if it weren't for the tourists, would enough people come?

What underpins all these dilemmas is an equally taboo thought about the late royal. In all the hours of news coverage and across yesterday's black-bordered front pages, the former Queen was described as a great unifying figure.

But her death has revealed some significant divisions in the 21st century Britain she leaves behind. The most obvious is the familiar gap between left and right. Not between Labour and Conservative, mind: Tony Blair avoided the Sissons manoeuvre, donned black tie and suit and went into his now-familiar eulogy mode, praising the Queen Mother's "grace, her sense of duty and her remarkable zest for life". Iain Duncan-Smith matched the PM, saying she was "the best of us".

But outside party politics, a left-right divide was perceptible. Traditionalists lamented the passing of an Edwardian lady who embodied now-vanished values of decorum and deference.

They saw her as a representative of an era when public figures remained private to all but their inner circle, their true selves essentially unknown.

The Queen might well be the only person now left in Britain, if not the world, who gives no interviews and whose thoughts remain a sealed secret. For conservatives, that buttoned-up reserve is a quality to be sorely missed.

As is the aristocratic, hierarchical world she was born into, grew up in and eventually dominated as Queen.

AN Wilson wrote in the Sunday Telegraph that to see her was to be "transported back to a more comforting world than that of the egalitarian present".

What we mourn, he declared, "is not simply a person, but a whole era of British history. There is no such thing any more as a governing class".

Liberals and the left also see the Queen Mother as the epitome of that bygone age, an emissary of a Gosford Park world where a lady could live for more than a century and never once open or close her own curtains, make a cup of tea or squeeze a tube of toothpaste.

But that is not an era progressives miss. And they cannot, with any sincerity, mourn its passing.

What will worry the palace is that this right-left divide is fast becoming a generation gap. For older Britons, the death of George VI's widow is yet another marker of the passage of time, pushing their wartime memories further into the past. But they are an ever-shrinking group.

By common consent, the Queen Mum's finest hour was the Blitz, when she toured the East End and stayed with her subjects as German bombs rained down on London.

But that was 62 years ago. Plenty of pensioners are too young to remember those events.

Tellingly, the Father of the House, Tam Dalyell, said yesterday that it was right to recall Parliament because, if it had not, his mother's generation would have been offended. Tam Dalyell is 69 years old.

For younger Britons, and not just teenagers and twenty-somethings, royalty exerts no such emotional hold.

The last time the Windsors unified the country was more than six decades ago: ancient history.

Younger viewers would have seen the weekend TV obits, with their interviews with earls, dukes and "ladies of the bedchamber" and felt they were watching a David Starkey documentary about medieval times.

The next fortnight will reinforce that feeling, casting royalty as a leftover of a long ago age.

So the passing of the woman born Elizabeth Bowes-Lyon can only be a multiple blow to the monarchy. The Queen is now her family matriarch, making her instantly seem a generation older.

A year that was meant to be one of golden celebration has now been marked by the death of a princess and a queen. An institution that desperately needs to seem part of the future will spend 2002 fixed instead on farewells.

Above all, the cordon sanitaire which the Queen Mother threw around the royal family – making it impolite to question the institution for fear of offending a sweet old lady – has at last vanished, gone forever.

Six pallbearers carrying the coffin of the Queen Mother from Royal Lodge in Windsor Great Park to the Royal Chapel of All Saints for a private service yesterday Photograph: Kirsty Wigglesworth/PA

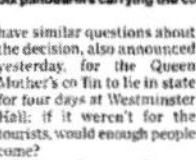

Inside

News, analysis and pictures on the Queen Mother's death **Pages 4 and 5**

Plus Obituary **Pages 18-21**

'Tourists cheerfully submitted to bag checks in return for having their photos taken alongside suitably glum-looking British policemen' **Emma Brockes joins the crowds of mourners, page 5**

'In claiming credit for the spirit of the Blitz, the now-anglicised house of Windsor was flaunting the medals of a defeat' **Christopher Hitchens, page 15**

'The funeral will tell us who we were, not who we are. It will be the formal laying to rest of an era that in other respects finished long ago' **Leader comment, page 17**

On Guardian Unlimited Latest news, archive articles and the chance to have your say at: guardian.co.uk/queenmother

2002

Well I certainly wasn't expecting THAT!
OUT NOW HP4
HARRY POTTER AND THE INTERFERING SOCIAL WORKER
AT LAST THE WAIT IS OVER

Crikey, Nan! Look at the time! Sorry I've gone on, but its been such a long time since my last visit, and I had so much to tell you!
Don't you dare apologise!
I get so few visitors here in the Home that I love to hear about you, that lovely boyfriend Brian, little Megan, naughty Ross The Dog and all those clients that keep you so busy. But I agree, it has been a long time since your last visit...
.... because I'm not your Nan. She's in the room next door.

Let's face it, Clare, things are as bad between us as they've ever been...
...but I can't accept that it's over. I refuse to give up on us, I refuse to believe that we can't turn things around, learn to love each other anew. If the will is there we can make it work. I firmly believe that where there is still communication there is still hope...
What? What? Look, you didn't ask for one, so I didn't make you one, OK.

A portrait of childhood
Libby Brooks explores the world of a four-year-old
G2

Melvyn Bragg
Capitalism v civilisation
G2

Roy Greenslade
Ken Livingstone and the Evening Standard
Media

50p
Monday
July 1 2002
Published in London
and Manchester
guardian.co.uk

The Guardian

Football goes home Brazil are champions for fifth time

Ronaldo goals erase pain of 1998

Richard Williams
in Yokohama

For the second time in his career, Ronaldo ended a World Cup final in tears yesterday. Four years ago the Brazilian footballer was in despair, a 21-year-old facing humiliation as crushing as it was mysterious. Yesterday his two goals in Yokohama's International Stadium gave Brazil their fifth title, bringing an extraordinary tournament to a deliriously romantic conclusion and drawing forth tears of a very different kind.

His mysterious illness on the day of the final in Paris in 1998 spread dismay through his team, giving France a relatively easy ride to the championship. Yesterday Germany were the victims as he took his revenge on fate and then dedicated the 2-0 victory to God, his family and his physiotherapist.

By scoring after 67 and 79 minutes, he left his opponents without a hope of recovery. The many yellow-shirted Brazilian supporters in the crowd of 69,029 exploded with a euphoria that would almost certainly have registered in Rio de Janeiro and Sao Paulo.

Brazil is football's spiritual home, and Ronaldo's renaissance is now one of the game's greatest stories. Since leaving the Stade de France he has spent more time with doctors than with coaches. Yesterday Gerard Saillaint, the surgeon who operated twice on his right knee, was his guest at the match.

So the 2002 World Cup finally did something predictable. Yet when the tournament began, less than a month ago, both the eventual finalists were rank outsiders. Despite winning the championship seven times between them, neither had shown any sort of form during the qualification rounds and both lost key players in the weeks leading up to the tournament.

In the end, perhaps these setbacks enabled them to make progress free from the usual pressures. They were also able to profit from the phenomenon that got the tournament off to such a striking start, the unexpected early departure of Argentina, Italy and France.

The 17th World Cup was the first to be held in Asia, and the first to be co-hosted. It was, indeed, a cup of two halves.

The trophy in the safe hands of Brazil, thanks to two goals by Ronaldo, below Photographs: Dusan Vranic/AP, Richard Sellers

Whereas the South Koreans supported their own remarkable team with a visceral passion that evoked football's oldest traditions, the Japanese responded to the arrival of Brazil and England with the kind of innocent and slightly synthetic enthusiasm that they might once have reserved for the simultaneous arrival of the Beatles and the Rolling Stones.

The 64 matches have been watched by a total of 2.7 million people, an average of just over 42,000 a game. The rows of empty seats at many of the matches were the result of administrative errors all round, the responsibility of the governing body in Switzerland and the ticket distributors in Britain as well as the local organisers.

Sharing a tournament between two countries inevitably reduces the event's cultural identity, an intangible quality that grows more precious in the memory. But Fifa's blazered functionaries are already talking about the possibility of holding the 2010 tournament in two African countries.

Fears that the presence of the English and German teams would lead to the opening of new markets for hooliganism in the far east were not realised.

For the England party and those who followed them around Japan, it was difficult to comprehend the impact of the tournament on the home front. All those giant screens in public places and the time off school and work looked less like a rediscovery of the value of nationhood than ▶ Page 3

Beautiful game reborn, page 3
Open door, page 17
Leader comment, page 19
Sport tabloid
Full coverage at guardian.co.uk/worldcup

20% house price boom forecast

Rupert Jones
and **Larry Elliott**

Britain's biggest building society will today intensify the Bank of England's dilemma over interest rates with a warning that house prices will rise by almost 20% in 2002 as the property boom rages unchecked for the rest of the year.

With the Bank's nine-strong monetary policy committee due to decide on borrowing costs later this week, the Nationwide will reveal that it has been forced to double its forecast for the increase this year in the cost of homes.

Surging demand for property fuelled by 4% base rates — the lowest in almost 40 years — and unemployment at levels unseen since the mid-1970s have forced the society to tear up its forecasts that the market will cool in the second half of the year.

In April the lender forecast that house prices would end this year 10% up on 2001, but it is understood Nationwide will today revise this upwards to around 18%-19% — 10 times the current rate of inflation.

The data from the Nationwide, accompanied by evidence of another large monthly jump in house prices in June, will add to fears at the Bank that inflation in the property market is running far too high for comfort. Prices are now rising at the fastest rate since the late 1980s, when annual increases of 30% were followed by a five-year bear market, negative equity and record home repossessions.

Despite mounting concern, however, earlier City expectations of an increase in rates this week have been dented by the fall in inflation to just 1.8% and by the turbulence on global stock markets after the $3.8bn fraud at the American telecoms giant WorldCom. Sir Eddie George, the governor of the Bank of England, said last week that the monetary policy committee still had time to assess whether higher rates were necessary.

Government steps to ease the pressure on the property market in the overheating south-east will be announced next week by Gordon Brown in his comprehensive spending review. The chancellor will relax planning restrictions and provide extra public money for house building in the hope that the measures will increase the supply of new homes and thereby take some of the heat out of the market.

Although Mr Brown said last week that he would support the Bank if it had to make "tough decisions" on interest rates, the Engineering Employers Federation stressed today that a "panic increase" at a time when inflation was low would harm manufacturing and endanger the prospects of recovery.

The Nationwide's new forecast for the property market represents the second time in three months the society has been taken by surprise at the strength of the boom. At the start of this year the lender forecast that prices would end 2002 6% up but revised this to 10% in April.

Nationwide is today also expected to announce that June saw another strong increase in prices after the 3.4% and 2.1% increases in April and May respectively. The average price in May was £102,886 compared with £87,267 12 months earlier.

The society has said that robust consumer confidence, seemingly undented by stock market falls and worries about the economy, was translating into a surge in buying activity as growing numbers flocked to buy their first home or trade up to a bigger property.

While saying that double-digit price growth is "ultimately unsustainable", Nationwide has attempted to dispel fears of another collapse. But some buyers and sellers will have been unnerved by a succession of reports saying the boom times are over for the buy-to-let market, and that some borrowers are over-extending themselves and could be left vulnerable if interest rates rise.

> The data will add to fears that inflation in the property market is far too high for comfort

The Nationwide's forecasts were backed up by a separate report on the housing market, also showing prices likely to increase by 20% this year.

The data by property research company Hometrack showed that prices had risen by 2% in June and 9.8% so far this year. The report said a slowdown in the rate of house price inflation was expected in 2003, but prices would still rise by 8%.

John Wriglesworth, housing economist at Hometrack, said: "I am not expecting it to slow this year — it's gone up 10% so far and we are expecting it to go up another 10%."

But Bridget Rosewell, a director of the Britannia building society and chief economic adviser to the British Retail Consortium, argues in the Guardian today that the market is not dangerously overheated.

"House prices are still rising, but this is not because consumers have gone off their heads," she writes.

"Most of the rises can be attributed to a simple phenomenon: lowered interest rate expectations."

She argues that with swings in interest rates unlikely and and inflation low and relatively stable, "nearly all the house price rises we have seen are a permanent shift, and the rates of increase will soon be able to slow down with no effort by the monetary policy committee".

Bridget Rosewell, page 23

KPMG conflicts of interest revealed

Jeevan Vasagar
and **Rob Evans**

The giant financial consultancy KPMG, whose polo-playing boss is paid £1.7m a year, has had at least five potential conflicts of interest in its dealings with the British taxpayer, a Guardian investigation has found.

KPMG is one of the big four who dominate the accountancy world, and is the latest auditor to be at the centre of controversy over scandals in the US. It audited Xerox, which on Friday admitted overstating its revenues during the past five years by almost $2bn.

We have found:

- KPMG was paid to advise Hertfordshire University on a contract to build student halls which was awarded to one of its construction company clients.
- KPMG advised the highways agency on a major road project awarded to another of its clients.
- KPMG took £128,000 from the government for an "unacceptable" investigation into the tax haven of Belize. It was doing extensive business with the offshore operators itself.
- KPMG was paid by the Foreign Office to investigate a series of other offshore tax havens in the Caribbean, where KPMG had its own lucrative offshore operations.
- KPMG has been allowed to place secondees in sensitive departments in the inland revenue, the Department of Trade and Industry and the serious fraud office, while specialising in advising firms and individuals on how to avoid British tax. In return for £500 KPMG last month told our reporter in London how to set up an offshore trust.

While the consultancy operates in more tax-avoidance offshore centres than other firms, KPMG has been paying British politicians and political parties. Both Toby Harris, leader of the London assembly's Labour group, and Steve Bassam, before he became a Home Office minister, have been on the KPMG payroll.

The firm also loaned a KPMG man, Rees Aronson, to serve as the Labour party's finance director in the year running up to the last general election. It sponsored and had a KPMG partner on the "independent" commission set up by the Labour IPPR thinktank to promote private finance initiative deals, which are lucrative for KPMG. The firm also helps the Tories, providing several Conservative frontbenchers with free research.

"These big accountancy firms can't simultaneously serve two masters," said Prem Sikka, professor of accounting at Essex University. "The question must be asked: are they taking the taxpayer for a ride?"

Prof Sikka, a strong critic of what he calls the "anti-social practices" of the big four, calls for wholesale reform in his book Dirty Business, to be published today. He says as much as £85bn in tax may be lost to Britain because of avoidance promoted by the big four.

Last year KPMG took in £7bn in fees from 152 offices across the globe. While Mike Rake, who heads KPMG in Britain, was paid £1.7m, the firm's 690 partners in Britain took an average of £413,000 in profits.

KPMG's head of corporate affairs, Gavin Houlgate, last night said the firm did not believe any conflicts of interest had taken place: "These events were all on the record. They are open and well-known."

Although the government has convened a review panel to look at auditing and corporate governance issues, so far this has only met twice. Any review is expected to include looking at new measures such as forcing companies to replace auditors every seven years and preventing accountants from being auditors and consultants for the same firm.

KPMG: government insider and tax avoidance adviser

The government's friend, page 4

Quick Index

27
9 770261 307712
CE ABFRRST

US veto puts Bosnia mission in jeopardy

Oliver Burkeman
in New York

The US gave the UN peacekeeping mission in Bosnia three days to live last night after dramatically vetoing a routine six-month extension in a rancorous dispute with its allies about the historic international criminal court, which came into existence at midnight.

The security council now has until 5am BST on Thursday to resolve the row, sparked by US demands that all its peacekeepers and other personnel be granted immunity from prosecution by the court, which is empowered to prosecute war crimes.

Earlier yesterday evening, facing unanimous opposition on the council, the US had vetoed plans to extend the mission for half a year, eventually agreeing to an emergency 72-hour extension.

John Negroponte, the US ambassador, said the veto was brought "with great reluctance", but that America would not ask its citizens abroad "to accept the additional risk of political prosecution before a court whose jurisdiction the government of the United States does not accept".

One European diplomat told the Guardian last night the veto was "a political point to say we're serious, so give us what we want — there will be an awful lot of political phone-calling over the next three days".

William Pace, head of the International Coalition for a Criminal Court, said of the veto: "History, I believe, will record the actions of the US administration of President George W Bush to wreck UN peacekeeping and the international criminal court as one of the most shameful lows in global US leadership."

Diplomats declared themselves uncertain yesterday as to whether an end to the 1,500-strong UN policing mission in Bosnia would also mean an end to the 18,000-strong S-For peacekeeping force, which is under the command of Nato but endorsed, until Thursday at least, by the UN. Nato officials insisted it would not.

Urging reconciliation, Kofi Annan, the UN secretary general, told the security council: "The world cannot afford a situation in which the security council is deeply divided on such an important issue, which may have implications for all UN peace operations."

Court fights for survival, page 15

2002

Wow! It says here that fathers shouldn't attend the births of their children after all! The Man's anxiety, awkwardness and confusion creates a 'stressful' atmosphere in which their contribution becomes, at best, a distraction and, at worst, an irritating liability!
Do you think it would be like that with Brian at the birth of a baby?
In fairness, Megan, I don't.
At the conception, maybe, but the birth, no.

What do I think? I'm bloody well 100% against it, and so is everybody I've ever spoken to. I regard it as a hideous, horrible, terrifying distortion of nature, and I would support an outright, unequivocal, indefinite ban for the sake of our children, and our childrens' children.
SOCIETY
QPR
Wow, Clare! I never realised you felt so strongly about cloning?
Cloning? I thought you said clowning.
SOCIETY
QPR

Come on, Megan, just ignore them. Its not as though they're doing anything.
That's exactly the point! There's something about young people hanging around street corners, with no discernible purpose, that I find very intimidating. Oh my goodness! They're heading this way!

'Capitalism is as bad as communism'
Zac Goldsmith in G2

55p
Thursday
November 7 2002
Published in London and Manchester
guardian.co.uk
* * * *

The Guardian

BBC cuts jobs and costs in £200m shortfall

Ian Griffiths

The BBC is being forced to cut costs and lay off staff because of a £200m budget shortfall.

News and current affairs programmes are expected to bear the brunt of job losses, but the BBC's board of management has ordered a clampdown on costs across the corporation.

Some departments have already been told to impose recruitment freezes. However, big-spending departments are also being forced to introduce job cuts. News and current affairs executives have been told that a recruitment drive planned for the World and 24 hour services must be reversed. Greg Dyke, the BBC's director general, believes that staffing levels are too high and must be reduced to a sustainable long term level.

An email is already circulating among news staff calling for voluntary redundancies, the first time that such cuts have been sought for at least two years. One source claimed that even more radical action is being considered. Compulsory redundancies are not being ruled out.

The shortfall in the news division is understood to be around £15m. One source said: "Basically, if we were to do everything that we want to do next year, we'd have to find an extra £15m."

The source said there were three ways of meeting the shortfall: an increase in the budget from central funds, redundancies, or a rethink of priorities.

The projected shortfall comes on top of an existing overspend in the news budget from the past year, following events such as the September 11 attacks, the war on terrorism, and the Bali nightclub bombing.

A BBC spokesman claimed that details of the budgeting problems were being twisted and that the cuts now being sought "were in no way radical". He said the focus was simply on efficiency gains, which would be ploughed back in to better programming, adding that the BBC was meeting the government's value-for-money demands.

The £200m mismatch in the corporation's finances arises from an arcane BBC accounting privilege which allows it to borrow centrally against the BBC's assets. This cash has been used historically to smooth out budgetary peaks and troughs between one accounting period and the next.

In the year ending March 31 2002 the BBC's income was £3.4bn but its costs ran to £3.5bn. Once other items such as tax and interest have been accounted for, the BBC had a deficit of £15.9m for the year. In 2001 that was a surplus of £75.5m.

However, close examination has revealed a significant projected overspend over the next two years.

Departmental heads have been told that in the current year, ending in March 2003, they will not be allowed to roll over any budget underspend.

In the past, a department which has not spent its full budget in the financial year has been permitted to carry the excess forward. Because of spending patterns, millions of pounds can be at stake.

BBC insiders are also suggesting that underspending departments will suffer a double penalty. Not only will they lose their budget carry forward, but their 2003-04 budget will be set using the actual spending in the current year as as a base.

The BBC is in the second year of a seven-year budgetary plan. However, the analysis of programmes commissioned for years three and four has revealed that the corporation has overspent significantly.

The corporation is under pressure to keep its financial house in order. Its objectives for the current year state that it must improve "efficiency in programme production whilst maintaining quality of output".

Jury finds Winona Ryder guilty of theft

Duncan Campbell
in Los Angeles

Actress Winona Ryder was convicted of shoplifting £3,900 worth of clothes at a Beverly Hills court yesterday. The twice-Oscar nominated actress is unlikely to be jailed and will probably receive probation or community service, when she appears for sentencing next month.

Ryder showed no emotion, sipping from a bottle of water, after the clerk of the court read the verdict. She was cleared of a charge of burglary, as the jury gave her the benefit of the doubt on a charge which involves using an implement to carry out the offence. But she was found guilty of two charges of grand theft and vandalism.

The jury had deliberated for five and a half hours before reaching their verdicts. Ryder, whose films include Girl, Interrupted, Beetlejuice, Little Women, The Age of Innocence and the recent Mr Deeds, was arrested at the Beverly Hills branch of Saks Fifth Avenue on December 12 last year. She was stopped by security staff and accused of stealing $5,560 worth of merchandise from the store.

The case against her was that she had been seen picking up 20 items as she moved through the store but had only paid for four of them. Store detectives said they had seen her cutting off the security tags from items while in a changing room. She was accused of having brought scissors to the store in order to clip off the tags.

When apprehended, according to Saks security manager Ken Evans, Ryder claimed she was rehearsing for a film. "She said, 'I'm sorry for what I did,'" Mr Evans told the court. "'My director directed me to shoplift for a role which I was preparing.'" She told another security officer that she thought she had left her credit card with an assistant earlier in the day and told her to leave it open.

Oscar-nominated Winona Ryder is guilty of shoplifting more than £4,000 worth of clothes Photograph: Adrees Latif/Reuters

The actress, who turned 31 during the trial and who makes $6m a film, did not give evidence, although her lawyer, Mark Geragos, said that she wanted to. Mr Geragos claimed that the security staff had wanted to "nail" her because she was a celebrity and had tailored their evidence to ensure a conviction. He produced one witness, Michael Shoar, a former Saks employee, who claimed that Mr Evans had told him he wanted to see the "rich Beverly Hills bitch" punished.

Ryder's parents, Mike and Cindy Horowitz, who live in northern California, were in court during her trial. Fans wore "Free Winona" T-shirts. She herself wore the T-shirt as an illustration for a magazine interview in the summer.

The trial was a bad-tempered affair with Mr Geragos being frequently scolded by the judge, Elden Fox. Mr Geragos accused the Saks security team of lying for their "15 minutes of fame" and said that the actress had always intended to pay for the clothes.

Prosecutor Ann Rundle told the jury that Ryder may have shoplifted for a thrill and that claiming that she was preparing for a part was no defence. She cited the character that Ryder plays in Girl, Interrupted, who liked to shoplift for thrills. She claimed that the defence version of events could only have been written in Hollywood.

After the case, Ms Rundle said she would not be seeking a prison sentence but probation or community service. She described Ryder, with whom she had spoken in court, as "a very nice individual" and said that the prosecution had been undertaken so that Ryder would "take responsibility for her conduct", not out of vindictiveness.

Ms Rundle expressed her sympathy for the Saks security team who had been followed and had had their lives examined by private detectives acting for the defence who were seeking to discredit them.

Bush wins hardline UN deal on Iraq

Dual victory as Congress falls to Republicans

Julian Borger in Washington

George Bush's presidency emerged triumphant on both foreign and domestic stages yesterday, as a UN deal was effectively brokered on a concerted hardline stance towards Iraq, and after Republicans seized total control of Congress in midterm elections.

Even as news of the election results was coming in the American ambassador to the UN, John Negroponte, declared that Washington would force a vote tomorrow on its Iraq resolution, drafted with British support, after nearly two months of negotiations.

The draft allows further security council discussions if Baghdad refuses to comply with comprehensive, unfettered weapons inspections, but it does not commit the US to wait for a new UN resolution before going to war.

US and British officials confidently predicted that France and Russia had in effect agreed to the broad lines of the resolution and that they would win majority support in the security council. Paris and Moscow said they would study the new draft before passing judgment on it.

President Chirac yesterday welcomed changes made in the US draft but called for "certain ambiguities to be removed".

French officials indicated that France would not use its veto, while Washington and London appeared convinced that Russia would tag along once France had made public its acceptance. China, the fifth permanent member of the security council, is widely expected to abstain.

In London, an upbeat Foreign Office said that the back of opposition to a tough resolution on Iraq had been broken. The focus now shifts to Tony Blair's efforts to persuade Labour and Liberal Democrat MPs to support the UN position, on which the prime minister has pledged a great deal of personal political capital.

Mr Blair will portray it as a diplomatic victory for multilateralism over Iraq, and not a blank cheque for an imminent US invasion.

Backbench Labour MPs, along with the Liberal Democrats who remain sceptical of the need for military action, will seek clarification of how any war would be triggered.

With the Bush administration poised to clear the final hurdle in its push for a tough UN resolution tomorrow, attention will now switch to Baghdad where the Iraqi regime will be under pressure to meet all demands or face imminent oblivion. Once the security council adopts the resolution, Baghdad will have seven days to respond. It is expected to accept the terms as refusal would mean instant war.

Within a month of the resolution being passed, Saddam will have to provide a full inventory of all his weapons of mass destruction. If those pitfalls are cleared it will be the job of the arms inspectors to ferret out any biological, chemical or nuclear weapons.

Under the terms of yesterday's resolution, the inspectors would have the right to inspect any facility, including palaces — a bone of contention between the Iraqi regime and previous inspection teams. The inspectors would also be able to take any Iraqi out of the country for interview, and to set up exclusion zones and corridors in which the Iraqi army would be forbidden from operating.

The Bush administration's success in corralling security council support on Iraq represents a foreign policy victory to match its resounding result in Tuesday's midterm elections. Mr Bush is now free of many of the constraints on his conservative domestic agenda.

The Republicans recaptured control of the Senate after an 18-month interlude during which the Democrats used a slim majority to foil some of the most controversial elements of the Bush agenda.

With all but two of the Senate's seats decided last night, the Republicans controlled 51 votes in the 100-strong chamber. A last minute surge of support, much of it due to a campaigning blitz by the president himself, toppled Democrats in most of the close Senate races, including the former vice-president Walter Mondale in Minnesota. Last last night Dick Gepardt announced he would not be seeking re-election as the Democrat leader in the House of Representatives. The Republicans strengthened their grip on the House of Representatives.

The victory immeasurably boosted Mr Bush's authority over his own party and dispelled many of the doubts lingering over his presidency since the 2000 election debacle.

Background, pages 4 and 5
Leader, page 25

MPs demand tape answers

Republican MPs last night called for Prince Charles to explain claims that a missing 30-minute cassette tape — recorded by Princess Diana — contains claims that a royal servant was raped twice by a man who works for the royal household. The crown prosecution service was sent a report on the alleged incident but ruled that there was not enough evidence to proceed.

Missing tape details alleged palace rape, page 2

2002

I don't get it. Why do couples need to 'spice up' their sex lives? For me, sex is like chips. I love chips. I've always loved chips. I'm as keen on chips today as I ever was and I've never once had to dress up, perform role play or try different positions to enjoy them.
But what if its not "chips" you're bored with, but your regular "chip shop." What if you want to try "chips" from a different "chip shop"? What do you do then?
I'd jump in the car, because the other chippie in our road never changes its fat.

What's with all the flowers, Clare?
Peggy upstairs is leaving today, So I went round all the florists in the area and bought every bouquet, spray and basket available. Cost a fortune, but it'll be worth it.
But you've had a vendetta with Peggy upstairs for as long as she's been here! You're going to give all these flowers to a person you can't stand?
Nope. And neither is anybody else.

OK, Kevin, to recap: Under the conditions of the Anti-Social Behaviour Order you are excluded from the following places:
Rugby Rd, Cromwell Avenue, Balfour Rd, Dover Rd, Warwick Drive, Alice Close, The Sparrow Estate, The Wren Estate, Lancaster Parade...
Hang on! I'm not excluded from Alice Close!
No, Kevin, you're not. But its where I live, and you can hardly blame me for trying to slip it in....

Beat the congestion charge
25 bikes to be won
Page 18

55p
Monday
February 17 2003
Published in London
and Manchester
guardian.co.uk

The Guardian

Million-strong demonstration will not deflect Iraq policy as ministers rally round prime minister

Blair to defy anti-war protests

Ewen MacAskill
and Michael White

Tony Blair refused to blink last night in the face of the biggest anti-war demonstrations ever held in Britain and worldwide.

Ministers and officials insisted the protests — which saw more than 1 million people march in London on Saturday — would not delay military preparations for war next month.

One well-placed source said: "It changes nothing at all. The quicker it is done, the better. To back down now would be the worst result possible. We would have no credibility if Saddam Hussein was still in place."

Ministers were wheeled out yesterday to buttress Mr Blair, who on Saturday claimed that there was a moral case for military action against Iraq.

In spite of their bullishness, there were signs that the scale of the protest, combined with the report by the UN chief weapons inspector, Hans Blix, on Friday, has disrupted US and British diplomatic plans.

A joint US-UK resolution authorising war that was to have been circulated at the UN security council at the weekend has been put on hold while Washington and London rethink their tactics.

The US and Britain say they still intend to seek a second resolution but must decide on its wording and on whether to present it to a sceptical security council this week or next.

The US national security adviser, Condoleezza Rice, confirmed yesterday that Washington was reviewing how to go about securing the resolution but was not considering any significant delay with regard to military action. She stressed that President Saddam had "weeks, not months".

The US and Britain still hope to have the second resolution in place when Mr Blix reports back to the security council on February 28.

Mr Blair will face calls to give the inspectors more time when he meets the German chancellor, Gerhard Schröder, and the French president, Jacques Chirac, at an EU summit on Iraq in Brussels tonight.

The summit was called at short notice by Greece, which holds the EU presidency, to try to secure common ground but there was little optimism in London that it would achieve much more than a reiteration of support for existing UN resolutions.

The London protest attracted people with an astonishing variety of backgrounds and political viewpoints. The numbers and diversity should be a cause of worry to a prime minister who prides himself on his awareness of public opinion.

Mr Blair, speaking at the annual conference of the Labour party in Scotland, said that while he understood the moral concerns of the marchers, the balance of morality lay with ending a barbaric regime.

While refusing to be dismayed by the scale of the protests, Downing Street aides took quiet satisfaction yesterday as cabinet members defended what the deputy prime minister, John Prescott, called Mr Blair's "courage, integrity and honesty" in the crisis.

John Reid, the Labour party chairman, took the marchers head on, saying they recommended doing nothing, and that such a moral choice meant sustaining a status quo "under which there are people being murdered, tortured and dying and starving".

Mr Blair's ministers insisted public opinion could flip in favour of war, provided there was a second UN resolution. They admitted it would be problematic for Mr Blair's relationship with his party if he failed to secure that.

One minister said cabinet resignations were unlikely to extend beyond the leader of the house, Robin Cook, and that while ordinary members would leave the party, he doubted if it would amount to the predicted exodus.

Yesterday, the leftwinger Alice Mahon spoke openly of a leadership threat if Mr Blair did not allow the UN's team more time: "Yes of course people are talking. There's no point in denying that."

Austin

NOW LET THEM TRY TO GET IN!

BAGHDAD

Threat of war, pages 2-10
Madeleine Bunting, page 21
Simon Tisdall, page 22
Leader comment, page 23
Letters, page 23

A Sunday jogger runs past graffiti on a hoarding protecting a statue of Achilles in Hyde Park Photograph: Stefan Rousseau/PA

In tomorrow's Guardian

Saving Grace

Grace is 30. Her husband and daughter are already dead through Aids. Without the right medicines she, too, will be dead within five years.

Jean Pierre Garnier is head of GlaxoSmithKline, which makes the drugs which could save Grace. In 2001 the firm paid him £3.5m, though he may earn double that.

The Guardian's Sarah Boseley met Grace and Jean Pierre. She then traced every link in the chain between the penniless shoe seller from Malawi and the millionaire chief executive.

Her astonishing 10,000-word report exploring why Grace can't get the drugs she needs is published in a special 12-page supplement tomorrow.

In today's Guardian

G2
The woman whose article on Miss World sparked riots in Nigeria tells her story.

Media Guardian
The comics cashing in on the Asian TV boom.

Sport tabloid
World Cup cricket, FA Cup football and Six Nations rugby.

Quick Index

CE ABFPRST

Flood of emotion and anger that rose to wash away years of dismay

Richard Williams

Somebody called it a movement. It was not a movement. It was a feeling. A feeling that drove wave after wave of people in a great river which began to flow a few minutes before noon and was still in full flood long after nightfall.

What astonished everyone who marched on Saturday – let's settle on a million, shall we? – was the apparently limitless variety of those with whom they shared the roads of central London. Not just a diversity of banner-bearing interest groups but of individuality, brought into focus by the single underlying feeling that gave this day its resonance.

That feeling was one of a generalised dismay directed squarely at the country's leadership. If you wanted to attempt the impossible task of identifying a typical marcher, you would probably settle for the middle-aged white man who marched past the barricaded end of Downing Street at about 1pm carrying a hand-lettered sign. What it said, in neat black letters about six inches high, came closest to summarising the message of the day. "Labour Party member no A128368 against the war," the man had written.

For although the river of people carried all kinds of flotsam and jetsam, the undercurrent was a mighty dissatisfaction with the performance of a leader who, 400 miles away in Glasgow, was at that very moment attempting to justify a stance that few appear to comprehend.

Whatever else it may have been, the march was a great shout of protest against a man for whom most of those present had voted in the last two general elections. After the long, alienating years of Thatcher, Tony Blair presented himself as one of us, part of the culture of modern Britain. But now one piece of foreign policy has provided the catalyst for the release of pent-up disenchantment. On Saturday all the dinner-party groans of anger – at the failure to restore the public services to something approaching a source of pride, at the corrosion of public trust by the incessant use of spin and at the publicity conscious consorting with charlatans and conmen – finally merged with the dismay over Iraq in this long warning cry.

Slogans dominated the day, but they were beside the point. Simple answers will not do, and the hundreds of thousands of placards distributed at the starting points served to diminish rather than amplify the impact of the gathering of so many people on a single pretext. In themselves, the people were ▸Page 2

Thousands of drivers leave it late as congestion charge starts

Andrew Clark
Transport correspondent

As many as 24,000 London motorists have left it until the last moment to pay their £5-a-day congestion charge, which comes into force today in an attempt by the London mayor, Ken Livingstone, to tackle the capital's chronic traffic jams. Vehicles entering central London from 7am this morning will be required to pay the fee. The rush hour will be greeted with protests by pro-car demonstrators and champagne celebrations among environmental activists.

As the countdown to the charge's introduction reached its final few hours, Transport for London announced that of the 100,000 eligible motorists expected to drive into town today, 26,000 had paid the charge and 50,000 had registered to pay on the day by text message.

The authority insisted it could cope with a last-minute rush. Its call centres will be staffed by 800 people, while hundreds of shops and petrol stations will sell tickets and a website has been upgraded to handle extra demand for online payments.

Many politicians believe mass non-payment could be the biggest barrier to the scheme's success. Mr Livingstone's backers say he needs to win over the "hearts" of Londoners as well as proving that the charge can work technically.

Lawyers acting for critics of the congestion charge said yesterday that they still intended to seek a judicial review of the charge, claiming they could be ready to file papers today.

Business leaders in London have overwhelmingly backed congestion charging on the grounds that transport delays cost the capital up to £4m a week. The mayor hopes it will cut traffic by 10% to 15%.

Tony Juniper, executive director of Friends of the Earth, said there was "no credible alternative" to the charge.

Norris to be candidate for mayor, page 11
How to text us your experiences on congestion charging, page 11
Leader comment, page 23

2003

Up here on the 15th floor, its like we don't exist. Out of sight, out of mind....
Nobody cares, nobody bothers nobody takes any interest. Except you...
...and I can't say how grateful I am.

This is ridiculous!
Are we going to have to do this every time you spot a former client?
Only the ones I pissed off.

The thing is, Clare, I need to know that you still find me attractive.

This man thinks the human race may be doomed

In Life, the new science section. Plus Online

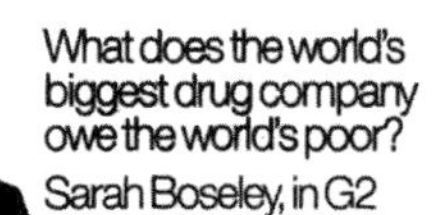

What does the world's biggest drug company owe the world's poor?

Sarah Boseley, in G2

United crash out in seven goal thriller

In Sport

55p
Thursday
April 24 2003
Published in London
and Manchester
guardian.co.uk

The Guardian

Galloway: others may have taken money

Richard Norton-Taylor, Sarah Hall and Jamie Wilson

George Galloway conceded last night that intermediaries in his fundraising activities could have siphoned off money from Saddam Hussein – but insisted he had never done so.

As he fought to counter allegations that he had received up to £375,000 a year from the Iraqi regime, Mr Galloway revealed the full amount given to the Mariam Appeal – the organisation he founded to fly a young Iraqi leukaemia victim to Britain for medical treatment and which then became a campaign against UN sanctions – and pledged to release further figures today.

Speaking from his holiday home in Portugal, Mr Galloway said there was a "possibility" that third parties had taken money from the former Iraqi dictator.

He also conceded he was open to criticism for collecting money from "unlikely quarters". But he insisted he personally had received "no money from anybody".

Mr Galloway's comments came after the Daily Telegraph printed documents, discovered in a burnt-out foreign ministry building in Baghdad and purporting to be from an Iraqi spy chief, that suggested he had demanded money from the Iraqi regime under the oil for food programme. In the latest memo, published in today's issue, it is claimed that officials close to Saddam sought to sever alleged links with the secret police, the mukhabarat, fearing disclosure of contact between the MP and the security agency would "damage him very much".

"Irrespective of the provenance of the documents the material in them is false," the MP for Glasgow Kelvin said yesterday. There was no evidence he had ever traded in oil or food or money, Mr Galloway added.

Yesterday the allegations intensified as the attorney general, Lord Goldsmith, in his capacity as protector of charities, confirmed he was considering whether to investigate claims that Mr Galloway had misspent money raised by the Mariam Appeal.

It has been alleged that he had spent the money – purportedly intended to treat sick Iraqi children – on travelling expenses. But Lord Goldsmith is taking legal advice to assess whether he has the power to investigate the appeal, which has not registered as a charity.

As MPs urged him to open the accounts, Mr Galloway revealed that the appeal had received about £800,000 over the past four years. More than £500,000 was provided by the United Arab Emirates and about £100,00 by Saudi Arabia.

The bulk of the remainder had been provided by the Jordanian businessman Fawaz Zureikat, a long-time opponent of sanctions against Iraq and the campaign's chairman. The rest came from a number of small donors, according to Mr Galloway.

As for expenditure, £150,000 was spent on the "Big Ben to Baghdad" bus – which travelled from London to Baghdad in 1999 – and about £60,000 on a sanctions-busting flight to Baghdad the following year.

A total of £80,000 was spent on the campaign's offices overlooking Trafalgar Square in central London. £35,000 was spent on three conferences, and £50,000 on sanctions-monitoring publications, publicity and advertisements.

Mr Galloway insisted the Great Britain Iraq Society, an organisation linked ▸ Page 2

Galloway controversy, pages 4 – 5
More at guardian.co.uk/politics/iraq

Behind the mask People protect against virus in Australia, India, Canada and China

Global battle against Sars panic

James Meikle
Health correspondent

The World Health Organisation strongly advised people yesterday not to travel to Beijing or Toronto, in a dramatic escalation of the global battle to control the spread of the Sars virus.

The British government immediately endorsed the new warning – despite Foreign Office insistence until now that the threat of infection in Toronto remained low – as the Tories accused it of maintaining a "lethal silence" on the threat to Britain.

More than 250 people have died among nearly 4,300 infected worldwide. The disease has now struck 25 countries in five continents with a number of governments taking drastic quarantine measures.

Chinese authorities closed schools in Beijing yesterday as China's death toll climbed to 105. Shanxi province was also included in the WHO warning.

Beijing authorities said they planned to quarantine people suspected of having Sars or who had been exposed to the virus.

In Australia, where just four cases have been reported, the New South Wales state government said it would fine or jail for up to six months anyone who refused treatment.

Hong Kong and Guangdong in southern China – where Sars, or severe acute respiratory syndrome, first made its appearance last November – have been under WHO health warnings against all but essential travel for three weeks, twice what is thought to be the maximum incubation period for the disease.

David Heymann, the executive director of communicable diseases at the WHO, said: "This is a very serious disease with a death rate now of about 5%."

The latest restrictions will reinforce gloom over economic slowdown as business and the tourism and travel industries become blighted.

The WHO plans an international summit of scientists to combat the disease in Geneva in June, although a network of research laboratories is already working round the clock to devise tests and treatments.

Officials in Canada, where there have been 16 deaths and more than 320 probable or suspected cases, have questioned the certainty of scientists who believe they have correctly identified the Sars culprit as a coronavirus related to one of the most common causes of colds.

There are already fears that the virus may be changing into a more virulent form.

The WHO said that in Toronto, "the outbreak has continued to grow and has affected groups outside the initial risk groups of hospital workers, families, and other person-to-person contacts. In addition, a small number of persons with Sars, now in other countries of the world, appear to have acquired the infection while in Toronto".

Canadian health officials and local politicians were outraged. "Where did this group come from? Who did they see? Who did they talk to?" an angry Mel Lastman, Toronto's outspoken mayor, asked at a news conference. "Let me be clear. If it's safe to live in Toronto, it's safe to come to Toronto. I dare them to be here tomorrow."

City health officials said the WHO advisory was irresponsible and regrettable. "The outbreak is not over but it is definitely under control," said Sheela Basrur, Toronto's medical officer of health.

Here, the government's chief medical officer, Sir Liam Donaldson, insisted last night that health services "remain vigilant" over Sars. The six probable cases in the UK had been promptly identified and cared for. "This is the correct approach at the present time and expert advice does not recommend mass quarantining of travellers returning from the far east or Canada."

He added: "The way Sars will progress is not predictable, so if there is any change in the situation here, we will not hesitate to take any necessary further action."

The Conservatives accused ministers and senior health officials of complacency. They suggested thousands of foreign and holidaying students returning to schools and universities from affected areas ought to have been quarantined. Liam Fox, the Tory health spokesman, said the government should have issued clear advice that such students should be isolated for 10 days rather than rely on screening at airports in Asia and twice-a-day health checks.

He added: "The experience in Canada shows what can happen if an outbreak occurs in a major western city."

Some schools, such as Eton, are refusing to take back those who have been to affected areas within the last 10 days. Harrogate Ladies' College put 42 pupils into isolation. Among universities, Portsmouth and Leeds suggested students should come home from overseas earlier than planned, "to enable them to avoid crowded places for three days after returning to the UK".

Patrick Dixon, of the London Business School, an expert on global trends, said: "This is potentially a far more serious epidemic than Aids. Unless the virus spontaneously mutates into a less serious form, the only hope we have is to mount an immediate aggressive global response at the highest levels against Sars, something we've not yet seen. "If things continue as they are, then a pandemic is surely only a matter of time."

Spread of Sars, page 13
More at guardian.co.uk/sars

Austin

FOR GOD'S SAKE! – SOMEBODY COUGH.

YES NO MAYBE SOME DAY

Blair tells IRA to give clear answers

Tony Blair yesterday challenged the IRA to give clear answers to three questions to enable the peace process to move forward: will it end violence, will it get rid of its weapons, and is its conflict over for good? Sinn Fein responded by saying the IRA's position was clear and accused Mr Blair of being unreasonable

Full report, page 2

Children held at Guantanamo Bay

Oliver Burkeman
in Washington

Children younger than 16 are being held as "enemy combatants" in the American detention camp at Guantanamo Bay, the US military admitted yesterday, a practice human rights groups condemned as repugnant and illegal.

Three boys aged between 13 and 16 are among about 660 inmates at the controversial camp, a US military official told the Guardian, on condition of anonymity. The official would not disclose their nationalities but said they had been brought from Afghanistan this year on suspicion of terrorism.

A spokesman at the base, Lieutenant Colonel Barry Johnson, said that as soon as the children's ages were confirmed in medical tests, they were moved to a "dedicated juvenile facility" at the camp, where they could socialise with each other.

"They are in a secure environment free from the influences of older detainees," Col Johnson said. "They are receiving specialist mental healthcare, in recognition of the difficult circumstances that child combatants go through, and some basic education in terms of reading and writing." Efforts were being made to contact their home nations, he added.

But the children would still be held indefinitely and would not be granted access to lawyers, he said, because the US continues to view them as "enemy combatants" – a term it has used to argue that the Geneva conventions do not apply to the inmates, who have not been charged with any crimes.

That would be the case "until we ensure that they're no longer a threat to the United States, that there's no pending law enforcement against them, that they're no longer of intelligence value," Col Johnson said.

Amnesty International called on the US to release the youths immediately or charge them, calling the detention "particularly repugnant".

The United States and Somalia are the only member states of the United Nations not to have ratified the Convention on the Rights of the Child, but the US is a signatory, and thus has "an obligation not to defeat the object and purpose of the treaty," Ms Wright said. "This is clearly

A detainee is led to his cell at Guantanamo Bay

totally at odds with the purpose of the treaty."

The precise legal ramifications are unclear, since many experts argue that the US is already in breach of international law by holding any of the detainees indefinitely without trial or charge, regardless of their ages.

Guantanamo Bay has been condemned by human rights campaigners since the first detainees arrived at what was Camp X-ray, in January 2002. Soon after, they were pictured cowed, blindfolded and bound in the intense Cuban heat.

Since then, the US has built Camp Delta, a permanent and better-equipped facility, and has been at pains to describe how the inmates' religious and cultural preferences are being catered for. Representatives of the International Committee of the Red Cross are in regular contact with the detainees.

But reports of hunger strikes and attempted suicides have continued to emerge from the base. Military officials have confirmed 25 suicide attempts by 17 people since the inception of the camp, with 15 this year, often by inmates attempting to strangle themselves.

One detainee, who reportedly fell into a coma after trying to hang, himself was back off life support this week, Col Johnson said, but there was no word on what the authorities would do with him next. The Pentagon has published regulations on how the inmates, who come from 42 countries, might be tried by military tribunal, but has not yet nominated any of them for trial.

The US court of appeals ruled last month that the government was entitled to deny due legal process to the detainees because they were not Americans and were not being held on US territory.

The three boys are not the only inmates under 16 to have been brought to Guantanamo Bay. Canadian officials had to negotiate for months in order to gain access to Omar al-Khadr,

a Canadian national who is being held at Camp Delta after being captured in July during fighting in eastern Afghanistan. He was 15 at the time his detention began; he is now 16.

More at guardian.co.uk/usa

17
9 770261 307941
CS ABFPRST

2003

For crying out loud, lads!!! You're just going to have to agree to disagree over salting aubergines. Mens' Group has other issues to discuss....

And when you find out that the Women's Group meetings ARE more fun? What then?
ROOM 8
LIFE DRAW

Dammit, Simon, we have an obligation to intervene when we see such vandalism! Just because it isn't our car being trashed, it doesn't let us off the hook morally. Yob behaviour has to be challenged!
They're still there.
I mean, society can only function when the individuals that make up said society take responsibility to protect it. I think it was Voltaire who once said.....

Wayne Rooney comes of age, interview in Sport **Plus** the guide, travel and 100s of jobs

£1.10
Saturday
October 25 2003
Published in London
and Manchester
guardian.co.uk
* * * *

The Guardian

Space Handbook
How to be bold – key ingredients for the elegant interior
40 page special in Weekend

Seamus Heaney
Ted Hughes, my partner in poetry
Review

Zoe Williams
Whatever happened to Blair's cool Britannia?
Weekend

Princes vent fury at butler

● Exclusive: 'weak' Charles to blame says former aide

● William and Harry plead for end to revelations

Ian Katz and **Stephen Bates**

The royal princes, William and Harry, launched a devastating assault on Princess Diana's former butler, Paul Burrell, last night following a week of tabloid revelations from private letters disclosed in a book to be published next week.

They accused him of a cold and overt betrayal of their mother. The unprecedentedly strong language of their intervention effectively undermines Mr Burrell's claim to be defending the memory of Princess Diana and discloses the sense of anger and betrayal the royal family feels about the book's publication.

In a terse, three-sentence statement issued from Clarence House, the princes said: "We cannot believe that Paul, who was entrusted with so much, could abuse his position in such a cold and overt betrayal." They said it would "mortify our mother if she were alive today" and called for Mr Burrell to "bring these revelations to an end".

Last night Paul Burrell responded by saying he was "saddened at the statement issued on behalf of Prince William and Prince Harry.

"My only intention in writing this book was to defend the princess and stand in her corner. I would also like to point out that, following the collapse of my trial at the Old Bailey last year, no one from the royal family contacted me or said sorry.

"Neither do I say sorry for writing this book of which I am extremely proud and I am convinced the princess would be proud of too. I have told the truth where the British public should know the truth."

He offered to meet both the princes to explain his actions. He told the Daily Mirror: "I want to look them both in the eye and tell them why I've written this book. I think they'll feel differently when they hear me."

Sealing a miserable week for the royal family, one of Prince Charles's most senior former aides tells the Guardian today that the heir is a weak figure who lacks self-belief and is incapable of standing up to his courtiers. Mark Bolland, the prince's former deputy private secretary, claims in his first newspaper interview that Charles was indirectly responsible for the airing of the embarrassing revelations in Mr Burrell's book because he failed to stop the butler's prosecution for alleged theft of Diana's possessions.

Mr Bolland says the prosecution was "a complete fuck-up that should never have happened ... And the Prince of Wales should have done more to stop it. But he's not a terribly strong person. I just think he lacks a lot of confidence. He doesn't have a lot of self-belief. He doesn't have a lot of inner strength".

Mr Bolland's attack will be particularly bruising coming from the once hyper-loyal spin doctor who was widely credited with masterminding Camilla Parker Bowles's stealthy passage into public life alongside the prince.

Mr Bolland says he believes Mr Burrell would not have gone public with his revelations, contained in his book A Royal Duty to be published on Monday, if he had not felt "hounded" by the royal family.

Extracts of the book were published by the Daily Mirror this week. They contained the revelation that Princess Diana had written a letter 10 months before her death alleging that there was a plot to kill her in a car crash.

According to Mr Bolland, Prince Charles could have averted the ultimately disastrous prosecution of Mr Burrell if he had been stronger in the face of pressures from the police and his own legal team.

He said, the prince was "not a strong person and in this particular case he was very, very weak".

Despite his insistence that a prosecution of Mr Burrell should have been avoided, Mr Bolland welcomed Prince William's statement: "It's a good thing to have done because he's standing up for his mother."

Bolland interview, pages 4 and 5
Mark Lawson, page 25

End of an icon

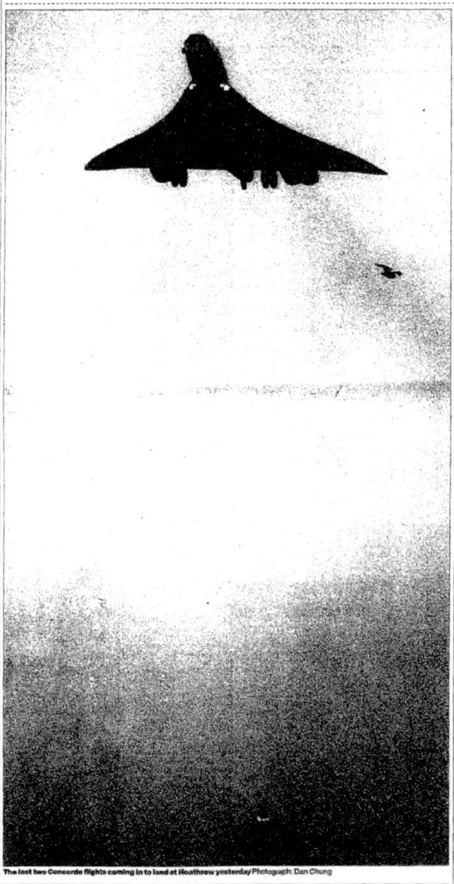

The last two Concorde flights coming in to land at Heathrow yesterday Photograph: Dan Chung

Time machine's final trip leaves an empty sky

Jonathan Glancey

The sky seems a little lower this morning; a cathedral without a spire, a mountain without wolves. Yesterday Concorde, the Anglo-French sky goddess, drooped her nose for the last time in commercial flight, coming in to land among commonplace Boeings and Airbuses at Heathrow airport.

And then she turned and pirouetted slowly into her hangar to meet and greet the massed ranks of waiting TV cameras, as 100 celebrities, captains of industry, competition winners, newspaper editors and at least one ballerina and a fashion model emerged from her nipped and tucked fuselage.

The last trip on Concorde G-BOAG from New York yesterday was not exactly as elegant as it should have been. The cabin was host to a media scrum, and for all the fine foods and wines, the journey felt rather like a trip back from a rugby match — as noisy as the aircraft's engines, and then some.

Down we came along the Thames over central London to join up with two other Concordes and to be welcomed by a crowd that was impossible to see through the aircraft's tiny windows.

Down came a dream that — as the pilot Captain Mike Bannister was keen to remind us — could fly faster than a bullet, faster than the earth rotated.

A time machine of sorts that could transport those who could afford a ticket from London to New York to arrive at least an hour before they took off.

Born into the glare of flashbulbs and global publicity, she was worshipped by the many who could never have afforded to drink champagne and dine on caviar in her pencil-thin cabin as she boomed across the Atlantic twice as high as jumbos and at twice the speed of sound.

The skies will seem quieter today too.

Concorde could always be heard before she was seen. That trademark thunderous rumble, as if the clouds were being pushed apart by some titan, caused heads to crane from city streets as she took off or came in to land.

Generations of the environmentally conscious thought of her as an evil, smoke-belching dragon, a gas-guzzling curse, pandering only to the swinish rich.

Who were the rich on board yesterday's flight? Bankers, yes, brokers, certainly — the advertising mogul Maurice Saatchi for one. There were few obvious stars. Joan Collins sat near the front, as she has done for many years. She said Concorde's going was a "travesty of civilisation". ▸ **Page 2**

Concorde by numbers, page 2
Take two, page 26
Leader comment, page 27

Asylum amnesty for 50,000 heralds tough new measures

Alan Travis
Home affairs editor

As many as 50,000 asylum seekers and their children are to be allowed to live and work in Britain under a Home Office amnesty.

The home secretary, David Blunkett, said he is to grant "indefinite leave to remain" to up to 15,000 asylum families who applied more than three years ago to "clear the decks" for tough new measures to be announced on Monday.

The one-off exercise was welcomed last night by refugee welfare organisations and will cover families with children who applied for asylum before October 2000 and who have "suffered from the historical delays in the system". They are expected to include some who have been in Britain for up to seven years.

But at the same time the home secretary announced that he is to withdraw all state support from those rejected families of asylum seekers who refuse to leave the country voluntarily when they are offered a paid route home. Families will also face the threat of their children being taken into care.

Mr Blunkett said the new asylum legislation, to be detailed on Monday, would encourage people to come to Britain to work legally while being "as tough as old boots" on those who abused the system.

He said the amnesty was justified because it made no sense to "drag people out of communities after so many years".

"Granting this group indefinite leave to remain and enabling them to work is the most cost-effective way of dealing with the situation and will save taxpayer's money on support and legal aid.

Many of the families covered by the amnesty who applied for asylum before the cut-off date of October 2000, when rejected asylum seekers lost their multiple appeal rights, can still challenge official removal directions in the high court under human rights legislation. In some cases it could be 2006 before they have to leave the country.

Currently 12,000 of the 15,000 families involved are being supported by the Home Office which said yesterday £15m in support costs and legal aid would be saved even if only 1,000 of them came off support. The amnesty decision was welcomed by refugee welfare groups last night but strongly attacked by the Conservatives.

Maeve Sherlock of the Refugee Council said: "It is the right and moral thing to do. Now the government must focus on getting decisions right much earlier, so people are not left in years of uncertainty."

But the shadow home secretary, Oliver Letwin, said the amnesty would make Britain a magnet for asylum seekers.

guardian.co.uk/asylum

43
9 770261 307668
CE ABFPRST

2003

I know how dismissive you are about 'self-help' books, Clare, but this one really is effective.
Its called 'Feel The Fear And Do It Anyway'. In fact, I think I'll get it for you.

What's this? Somebody's birthday?
My Dad's. On his behalf I've adopted a rare Sequoia tree in Oregon State, U.S.A.
What an original gift! You must have put a lot of thought into it.
I did! I couldn't choose between the tree, a tarot reading or a salad sprouter...
....but on balance I decided the tree thing would piss him off most.

You know, I really resent what's happened to the date September 11th.
Because its been appropriated by The Right to justify their own narrow political agenda, reducing a cataclysmic human tragedy to the level of a cheap campaign slogan?
Because it's my birthday.

Martin Johnson exclusive

England's captain tells the inside story of how the World Cup was won in a 20-page souvenir tabloid

55p (IR €0.80)
Monday
November 24 2003
Published in London
and Manchester
guardian.co.uk

The Guardian

Georgia leader quits in velvet coup

Shevardnadze forced out in tense standoff

Nick Paton Walsh in Tbilisi

Eduard Shevardnadze last night ended his 30-year domination of Georgia, stepping down as president after weeks of protest, in what his opponents hailed as a velvet revolution.

The former Soviet foreign minister, lauded by the west for his role in ending the cold war, but hated at home for a presidency that turned authoritarian and corrupt, and that was tarnished by a series of fixed elections, looked exhausted after a series of defections by close colleagues.

"I have quit. I see that this [the political crisis] could not have ended bloodlessly and I would have had to exercise my power. I have never betrayed my people, and therefore I believe that, as president, I must resign," he said.

The 75-year-old, known as the grey fox for his wily political manoeuvring, made a joking reference to his resignation as Soviet foreign minister in 1990 in protest at plans to quell unrest in the Soviet Union: "I am well accustomed to resignations. I have a lot to do and have enough to write about already. I feel happy to have the chance to do something as long as I live," he said.

The opposition leader, Mikhail Saakashvili, said the speaker of the outgoing parliament, Nino Burdzhanadze, would take over as acting president. The constitution provides for her to remain president for 45 days pending elections.

"Now it is important that ... Shevardnadze and the police of Georgia and the armed forces, as well as the acting president, preserve stability and calm in the country," said Mr Saakashvili. He urged protesters to remove their barricades in Tbilisi.

Mr Shevardnadze's resignation ended a tense standoff that had threatened to turn violent on several occasions but that rarely lost a unifying sense of Georgians rising up to reclaim their poverty-stricken land.

After an intense meeting between Mr Shevardnadze, opposition leaders and the Russian foreign minister, Igor Ivanov, at Mr Shevardnadze's residence in the capital, a middle-aged soldier, Tamaz Gebashvili emerged to say: "He's gone". Protesters grabbed him and threw him in the air, cheering.

Mr Shevardnadze's resignation was confirmed 40 minutes later when Mr Saakashvili emerged to an ecstatic crowd.

"He said that he had thought about resigning before and did not want bloodshed. We asked him to resign, and he said yes. He will stay in Georgia, probably here," he added, pointing to the residence behind him.

Mr Saakashvili said that Mr Ivanov, who spent much of yesterday in transit between the president and his opponents, had left the room prior to the resignation.

Mr Saakashvili later called Mr Shevardnadze "courageous" and called on Georgia to provide the former president guarantees of security.

Zurab Zhvania, another opposition leader, said Mr Shevardnadze had wanted to resign earlier but had been convinced by his inner circle who had "been urging him to hold on to power by violent means".

Tbilisi was ablaze with street parties, cheering and fireworks, and cars full of Saakashvili supporters racing through the streets chanting "Misha, Misha" and "Free Georgia".

Widespread fraud in November 2's parliamentary elections — deemed "spectacular" by international observers — brought tens of thousands of Georgians on to the streets. At times they gridlocked the city centre, blockading the parliament building.

Tension grew during the week, as Mr Shevardnadze repeatedly warned of civil war and his officials threatened to crack down on protesters. But Mr Shevardnadze was dealt a severe blow by his security chief, Tedo Japaridze, who has close ties to Washington. Mr Japaridze said the elections were fraudulent and demanded new ones, the first sign that the president's inner circle was fracturing.

On Saturday, Mr Shevardnadze convened parliament, with apparently enough MPs present to appoint a new speaker. Mr Saakashvili and his supporters burst into the room, fighting off security guards. The president was ushered out by his security and later declared an "armed coup attempt" had taken place.

Yesterday the square before parliament filled with an estimated 30,000 protesters, deserting troops mingling with pensioners, students and MPs. Television carried repeated reports of national guard units, police, interior troops and presidential security deserting the president.

As dusk fell, Mr Saakashvili appeared before the crowd and said that if Mr Shevardnadze did not come and speak to them by 7pm, they would go to him at his residence.

An appeal from Mr Ivanov set the deadline back an hour. At 8pm news came of the resignation. Waiting at the gates with her two daughters, Maga Podskhvelia, 38, said: "Today we can have stability in Georgia because Shevardnadze has gone."

Mr Shevardnadze's old comrade in cold war arms, Mikhail Gorbachev, said: "Eduard is not a coward and probably understood [he had] to make this step so that Georgia did not break up. I think he was right."

Georgia crisis, pages 14-15
Comment, page 20

Golden boy England's reluctant hero heads for home

Jonny Wilkinson, whose last minute drop-goal sealed England's victory, with the Webb Ellis Cup Photograph: De Martignac/Equipe

A month of celebrations for World Cup winners

Paul Kelso
Sports correspondent

England's victorious rugby team will return to the UK tomorrow with the World Cup to begin a month of victory celebrations unprecedented in the history of their sport.

Their dramatic extra-time victory over Australia in Sydney on Saturday prompted nationwide celebrations that will continue until Christmas with a series of events to mark the success.

The team, which yesterday received the congratulations of Tony Blair and the Queen, is likely to be rewarded with a Downing Street reception and a "victory tour" of the capital in an open-top bus.

The team will also play a celebration match against the New Zealand Barbarians at Twickenham on December 20, and yesterday Tessa Jowell, the culture secretary, hinted at the possibility of a public holiday in the players' honour.

"We will look at all the appropriate ways of marking this ... but you can be absolutely sure that the team will be honoured in the way that everybody in England wants to see them honoured," she said.

Mr Blair, who watched the game at Chequers, said: "This was a fantastic day for English rugby and for England. The team can be proud of their performance, their spirit and above all their character. It was a victory they worked for and the whole country can be proud of them."

The team are certain to dominate the New Year's honours list, with the coach, Clive Woodward, expected to receive a knighthood and the captain, Martin Johnson an OBE.

Jonny Wilkinson, who is in line for an OBE after his drop-goal sealed victory for England with 20 seconds remaining in extra time, will find himself at the centre of the wider public's new-found passion for rugby.

The last time hundreds of English fans turned up at an airport to greet a returning England team was after the 1990 football World Cup when they lost the semi-final on penalties. Then the popular hero was Paul Gascoigne, and he greeted his public wearing a pair of false breasts.

The contrast with Wilkinson could not be more marked. If he could, the modest 24-year-old, who was among the first to leave England's victory party on Saturday, would avoid the limelight altogether but he is unlikely to be afforded that privilege. His decisive role in the victory will see him in huge demand, and he is expected to more than double his earnings, to around £5m a year. All the players are expected ▸ Page 2

Special 20-page sport tabloid
Peter Preston, page 19
Leader comment, page 21
MediaGuardian, pages 8-9

In rugby's heartland, heroic drinking gives way to sober reflection

Matthew Engel

The morning after is the time reality sets in, and reality comes no colder than it did yesterday at St Catherine Meadow, home of Spartans Rugby Football Club.

Here we were on day two of the Great English Rugby Boom. And nine aspirant Jonny Wilkinsons, plus one chunky 10-year-old prop forward, all from local primary schools, turned up for the normal Sunday morning session of mini-rugby, the form of the game supposed to unearth the lads who will win the World Cup again in 2015.

Unfortunately, the adults failed to make it. The gate was locked and the club was deserted. The kids had a makeshift knockabout in the bleak car park, practising their scrummaging like young stags in the rutting season, while the parents wondered whether English rugby was now too hung over to attend to normal business.

Then word came through: mini-rugby cancelled; breakdown in communication; apologies. "Rugby's going to have to get its act together," seethed one mum. And if rugby can't get its act together here, it can't happen anywhere. For this is Gloucester, the heartland of the English game.

All over the country, people who don't know the difference between a wing three-quarter and a ha'penny stamp spent Saturday night dancing on tables, "doing the Jonny" with their arms, yammering on about 1966 and pledging undying allegiance to a game that mixes nitpicking complexity, simple artistry and even simpler violence. But among true rugby folk, reaction to England's victory over Australia was at once drunker — and more sober.

This is a city where there are more than a dozen high-class clubs, their strength still based largely on the city's selective rugby-playing grammar schools. Here the sporting landscape is dominated by the premiership rugby team, the Cherry-and-Whites, and the soccer team — Gloucester City FC of the Dr Martens League Western Division — are so overwhelmed that they only make page 27 of the Saturday Pink 'Un.

And the crowd who watched the game in the most rugby-crazed pub in the country's most rugby-crazed town on the most rugby-crazed day in English history cannot possibly have been out boozing on Saturday night. The limits of human endurance are such that they must have been comatose.

Opposite Kingsholm, the Gloucester rugby ground, an all-ticket crowd started drinking pints round about 8am in the White Hart, the pub run by the former England forward Mike Teague. Much the same was going on down the road in the Queen's Head and the Kingsholm Inn, and in the other 14,997 English pubs reputedly open for the occasion, although elsewhere the drinking may not have been on the same heroic scale.

For these were no fair-weather fans. When the whistle blew for infringements, many of them actually understood why. In this pub all five screens are tuned to rugby even when Old Fartonians are playing Lymeswold on Sky Sports 49. And the customers, many of them with forearms like oak trunks and the capacity of oil tankers, represented the spirit of old rugby, that game of sang-froid and singsongs. And they were paying homage to this new game of Woodward and Wilkinson, in which England practise beforehand and go on to win.

At the height of the drama, the White Hart reacted the same as everywhere else. They explained Australia's last-minute penalty in the usual technical terms: "The referee's a twat". In extra time strong men nuzzled closer to each other for reassurance. Some tried to turn away, but there were too many screens; there was nowhere else to look. And when victory came, a "Yes!" rang out that could have been heard all the way to Sydney. Their emotions were drained, even if their bladders were not.

Someone said to Teague that it had worked out well for him: "Think of all the extra beer you sold in extra time." He reacted with contempt. "Think of the prize!" he said righteously. "The greatest prize of all!"

In any case, he was still selling just as much beer in mid-afternoon. But by now a certain thoughtfulness had crept in. "In a way I feel resentful about all the people jumping on the bandwagon," said Steve Barrett, a Gloucester season-ticket holder who sounded mighty perceptive for someone who had drunk six pints of Guinness washed down with four of Strongbow. "But how else will you get peo- ▸ Page 2

2003

So, I've got the wine, you've got the cake, Cheryl's bought some balloons, Errol is sorting out snacks and munchies, Mel's arranging plates and cutlery, and Finn has agreed to bring in a sound system and be DJ.
VIN ROUGE
Gosh, Clare, I'm so excited. It's such fabulous news about Jeff's new job, I wish we could start celebrating now!
Patience, Megan, patience...
VIN ROUGE
Let's at least wait for the bastard to leave the building first.

The first day of a fitness regime is always the hardest, Brian. But you just have to stick with it....
...and pretty soon you'll have no problem lacing up your trainers. Now off you go for your run.

For crying out loud, Sis! What kind of aunt do you think I am? Of course I didn't tell her that Santa doesn't exist!
What I told her was that Santa is a reactionary stooge of the adult world, his presents a weapon of social control to ensure good behaviour and conformity in children. Not the same thing at all!
harry.venning@lineone.net

2004

Late in 1996 I received a letter from Anil Gupta, a comedy producer at the BBC, who suggested that Clare In The Community could be adapted into a television sitcom. With my good friend David Ramsden as co-writer, we wasted no time in putting pen to paper, and just eight years later Clare In The Community was on the radio.

The story of Clare's agonising eight year trek through the wilderness of development hell has no place here, except to note that before Sally Philipps made the character her own on Radio 4, she had already been played by Nicola Walker and Julia Sawalha in BBC and ITV pilots respectively.

Three actors, three very different interpretations. Who'd have thought a two dimensional character could have such depth?

Clare was first broadcast on Radio 4 in November 2004. Some people got it - others didn't.

Enough people liked it to prompt a further eleven series and several one-off specials, totalling thirty six hours and forty five minutes of material in all. That's almost enough to keep you fully occupied on a round the world flight, provided your plane crash lands in the middle of the Atlantic on the way home.

2004

The Reviews - some got it

I'm crossing my fingers that the second episode of Radio 4's new sitcom Clare In The Community will be as funny as the first. ***It's the sharpest script I've heard for years.***
Sue Arnold, THE OBSERVER

Two episodes in, it's clear that ***Radio 4's found a really funny sitcom****. Hurrah- there are four episodes still to come!*
Camilla Redmond, THE GUARDIAN

The heart sinks at the prospect of a sitcom based on a Guardian strip cartoon about a social worker- but don't be put off. ***This is actually very funny. Honestly. Truly.*** *It's quick paced with an intelligent script, and this episode has a great, if risky, pay off.*
Top Choice, Weekend, THE MAIL

Programme of the week is this new sitcom based on a cartoon strip in The Guardian. Sally Phillips manages to make this politically correct monstrosity mildly sympathetic by the end- by which time the tone has changed from bitter to ***wildly funny. All very acidic and highly enjoyable.***
Culture, THE SUNDAY TIMES

What a ***crackingly good sitcom*** *this is. Laugh out loud funny.*
Susan Jeffries, DAILY MAIL

A completely ***engaging narrative, beautifully observed characters and lots of very funny material****. A radio sit-com that pleasingly stresses the "com" rather than the "sit".*
SONY RADIO AWARD PANEL 2005

Some didn't...

FRIDAY

Radio

Social worker Clare is a saint to her profession – even when she's called on to babysit a "difficult" teenager

Clare in the Community

11.30am R4

For nearly ten years, Clare has been self-righteously commenting on the social worker's lot in a cartoon strip in the caring professional's newspaper of choice: *The Guardian*. Now, Harry Venning's character takes on a new life at the centre of a sitcom that she'd probably accuse of "reinforcing negative stereotypes", for she's portrayed in it as a control freak who prefers interfering in other people's lives to sorting out her own. Recorded in front of an audience, this is workmanlike stuff with a soapy dimension. The jokes may not be that special but the delivery is – thanks to Sally Phillips. She heads a cast that also includes Gemma Craven as Clare's colleague Helen, and Nina Conti as social work student Megan. Tonight, Helen has her first date since the invention of the internal combustion engine, but where can she turn to find a babysitter?

2004

Christmas in cartoons
With Steve Bell, Robert Thompson, Andrzej Krauze, Harry Venning ... in G2

Sport quiz 2004
Who coached Greece to football glory? What was the name of Pinsent's boat?

80p
Thursday
December 23 2004
Published in London
and Manchester
guardian.co.uk

The Guardian

Labour plans flood of bills for third term

Programme includes reform of schools, Lords, welfare and health

Patrick Wintour
Chief political correspondent

Labour is planning to counter criticism that it has lost its way in power by privately preparing up to 60 new bills ready for a probable third term.

Ministers are desperate the programme as the most Blairite yet put before the country. At its heart will be the extension of home ownership, *better public health, a democratic second chamber, welfare reform and greater support for parents and young children.*

A more parent-friendly schools policy is also being examined by the new education secretary, Ruth Kelly, following criticism that the five year plan published in the summer lacked focus.

One idea is to increase streaming in schools. At present 40% of classes by secondary education are mixed ability, despite a promise to extend streaming according to ability in the 1997 Labour manifesto.

Ministers claim the government is months ahead of the comparative legislative plans made before the 2001 election.

They say the planning reflects Mr Blair's impatience not to see his final period of government dissipated in the way the second term record majority became outnumbered by the long controversy.

Labour's election high command comes with guidance polls showing an eight-point lead, and the generally advanced planning underlines ministerial confidence that they can be re-elected with a three figure majority.

It was being stressed that Downing Street does not want a Queen's speech after the election that merely carries forward uncompleted legislation, but instead augurs "brand new legislation", based on manifesto commitments, to inject political momentum.

Mr Blair, in practice, will have only three years further

to full power after the general election and clearly wants to leave an unmistakable legacy. He has already announced that he will not seek a fourth term.

The degree of planning — described as "epic" by one ministerial source — would mean the government could probably handle a February election and have enough legislation on the stocks to fill a parliamentary session starting in early spring.

Labour's campaign strategists have already reportedly booked a two-week long stint of billboard advertising for the new year. The party has secured 1,300 poster sites for around £1m.

But campaign chiefs continue to reject speculation about a snap February poll. They claim the electorate would expect Mr Blair to serve four full years and if he went to the country early it would feed damaging suspicions that he was hiding bad news on the economy, including imminent big tax rises.

The IMF this week warned that the chancellor, Gordon Brown, needed to cut planned borrowing by £10bn a year over the next five years. The Treasury, however, remains confident such dire forecasts can be proved wrong.

A meeting of Labour's gen-

eral election strategy committee last week again confirmed that the economy will be central to the campaign.

With only two more departmental five-year plans to be published from the Department of Work and Pensions, and the Office of the Deputy Prime Minister, the bulk of the policy work is now in place. They are likely to be endorsed at a special Labour policy forum on January 29.

Nevertheless, internal discussions are still under way on the extent of welfare reform, especially how to help women improve their pension entitlement.

The Treasury is looking at ways that women with broken national insurance records or low part-time jobs can build up decent entitlements.

Its review, welcomed by women Labour MPs, stops short of the proposal for a non-means tested citizen's pension, an idea floated by the new work and pensions secretary, Alan Johnson, but which might cost £6bn.

Only 18% of women receive a full basic state pension when they retire.

Debates are also continuing over how to provide incentives for hundreds of thousands of incapacity benefit claimants to find work, and the government is still looking at imposing new requirements on lone parents seeking state benefits, as long as they are offered decent childcare provision.

In another area of debate, the election coordinator Alan Milburn is pressing for tenants to be able to take equity shares in social housing as a way of boosting an asset owning democracy and social mobility. Tenants who wanted to buy their rented house would be eligible for an interest-free equity loan from the landlord equal to the right to buy discount they would have received.

Jackie Ashley, page 20

This year's must-have present
Yes, it's a goat

A goat or an iPod? The Oxfam catalogue's top-selling gift is the goat. It has sold more than 30,000 as gifts for villages hit by famine

Patrick Barkham

One is small, shiny and plays thousands of your favourite songs when you carry it with you. The other is large, hairy, makes a bleating noise and would butt you if you tried to pick it up.

But iPods and goats are the must-have Christmas gifts this year. And both, it seems, are in short supply. Oxfam has sold more than 30,000 goat gifts; Cafod — the Catholic Agency for Overseas Development — has sold 13,000 — at £25 a goat. The charities are using the gift money to buy the obstreperous

beasts for villages stricken by famine.

"It's been incredible," said Debbie Wainwright of Cafod. "We've raised nearly £800,000 from Christmas gifts this year and our top selling gift is the goat. One school raised £5,000 to buy goats."

Devotees of Radiohead, who have made it a Christmas tradition to buy guitarist Ed O'Brien bizarre gifts, have got him dozens of £24 Oxfam goats this Christmas. "I have decided I want to populate the world with my goats," wrote one fan on a Radiohead message board. Cafod is buying goats for

people in Eritrea, Kenya and southern Sudan. Oxfam's goats will go to 30 countries.

As well as producing milk, offspring and manure for crops, goats are notoriously hardy.

Under Oxfam's scheme, the animals are given to village committees, who decide who most needs them.

"It's been a phenomenal success," said Douglas Graham of Oxfam. "People like laughingly, but they also understand when they are buying something less tangible. I'd rather have a goat than an iPod."

Leader comment, page 21

Letter, page 21

Prince's group gets £1m to help regulate healers

Sarah Boseley Health editor

A foundation set up by Prince Charles was given nearly £1m by the government yesterday for the delicate task of getting the experts to look for alternatives in alternative medicine.

The Prince of Wales established the Foundation for Integrated Health to press for more complementary and alternative therapies within the NHS at a time when most conventional doctors had no time for them.

At a speech last month in Devon, the prince said that when he suggested a more holistic approach to the first

tish Medical Association 20 years ago, "all hell broke loose".

But now the foundation has officially moved into the mainstream, taking on a central, government-sponsored role in what the health minister, Lord Warner, called "a new drive to improve the regulation of complementary and alternative healthcare".

The government will give the foundation £900,000 to support the work it has already begun in "developing robust systems of regulation for the main complementary healthcare professionals".

The foundation is involved in drawing up statutory regu-

lation for those who practise acupuncture and herbal medicine. The proposals have gone out to consultation and are expected to be published by the government in final form in January. Only those who are fully trained and hold the recognised qualification will be able to describe themselves as an acupuncturist or herbal medicine practitioner.

The new and more difficult challenge is to tackle the professions where qualifications and skills are more variable, such as aromatherapy and reflexology. Michael Fox, the foundation's chief executive, said he believed the professions needed to move swiftly towards regulation, but that there were difficulties.

Take reflexology — the sessions which may not last terribly long. There are also some very good ones that last full-time over three years. The difference in terms

Page 3

Stars sign letter in support of playwright in hiding

Tania Branigan

Leading figures from the arts world are among more than 700 signatories of an open letter supporting the Sikh playwright who has been forced into hiding by death threats.

Actors, writers, directors and others — ranging from Priscilla Scales to Tariq Ali, via Terry Jones and the poet Benjamin Zephaniah — have signed the statement, published today in the Guardian.

The gesture is all the more significant as Gurpreet Kaur Bhatti has asked for plans to hold readings of her play, Behzti, to be axed, as they appeared to have prompted further threats against her.

Other supporters include directors Jude Kelly and Richard Eyre, writers Arnold Wesker, Willy Russell and Jonathan Coe, and actors Sheila Hancock, Timothy West and Samuel West. The cast of the play have also signed.

They say: "It is a legitimate

function of art to provoke debate and sometimes to express controversial ideas ... Those who use violent means to silence it must be vigorously opposed and challenged."

The letter warns that everyone has lost out due to the cancellation of the play. Birmingham Repertory Theatre said it could not protect the safety of its audience or staff following a violent protest at the weekend.

Protesters say Behzti ("Dishonour"), which depicts rape and murder inside a temple, demeans the Sikh faith.

But in the letter its defenders say: "We all have the right to protest peacefully if a work of art offends us. We do not have the right to use violence and intimidation to prevent that work of art from being seen by others.

"To verbally and physically threaten a writer, audience members, performers and theatre staff is unacceptable. To attempt to censor a play be-

cause some incident in it would thereby be rendered less offensive to some people if they were set elsewhere is unacceptable. To stop the production of a work of art by means of force and continued threats of force is unacceptable.

"Doubtless, some will see the fact that the play's production has been brought to an end by this campaign of intimidation as some kind of victory. The reality is we all lose by it."

Theatres nationwide had backed proposals to hold readings of the script followed by discussions involving its Sikh critics, but plans were shelved.

"Someone called me last night on her behalf. Because of increased threats she has asked if I would drop our plans," said Neal Foster, the theatre manager of the Birmingham Stage Company, who proposed the readings. He is understood to have received death threats himself.

guardian.co.uk/medicine

2004

I'm flattered, Megan, I really am. Honestly, I think you're a great girl, and under different circumstances... oh, I don't know.... since I hit 40 I've been going through this mid-life anxiety thing, its brought up all manner of fears and insecurities...
...truth is, I'm worried about the gap in our ages.
Oh, come on, Keith. Ten years isn't that much.
Exactly. Frankly, what I'm looking for is a Trophy Girlfriend, and that means 20-25, tops.

Oh my God! That is such a depressing sight. Every day its more obvious and apparent.
Too right it is, Brian! This is a shop, not M.I.5 HQ! Yet here we are broadcast on CCTV.
Q HERE
Its just another example of the intrusive nature of modern surveillance, the creation of a paranoid society obsessed with spying on each other, leading to the inevitable disintegration of civil liberties...
You're talking about your bald patch, aren't you?
Yes, actually.
Q HERE

I'm not disagreeing with you, Clare. I know that owning a car is morally unjustifiable and I should support public transport. I'm fully aware of the pollution and devastation cars cause the environment.
I take your point that owning one tacitly encourages further road building. I accept that not driving a car would be better for me, the country and the planet. All I'm saying is...
...that this isn't the best time to remind me.
POLICE
Well, can't hang around chatting. Thanks for the lift.

2004

HTON GAY PRIDE 2004
Of course, when I first started going to Pride I was about the only straight person there!
Of course, when I first started going to Pride I was about the only straight person there!
Of course, when I first started going to Pride I was about the only straight person there!
Of course, when I first started going to Pride I was about the only straight person there!
Of course, when I first started going to Pride I was about the only straight person there!
Of course, when I first started going to Pride I was about the only straight person there!
Of course, when I first started going to Pride I was about the only straight person there!
Of course, when I first started going to Pride I was about the only straight person there!
Of course, when I started going to Pride I was about the only straight person there!

Admit it! I'm nobody! I'm nothing. Even you just regard me as a statistic, another sad case study devoid of any real identity.
That's just not true, Mr...
... Jenkins.

I've heard of social workers burning out, but I never thought it would happen to me. I could handle the pressure, I could handle the stress.....
But look at me. I can't go on, I'm finished! You must think I'm pathetic!
Not at all, Ben. Ask anyone....
The first day in the job is always the hardest. Why not try and hang in there until lunchtime when things might look better.

2004

You know, it's only at this Men's Group that I can express my feelings, make myself vulnerable. I envy you guys in your steady relationships, I wish I had the courage to commit. Instead I take the coward's course of empty sexual encounters, continuously bedhopping from one conquest to the next, targeting girls half my age because they present less of an emotional or intellectual threat.
Oh, *@#☠ off!

Hail fellow, well met! Top of the morning to you, and what a glorious morning it is too, brimming with hope and expectation, resonant with promise, full of the joys of spring as the sunbeams of optimism burst through the dark clouds of despair.
Its nice to see you so cheerful.
Well, its not often your most difficult client dies AND you wangle a day off to go to the funeral.

So, Sarah, what was the pain like?
Whoaa, Clare! Hold on one second!
Childbirth is a fulfilling, empowering and totally positive experience, and the use of negative language to describe it is wholly inappropriate. I don't use the word 'pain', I use the word 'energy'.
So, what was the energy like?
Absolutely excrutiating.

2004

Well, Brenda, its good of you to come back here and remind your former colleagues how meteoric your career in management has been. But let me just say one thing.
I could never play the politics game. I could never ingratiate myself with my superiors. I could never do any of that sick making, sycophantic arse licking that you're so good at!
And you'd like me to teach you?
Could you?

Its a lovely house, Libby, but aren't you worried these high density developments are eradicating the green spaces?
Call me selfish, Clare, but I just wanted to move somewhere with a garden for the kids to play.
Nip out and tell your sisters to come in for their tea, would you, Tim.

Anyway, things were about to kick off for the tenth time that day when I said to Brian "when a disagreement turns into an argument there are no winners".
Thanks
Profound.
What did Brian say?
Nothing. Nailed the bastard completely.
Nice one.

2004

You look engrossed.
I'm reading a review of Sue's new book, "In my Own Right: The Struggle For Female Identity"
Sue?
Sue Kubicki: Tall, elegant, long red hair, round glasses, very distinctive laugh.
Nope. None the wiser.
Smart. Sharp. Witty. Lectures at the University. Wrote that novel that they serialized on Radio 4.
I don't think I know her.
Yes you do. Bill and Sue.
Oh! BILL and Sue!
G2

How can you deny it? It's here in black and white! You had both a starter and a pudding, plus extra chips.
Yes, but I didn't have any wine! You lot worked your way through at least five bottles!
What!!? You had at least two glasses of wine!
ENOUGH!!
For crying out loud!! Can we please stop arguing about last year's bill and just order?

I hate Xmas. It was Xmas when my breakdown occurred. I took 25 kids in care to a pantomime. I was so traumatised that, to this day, any reminder of the experience can trigger terrible, terrible psychological repurcussions.
Still, the important thing is...
... it's behind you.
AAAAAAA AAAAAAA AAAAGH!
Oops!

2005

Radical redesign
How we remade the paper from the bottom up

Page 2

Goodbye to the broadsheet. Our current design has lasted from 1988 until today

Six days a week
Your new sport section plus G2 and the new G3s

Back page

Preview edition
actual size
First edition published
Monday 12.09.05
guardian.co.uk

theguardian

From Monday: a new, smaller Guardian, the UK's most colourful national paper

The new-look Guardian will have colour on every page of every section but one thing will remain the same – our reputation for supplying first class news, features and comment

[illegible]

[illegible]

Any questions?

The Guardian's new format and redesign are the biggest changes to the paper for many years. If you have a question or want to contact us, please ring [illegible] or email [illegible]

The Guardian years

1821 [illegible]

1855 [illegible]

1872 [illegible]

1908 [illegible]

1936 [illegible]

1952 [illegible]

1959 [illegible]

1988 [illegible]

1992 [illegible]

1999 [illegible]

2002 [illegible]

2005 [illegible]

2005

What's that music?
Beethoven. The shopping centre plays classical music in the belief it'll disperse groups of youths.
Come on. Lets go. I'm not going to listen to this crap!
XMAS SALE
50% OFF

Well it seems to work.
Depressing, isn't it. Much as I'd like to think otherwise, I'm afraid kids today are totally predictable, unimaginative and narrow minded.
XMAS SALE

It's bad enough hearing Beethoven mangled over a tannoy, but this 'Eroica' is the totally lacklustre 1976 Deutsche Grammaphon recording.
Yeah.

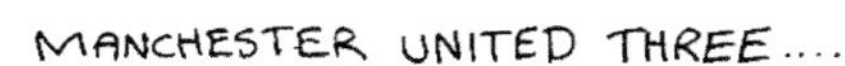

MANCHESTER UNITED THREE....

Stuff summer! This is what life is all about! Saturday, 4.45pm, Final Score, watching your beloved team's result come through. God is in heaven and all's well with the world.
The Guardian

...TOTTENHAM HOTSPUR NIL.
You bunch of overpaid ****! Call yourselves a ****** football team! You're ****!
The Guardian

Whilst I support your contention, Megan, that 'You need to be able to laugh to do this job', I can't help thinking Bob may have moved on a couple of stages from that.
HA! HA! HA! HA! HA! HA! HA! HA! HA! HA! HA! HA!

2005

Inside the life of a child prodigy

What cocaine says about you

theguardian

After eight years in power Tony Blair hears a new word: Defeat

Sketch
Hubbub then humiliation

Simon Hoggart

Labour rebels leave terror plan in shreds and question PM's future

Terror defeat

International

57 killed in Jordan suicide attacks

National

Nurses get power to prescribe all drugs

Financial

Tesco too dominant says ex-OFT chief

Science

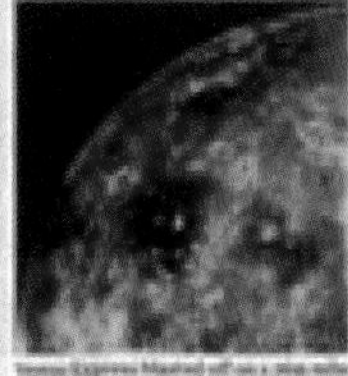

2005

Hello, Clare, how's it going? You've lost a bit of weight.
Have I? What's it to you?
You deign to approve of my body shape because it conforms to your narrow and oppressive male image of female beauty, and I'm supposed to be flattered. Sorry, Stan, I don't think so!

Don't get me wrong, Megan. I think it a commendable gesture, and its to your credit that you want to show solidarity with the disaffected and demonised urban youth...
I just wonder if this is the best day to wear your hoodie.
LITTER

Come on Kayleigh, this will be your first chance to vote! You can't afford to be apathetic!
Why not?
Because you can make a difference! This offers an opportunity for you to create the kind of world that you want!
Can't be arsed.
On Thursday May 5th you can make your voice heard!
Mind you, that Mr. Howard seems to be thinking what I'm thinking...
On the other hand, Thursday is good for telly: Hollyoaks, Eastenders, Footballers' Wives. You wouldn't want to miss any of those...

2005

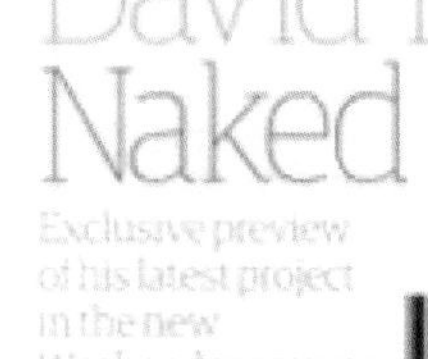

David Bailey's Naked people

Exclusive preview of his latest project in the new Weekend magazine

Christian O'Connell
Crying over sport
Sport, page 16

The way we live now
New today 8-page Family section

Free inside 56-page fashion handbook
Inside Weekend

£1.20
Saturday 17.09.05
Published in London and Manchester
guardian.co.uk

theguardian

Radical plan to stop Muslim extremism

Vikram Dodd

[illegible]

11»

BBC money may go to C4

[illegible]

4»

Under this picture, a master. But who?

[illegible]

Column five
Life through a rolled-up fiver

Emma Brockes

[illegible]

National
Eight jailed for airport theft bid

[illegible] 4»

International
China to be biggest exporter by 2010

[illegible] 15»

Financial
British Gas tells staff to sell or face sack

[illegible] Money»

News

3»

[illegible]

Sport
Prince William next FA president

[illegible] Sport, 4»

2005

You and your broken ankle stay right here, Mrs. Hobbs, and I'll go and fetch you a wheelchair that doesn't have dodgy brakes.
LIFT
X-RAY DEPT.

The Rose And Crown? Ten minutes? Cheers, Megan. I can't stand another wednesday night in front of the telly, watching Brian get all hot under the collar at the sex scenes in 'ROME'.
See you later, Brian.
That's ridiculous! A woman of her social rank would NEVER make love in the prescence of her servants! WHAT! There is absolutely no historical evidence that Roman women shaved their pubic hair!.... For pity's sake! You wouldn't just throw your toga praetexta on the floor like that, you'd fold it neatly....

Wow, that's a very depressing sight. What do you think caused it?
Poverty.
FIRE
Poor householders, desperate to save money, employ people on low incomes to do specialist work they're unqualified for. You mark my words, this'll be down to the electrics.
How can you be so sure?
I put them in.
FIRE

2005

Simon Schama:
America will never be the same again

G2 Page 8

Lady Macbeth, four-letter needlework and learning from Cate Blanchett. Judi Dench in her prime

G2, page 12

Chris Patten:
How the Tories lost the plot

This Section Page 32

Amy Jenkins:
The me generation is now in charge

G2 Page 2

£0.60
Monday 12.09.05
Published in London and Manchester
guardian.co.uk

theguardian

Backlash over Blair's school revolution

City academy plans condemned by ex-education secretary Morris

An acceleration of plans to reform state education, including the speeding up of the creation of the independently funded city academy schools, will be announced today by Tony Blair.

But the increasingly controversial nature of the policy was highlighted when the former education secretary Estelle Morris accused the government of "serial meddling" in secondary education.

In an article in tomorrow's Education Guardian she writes: "Another round of structural change won't by itself achieve universally high standards. Worse than that it could be a distraction. In five years' time, whose children will be going to these new academies? Will choice and market forces once again squeeze out the children of the disadvantaged?"

Today, the prime minister will say: "It is not government edict that is determining the fate of city academies, but parent power. Parents are choosing city academies, and that is good enough for me."

He will also set out the future of local education authorities as "commissioners of education and champions of standards", rather than direct providers.

The academies replace failing schools, normally on new sites, in challenging inner-city areas. The number of academies will rise to between 40 and 50 by next September. This month 10 city academies started, bringing the total to 27, and Mr Blair will insist the government is on target to reach 200 by 2010. City academies have proved to be among the most hotly debated aspects of his public sector reforms. The Commons education select committee has criticised them as divisive and teaching union leaders have also denounced the expansion of an "unproven" scheme.

However, this will not deter Mr Blair who will point out that in the last academic year the proportion of pupils receiving five good GCSEs in city academies rose by 8 per cent, four times the national average.

4»

Patrick Wintour and Rebecca Smithers

UK link to terror snatches

The United Nations is investigating the CIA's use of British airports when abducting terrorism suspects and flying them to prisons around the world where they are alleged to have been tortured. The inquiry, led by Martin Scheinin, a special rapporteur from the UN Commission on Human Rights, comes as an investigation by the Guardian reveals the full extent of the British logistical support. Aircraft used in the secret operations have flown into the UK at least 210 times since the September 11 terror attacks. Foreign Office officials have denied all knowledge of the secret flights, telling MPs on the foreign affairs select committee that the ministry has "not granted any permissions for the use of UK territory or air space", and suggesting to the Guardian that it was "just a conspiracy theory". Privately, Ministry of Defence officials admit that they are aware of the flights, and that they have decided to turn a blind eye. "It is not a matter for the MoD," said one. "These craft use our airfields. We don't ask any questions. They just happen to be behind the wire."

13»

Ian Cobain and Richard Norton-Taylor

Belfast Second night of rioting

A soldier on patrol behind a burning barricade in Springfield Road, Belfast, after hundreds of rioters took to the streets for a second day. Page 3 »

Column five
The shape of things to come

Alan Rusbridger

Welcome to the Berliner Guardian. No, we won't go on calling it that for long, and yes, it's an inelegant name. We tried many alternatives, related either to size or to the European origins of the format. In the end, "the Berliner" stuck. But in a short time we hope we can revert to being simply the Guardian.

Many things about today's paper are different.

Starting with the most obvious, the page size is smaller. We believe the format combines the convenience of a tabloid with the sensibility of a broadsheet. Next most conspicuously, we have changed the paper's titlepiece and headline fonts. Gone is the striking 80s David Hillman design – adapted over the years – which mixed Garamond, Miller and Helvetica fonts. In their place is a new font, Guardian Egyptian, which is, we hope, elegant, intelligent and highly legible.

The next difference you may notice is colour. The paper is printed on state-of-the-art MAN Roland ColorMan presses, which give colour on every page – something that sets us apart from every other national newspaper. The effect will be to give greater emphasis and power to our photography and, we hope, make the whole paper a touch less forbidding than it sometimes may have seemed in the past.

G2 has also shrunk: it is now a full colour, stapled news magazine with newspaper deadlines. Sport has expanded into its own section – at least 12 pages every day, again in full colour.

As the week progresses you'll notice further changes. There are one or two new sections. There will be new columnists, both in G1 and G2 – most notably the pre-eminent commentator Simon Jenkins, who joins us from the Times to write on Wednesdays and Fridays.

Continued on page 2 »

National

War crimes suspect evades arrest

Detectives waiting at Heathrow airport to seize a former senior Israeli army officer for alleged war crimes in occupied Palestinian lands were thwarted when he failed set foot on British soil. A judge had issued a warrant for the arrest of Doron Almog but it is believed the retired general was tipped off while on an El Al flight and stayed on the plane to avoid capture until it returned to Israel. The arrest warrant issued on Saturday at Bow Street magistrates court, central London, alleges that Mr Almog committed war crimes in the Gaza Strip in 2002 when he ordered the destruction of 59 Palestinian homes near Rafah.

5»

Law

Judges may block deportations

The government faces a confrontation with judges over its attempts to deport terrorist suspects to Middle Eastern and north African countries with poor human rights records. Four appeal court judges who may have to decide whether deportations can go ahead have told the Guardian they will refuse to rubber-stamp the UK's human rights deals with countries such as Jordan and Algeria. Despite being urged by the home secretary to respect the country-to-country agreements, the judges say they will demand evidence that the assurances are "worth the paper they're written on".

15»

International

Israeli troops leave Gaza after 38 years

Israel lowered its flag in the Gaza Strip for the last time yesterday as the government declared an end to 38 years of occupation and troops withdrew from demolished Jewish settlements. The last troops were expected to leave overnight. Palestinian leaders described it as a "liberation", but said Israeli controls on border crossings and other restrictions maintained the occupation. Thousands of Palestinians gathered on roads leading to the settlements, ready to stream the rubble once the last troops were gone. A 12-year-old boy was seriously wounded by gunfire from an Israeli tank still guarding the settlements.

17»

Financial

Sky's Premiership rights under threat

BSkyB's 13-year monopoly over live broadcasts of Premier League football games is under immediate threat. Media regulator Ofcom has told the European Commission it should force whoever holds the Premiership TV rights to sell a number of games to rival broadcasters. A separate regulatory plan under consideration in Brussels could see individual broadcasters limited to 50% of the live games put up for sale. The League, meanwhile, is resisting all attempts to remove its "exclusivity premium," arguing that clubs' finances will be undermined. The current rights deal expires in 2007.

26»

Bigger
isn't always
better...

2005

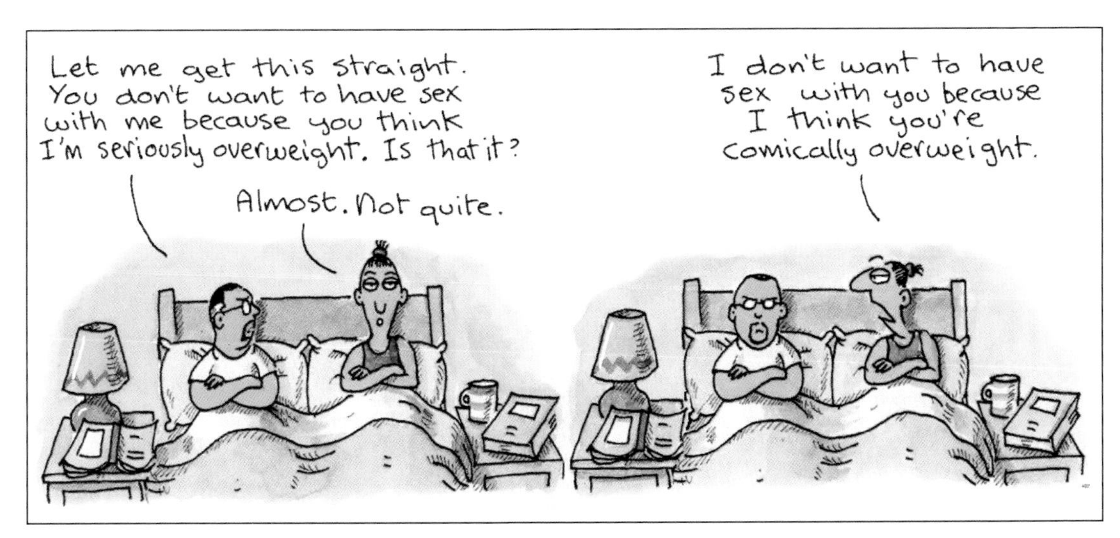
Let me get this straight. You don't want to have sex with me because you think I'm seriously overweight. Is that it?
Almost. Not quite.
I don't want to have sex with you because I think you're comically overweight.

So, for future reference, there is such a thing as a too bio-degradable eco-friendly coffin

I tell you, Clare. My training as a Child Psychologist has revealed a whole new world to me. For example, the way that little lad is playing with his building bricks is a cry for help.
Incredible!
Although its not all training. A lot of it is intuition.
Well of course

2006

David Foster Wallace

How Roger Federer made tennis a beautiful game. G2 Page 6

Plus: Kay Mellor on life in Britain's most female friendly town
G2 Page 13

£0.70
Thursday 07.09.06
Published in London and Manchester
guardian.co.uk

the guardian

Newspaper of the year

The day Blair accused his chancellor of blackmail

12 hours of rows and resignations

- Brown demands PM go by Christmas
- Shouting match as PM refuses joint premiership
- Blair likely to make public statement today
- Cabinet divisions begin to emerge
- Seven MPs quit government jobs

Patrick Wintour
Political editor

Fighting for power

Full coverage of Labour's day of drama
» Pages 2-6

Sudoku

Is on p39 today »

National

PlayStation 3: This year's can't-have gift

International

Teenager speaks of her dungeon ordeal

2006

OK, Sophie, we are going to throw the 'Emotion Ball' to each other and explore the feelings that come up!
Right. Well maybe we can start by exploring feelings of loss....

For heaven's sake, we are all responsible adults. Is it asking too much of Management to treat us a such?
I agree...
Its about time they gave their ridiculous 'Health And Safety' emails a rest.

I'm sorry if you feel I am behaving unfairly and unkindly towards you, Brian, but I did warn you when we first met. Subequently, I reserve the right to be grumpy, irritable and short tempered in the morning.
But it isn't morning.
It is somewhere.
the guardian
the guardian

2006

So, you teach an Assertiveness Training course.
That's right.
Any good?
Well I've never had any complaints.
Yeah, but that could just as easily be because you're rubbish.

Hi, I'm a social worker. Is your Mum home?
Sorry, no. I've been mummy since our real one left six months ago.
27
I'm going to need some back-up urgently...
27

We're Megan and Clare, right? Two named women having a conversation about something other than men. We have just passed The Bechdel Test!
That's fantastic!
I wish I had a boyfriend I could tell.

2006

Megan, this woman is living in the most insanitary, dirty and appalling conditions that I have ever witnessed as a social worker. I think we both know who needs to be contacted.
Absolutely.
Hello, Channel 4? Could you tell me if "How Clean Is Your House" offers some kind of a finder's fee?
Actually I was thinking of the Mental Health Team, but what the hell.

Come on, Megan. You've been clutching those flowers for 24 hours now.
I just can't help myself, Clare.
Oh, Clare! Is there any gesture more romantic than having a dozen red roses delivered to the workplace of the one you love on Valentine's Day?
No, Megan. Probably not.
But they're Helen's. Give them back.
No! Shan't!

How dare I call you a child, Brian? I shall tell you.
Firstly because you made plans to go to a football match without consulting me first, thereby undermining the mutually responsible nature of our relationship...
Secondly, because you became incoherent with rage when I was obliged to veto those plans...
And thirdly because I can see your reflection in the television screen.

2006

Be Kind
ARSEnal
although Tottenham are very good too
Debbie is not a slag she is a sexually active but responsible young adult
TOLERATE MINORITIES
HAZZA
(If my Tag offends you please call 07957 819281 and I will remove it)
Colin Nesbitt is entitled to his sexuality
... and then other times I get the feeling all the pro-social initiatives are working....

"Girls' Book Of Fab Women", "Women Who Changed The World", "Bedtime Tales Of Brilliant Women". Wow! So many books encouraging girls to grow up and be anything they want to be: politician, footballer, scientist, explorer...
Senior manager in publishing?
Who knows, Megan? Maybe one day....

Clare! At last! What are you doing down there? Not trying to avoid me, I hope.
Ha ha ha! No, I just dropped a contact lens.
We all did.

2006

Come on, guys. I know the personnel situation is critical to the point of desperate, but if Meryl chooses to leave the team I think we just have to accept it.

WELL DONE MEGAN
LONDON MARATHON 2006
The thing is, its been nearly two weeks, so we should either take it down or find out what happened to her.

Well, these have been three of the nicest hours I've spent in a long time. There's nothing like a leisurely catch up with an old friend that you have bumped into down at the shops.
The irony is that I only came out to buy one thing, and I can't even remember what it was!!

2006

Clare, you're down, I know. But perhaps it may help to know that research has identified several seasonal, economic and social factors that converge on today's date to make it the most depressing day of the year.
Strangely enough, Megan, it does help. I'm comforted by the knowledge that at least I'm not going to feel any worse.
Good!
Hang on, my mistake, its not today, its tomorrow.

I feel I'm always disappointing people.
When you feel like that, Joel, I want you to say to yourself: "I AM ENOUGH!"
I am enough.
Come on, Joel, do it with a bit of conviction!

Truth be told, Saskia and I rather expected the pace of gentrification to be a bit more rapid.
19

2006

I can't believe this, Brian! I come home early and find you logged on to something called 'Red, Hot and Danish'!
Its not what it seems! I thought it was a website about bacon.
Clare, please, you've got to believe me!!!
Sadly, Brian, I do.

Oh, come on, guys! Even if it was the team upstairs that stole our chocolate biscuits, couldn't we just wait until morning and ask for them back?
PHYSICAL

You know, Sis, I sometimes think you push Abigail into far too many extra-curricular activities.
Nonsense!
Well OK, but could you at least try and space them out a bit?

2007

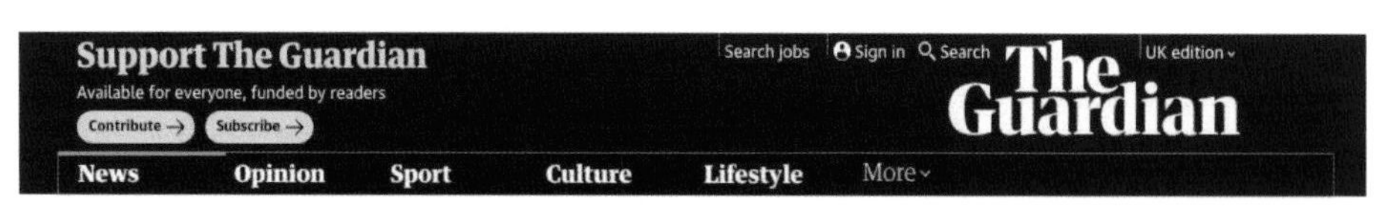

Environment ▸ Climate change Wildlife Energy Pollution

Environment

Scientists offered cash to dispute climate study

Ian Sample, *science correspondent*

@iansample

Fri 2 Feb 2007 15.11 GMT

740

▲ The Arctic habitat of polar bears is under threat as climate change causes ice to melt. Photograph: Joseph Napaaqtuq Sage/AP

Scientists and economists have been offered $10,000 each by a lobby group funded by one of the world's largest oil companies to undermine a major climate change report due to be published today.

Letters sent by the American Enterprise Institute (AEI), an ExxonMobil-funded thinktank with close links to the Bush administration, offered the payments for articles that emphasise the shortcomings of a report from the UN's Intergovernmental Panel on Climate Change (IPCC).

Travel expenses and additional payments were also offered.

The UN report was written by international experts and is widely regarded as the most comprehensive review yet of climate change science. It will underpin international negotiations on new emissions targets to succeed the Kyoto agreement, the first phase of which expires in 2012. World governments were given a draft last year and invited to comment.

The AEI has received more than $1.6m from ExxonMobil and more than 20 of its staff have worked as consultants to the Bush administration. Lee Raymond, a former head of ExxonMobil, is the vice-chairman of AEI's board of trustees.

The letters, sent to scientists in Britain, the US and elsewhere, attack the UN's panel as "resistant to reasonable criticism and dissent and prone to summary conclusions that are poorly supported by the analytical work" and ask for essays that "thoughtfully explore the limitations of climate model outputs".

Climate scientists described the move yesterday as an attempt to cast doubt over the "overwhelming scientific evidence" on global warming. "It's a desperate attempt by an organisation who wants to distort science for their own political aims," said David Viner of the Climatic Research Unit at the University of East Anglia.

"The IPCC process is probably the most thorough and open review undertaken in any discipline. This undermines the confidence of the public in the scientific community and the ability of governments to take on sound scientific advice," he said.

The letters were sent by Kenneth Green, a visiting scholar at AEI, who confirmed that the organisation had approached scientists, economists and policy analysts to write articles for an independent review that would highlight the strengths and weaknesses of the IPCC report.

"Right now, the whole debate is polarised," he said. "One group says that anyone with any doubts whatsoever are deniers and the other group is saying that anyone who wants to take action is alarmist. We don't think that approach has a lot of utility for intelligent policy.

2007

I'm not disagreeing with you, Brian. Of course you should embrace your body image. I just think you should lose 30-40lbs before you do it.

Thank heavens for some decent weather. I swear, I'd have gone totally stir-crazy if I'd spent another lunch break cooped up indoors, everyone on top of each other.

HERE TO H
YOUR COMMUNITY RESOURCE
CARING FOR ALL
You know, Megan, I think we might come over as more accessible if you ease up a little on the 'one free pen per person' rule.
ASW

2007

So, do you want to discuss 'What A Great Opportunity This Holiday Offers To Re-connect On A One-To-One Level' again, or do you just want to sit here in silence?

Drawing, Clare?
Indeed I am. It is an invaluable tool when working with children.
Pictures help little minds to understand big concepts.
Yes, but is it art?

I'm desperate. There's a rumour going round that a medical research trial will pay £18,000 if you have a little toe amputated.
But Mr. West, what effect would that have on your balance?
Put it in the black, hopefully.

2007

Let's face it, Megan, this was one argument we were never going to win. Why should Brian, or any non-smoker, have to inhale our fumes?
I mean, is it really asking such a lot of us smokers that we step outside the pub for a cigarette? I don't think so.
It's just common courtesy.

I suppose the question has to be asked, "When does a robust management style turn into bullying?"

Tristan and Sophie have just finished renovating yet another dilapidated farmhouse in France.
They're gites.
The Guardian
G2
I know, I know, but so long as there's the chance of a free holiday I say keep in with them....
The Guardian
G2

2007

Yes, I am the lynchpin in this office. Yes, I provide emotional and professional support, 24/7. Yes, both clients and colleagues are dependent on me. But this year, for the sake of my mental health, I decided I'd be selfish and take a holiday.
You've been on holiday?
PLEASE WASH UP
PLEASE WASH UP
PLEASE WASH UP

The mud, it got in your hair, your eyes, your nose, your mouth. Of all the horrors that's what I remember most. That, and the fact that I lost all of my friends on the first day.

Still, credit where it's due, Mr. Davitt. Not many people your age would even consider going to Glastonbury.

I appreciate how important this team meeting is, Clare, but don't you think we should postpone it until everybody has got over their Norovirus?

2007

I just find it absurdly PC, that's all. Especially since 'man' in original anglo-Saxon was gender non-specific.
That's all very well, but in common usage 'man' equates to 'male', and as such becomes a sexist term when applied to a mixed-sex profession. How about 'Firefighters'?
OK, I'll go with Firefighters.
Agreed! Lets call the Firefighters.

Don't get me wrong. I love the dog. But I didn't get him to be cute, I got him as a practical tool to help overcome obstacles and normalise my life.

But wherever we go he becomes the focus of attention. I find this personally demeaning and professionally distracting, making me feel even more marginalised!
Yes, I hear what you're saying.

But he is an ooky schnooky wooky!!!

OK, at this point I think I should mention a few things. First, I'm not a parent. Second, I've never conducted an ante-natal class and am just covering for a friend...

...and third, I think I may be holding this 'birthing position flash card' upside down.

2007

Ours is a high stress job, Megan, and so many social workers choose self-destructive ways of coping. So you joining an orchestra last night is a great idea. What's the problem?

Well it's more about what happened after orchestra finished.....

2007

I'll give you an example of how obscene the arms trade is: This house, and everything in it, would just about pay for a single surface-to-air ballistic missile.
Mind you, when we first moved in it was only worth a small tank, so we obviously bought at the right time.

Brian, what can I say! I've never played squash before! I didn't know I could hit the ball that hard! I didn't see you until too late! I don't know what to do!!!
For Pity's sake, fetch someone!
Did you hear that, Brian? The onus is on you to get out of the way, so the point is mine.

Whiney Wendy is at it again: Banging on about how disillusioned she is with social work because she feels so powerless to change anything.
What whiney wendy fails to grasp is that the experienced social worker only exerts her energies upon those things that are capable of being changed.
Such as the Office Xmas Meal seating plan. I'll stick her at the other end of the table next to smelly Pete.
Good idea.

Inside Souvenir supplement plus 30 pages of unrivalled coverage

£0.80
Thursday 06.11.08
Published in London and Manchester
guardian.co.uk

theguardian

Obama's new America

President-elect Barack Obama and his daughter Sasha salute supporters in Grant Park, Chicago Photograph: Eric Thayer/Getty Images

First black leader to hail 'birth of freedom' at inauguration

Ewen MacAskill
Suzanne Goldenberg Washington

Barack Obama will pay homage to Abraham Lincoln when he takes the oath of office as America's next president in January, urging his fellow citizens to unite in "a new birth of freedom".

Obama, who chose to launch his election campaign last year at the spot in Illinois where Lincoln began his, will express a hope that as the 44th president he too will usher in a new American era.

The Democratic president-elect, enjoying messages of congratulations from leaders round the world, spent the day closeted with his advisers in Chicago planning the team that will move into the west wing and executive office as President George Bush prepares to move out.

Bush, in offering his congratulations, promised full cooperation with the incoming administration, and hailed the historic nature of Obama's victory. "No matter how they cast their ballots, all Americans can be proud of the history that was made yesterday," Bush said in remarks delivered from the White House rose garden.

"This moment is especially uplifting for a generation of Americans who witnessed the struggle for civil rights with their own eyes – and four decades later see their dream fulfilled".

He said he had invited Obama and his wife, Michelle, to the White House before the inauguration on January 20. Although that is 75 days away, Obama's team demonstrated urgency yesterday by opening a transition office on Capitol Hill.

The Democrat's aides are expected to begin moving into key departments such as the Treasury within days to work with the outgoing administration. The priority is to get an economic stimulus package in place as quickly as possible.

As America celebrated yesterday, the stockmarkets suffered another difficult day; the Dow Jones index dropped by 3% because of recession fears.

In an another indication of the shift in power, Obama is to begin receiving intelligence briefings from the CIA from today. "He will see the full range of capabilities we deploy for the United States," the CIA director, Michael Hayden, said in a letter to employees.

Obama's sweeping victory to become the first black president elicited emotion across the political spectrum yesterday. The Republican former secretary of state Colin Powell, who watched the results come in from Hong Kong, was brought to tears. "The fact that he's also black just has turned America on," Powell told reporters. He paused for a few seconds, before adding: "Very emotional."

Bush's current secretary of state, Condoleezza Rice, also noted the historic nature of the result, saying American

Continued on page 3 »

guardian.co.uk »

Full results and analysis
The story of a historic victory from our unrivalled team in the US

Interactive
Click-through to the best of the Guardian's coverage: top stories, blogs, videos

Debate
Martin Kettle: After the triumph, holding on to the the support through to 2012

Journey of generations that passed in a moment

Gary Younge
Chicago

There are times when the usually glacial pace of social progress accelerates to such a degree that you feel you are experiencing it in real time. Stand in the present and history comes rushing towards you, making you feel lightheaded.

The second that Ohio fell to Barack Obama on Tuesday evening, effectively handing him the keys to the White House, was one of those dizzying moments. A man born three years before African-Americans had secured their right to vote had risen by popular acclaim to the highest office in the land before he reached 50.

A political journey that should take generations felt as though it had occurred in a moment.

At the President's Lounge, a bar in Chicago's black southside, the soundtrack to that moment gave voice to decades of thwarted dreams. First they crooned soulfully to Sam Cooke's Change is Gonna Come. Then they bellowed boisterously to McFadden and Whitehead's Ain't No Stoppin' Us Now: "If you've ever been held down before, I know that you refuse to be held down any more."

Outside car horns beeped and Chicago police shouted Obama's name at passers by through loudspeakers. They were cheering for their native son, but the festivities were not bound by geography or race. Tens of thousands across the country took to the streets to celebrate. In Harlem, subway trains erupted into spontaneous applause. In Detroit, the home of Motown, they danced in the street.

Like Joe Louis's defeat of Max Schmeling back in the 30s, this was black America's gift to a grateful if not always gracious nation. "It was vindication," wrote Maya Angelou of Louis's win. "Some black mother's son, some black father's son, was the strongest man in the world."

Now Obama is the most powerful man in the world. Only he is the son of some white Kansan mother and some black Kenyan father – a biracial man with a Muslim name in a country at war in the Gulf. No matter how long one pores over the electoral map, his victory still seems unlikely if not implausible.

But the very things Republicans hoped would alienate him from the average American apparently made him appealing to some.

As the campaign gathered pace, it seemed as though there was a little bit of Obama for everyone: the immigrant, the midwesterner, the Hawaiian, the

Continued on page 2 »

2008

Hi Brian, I'm back! The meeting was cancelled, so I came straight home...
Clare, I swear, I was watching porn!
Don't lie to me, Brian. I know the Top Gear theme when I hear it.

The election of Barack Obama is bound to resonate with black and mixed heritage people throughout the UK.
Having witnessed what once seemed inconceivable in the USA, they will ask how long before something similar happens here.
A black Prime Minister.
Actually I was thinking of Dr. Who, but yeah, why not!

What do I say?
Anything. Anything you want. That's the point of the documentary: To simply record the authentic voice of a social worker.
Well, it's a challenging job, but I work with a friendly team, and its always nice to know you're helping people...
Cut!
OK, I'm going to stop you there and go record the authentic voice of a more interesting social worker.

2008

Whilst I agree that he took the UK into a bloody and illegal war, and whilst I share the rage that drove you to hurl your shoe in the traditional Iraqi act of protest, I fear the person you've brained is actually the actor Michael Sheen.

OK, we'll depart from the agenda at this point, as it appears Megan would like to raise the subject of the washing up rota.

You are so lazy, Brian. I said play with my nieces, not stick them in front of the TV!
It's Scooby-Doo! A recent report said it's the healthiest TV show for children.
Actually the report said that Scooby-Doo depicted a healthy and active lifestyle.
It wasn't recommended as an alternative to actual physical play.
Curses! I would have got away with it if it hadn't been for those pesky kids!

2008

What's up, Clare? What's with the furrowed brow?
Our team clerk is retiring. We've bought her this silver plate and we're going to have it engraved with her name and a few words of appreciation.
Fifteen years she's worked with the team. Never missed a day, never made a mistake. First to arrive in the morning, last to leave at night. A constant support to the older social workers, a mother to the younger ones.
Hard to find the words, eh?
Oh no, we've got the words. Can't remember her name.

Admit it, Clare, you don't like having me as your student. You think I'm a spoilt and naive 'little rich girl' playing at social worker!
Well, Rosamunde, I certainly think its insensitive to make home visits on a sink estate wearing a cashmere winter coat, with matching accessories, by Georgio Armani!
Yeah? Well that just shows what you know...
They're last season's!

OK, before the client comes back I've got to correct you on the pronounciation of the name.
It isn't "Cat-tree-oh-na", its "Ca-tree-nah". Its Scottish. Got it?
Got it.
Hello, Mrs Mills. May I introduce my new student, Catriona.

2008

Modern teenagers think they invented wild nights, binge drinking, drug taking and parties, but they should have seen me at their age.
Back in the sixties?
Back in the nineties. I really caned it.

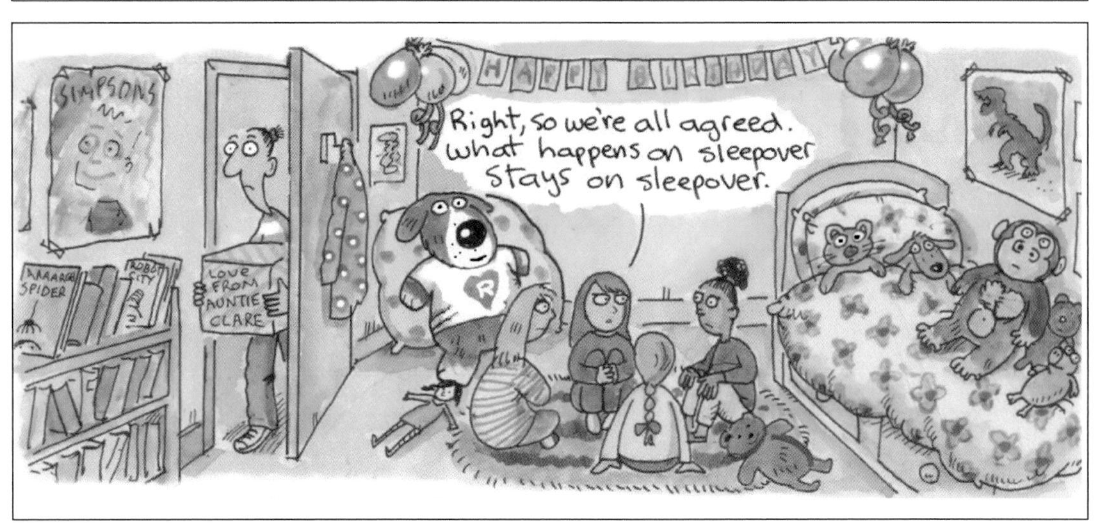
SIMPSONS
SPIDER
ROBOT CITY
LOVE FROM AUNTIE CLARE
Right, so we're all agreed. what happens on sleepover stays on sleepover.

May I suggest Men's Group just lets the big spider leave of its own accord, and then we can continue our 'Masculinity In Crisis' discussion.

2008

For crying out loud, Jasmine! If you're going to be my student the least you can do is try and keep up when we go out on home visits.
That's not fair!!! I could keep up if I wasn't wearing brand new boots.
Does Clare know?
Of course she knows. I'm breaking them in for her.

Hey, Brian, you know we had that long discussion on environmentally responsible tourism, and how the only option was to stay in Britain despite the crappy weather.
Yes.
Well I think I know a way to holiday in Spain yet halve our carbon footprint whilst doing so.
Brilliant, Clare, what is it?
You don't go.
ESCAPE
SUN HOLS

That's really nice of you, Shaun. When I see Megan I'll make sure to tell her what you said.
Young people are so fabulously imaginative in their use of language. Who else would reverse "sick" to mean "great"?

2008

Yes, she grew up in a care home. Yes, she became a social worker to help kids like herself. And yes, what you're suggesting would make a realistic and plausible third act...

...I just can't see children watching a TV show called 'Tracy Beaker Burns Out'.

I'm sorry, but I find your behaviour totally irresponsible. The BMA's findings on the subject are unequivocal.

Any more than two units per day constitutes a health risk, whilst keeping within the limit actually reduces the possibility of heart disease

For crying out loud, Grandma, anyone would think you didn't want to make it to 97.

So, guys, this is "Walking And Talking Therapy". The combination of exercise, the outdoors and the company of a dog is believed to dissipate stress and anxiety.

At least, that's the theory.

2008

Well, I have to say, fifteen years is a damn good innings, but the problem at this stage is that things don't just go wrong, They go wrong, stay wrong and invariably get worse. So, I suppose the question is: whose benefit are you keeping him around for?
Mine, I suppose.
He gets up and walks the dog in the morning for one thing.

Ice, frost, sub-zero temperatures. These conditions can be treacherous for the elderly. I think we should check up on Mrs. Hobbs.
Agreed.
For crying out loud, Mrs. Hobbs, will you pack it in!
Same every year.....
Harry Venning

Wouldn't it just be easier to invite Maureen?

2009

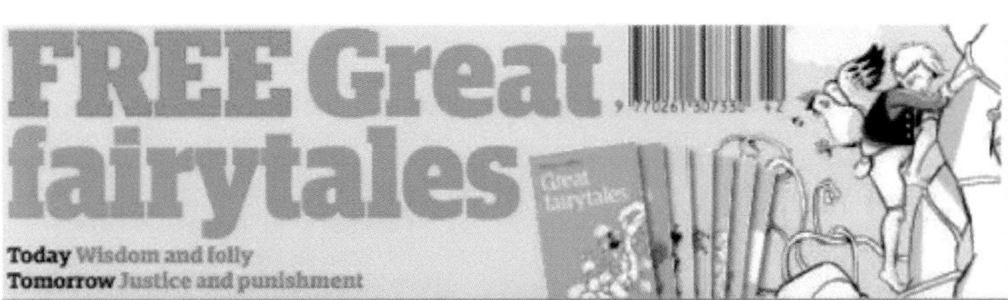

FREE Great fairytales
Great fairytales
Today Wisdom and folly
Tomorrow Justice and punishment

How much TV should your children watch?

G2 cover story

£1.00
Wednesday 14.10.09
Published in London and Manchester
guardian.co.uk

theguardian

Oil firm drops bid to gag Guardian over MP's question

- Web users publish details of legal issue raised in parliament
- Labour member asked about injunction over toxic waste case

David Leigh

An unprecedented attempt by a British oil trading firm to prevent the Guardian reporting parliamentary proceedings collapsed yesterday following a spontaneous online campaign to spread the information the paper had been barred from publishing.

Carter-Ruck, the law firm representing Trafigura, was accused of infringing the supremacy of parliament after it insisted that an injunction obtained against the Guardian prevented the paper from reporting a question tabled on Monday by the Labour MP Paul Farrelly.

Farrelly's question was about the implications for press freedom of an order obtained by Trafigura preventing the Guardian and other media from publishing the contents of a report related to the dumping of toxic waste in Ivory Coast.

In yesterday's edition, the Guardian was prevented from identifying Farrelly, reporting the nature of his question, where the question could be found, which company had sought the gag, or even which order was constraining its coverage.

But overnight numerous users of the social networking site Twitter posted details of Farrelly's question and by yesterday morning the full text had been published on two prominent blogs as well as in the magazine Private Eye.

Carter-Ruck withdrew its gagging attempt by lunchtime, shortly before a 2pm high court hearing at which the Guardian was about to challenge its stance, with the backing of other national newspapers.

MPs from all three major parties condemned the firm's attempt to prevent the reporting of parliamentary proceedings. Farrelly told John Bercow, the Speaker: "Yesterday, I understand, Carter-Ruck quite astonishingly warned of legal action if the Guardian reported my question. In view of the seriousness of this, will you accept representations from me over this matter and consider whether Carter-Ruck's behaviour constitutes a potential contempt of parliament?"

The Commons question reveals that Trafigura has obtained a hitherto secret injunction, known as a "super-injunction", to prevent disclosures about toxic oil waste it arranged to be dumped in west Africa in 2006, making thousands of people ill.

Farrelly is asking Jack Straw, the justice secretary, about the implications for press freedom of a high court injunction obtained on 11 September 2009 by Trafigura "on the publication of the Minton report on the alleged dumping of toxic waste in the Ivory Coast, commissioned by Trafigura".

The Guardian is still forbidden by the terms of the existing injunction, granted by a vacation duty judge, Mr Justice Maddison, to give further information about the Minton report, or its contents. Last month, Trafigura agreed to pay more than £30m in compensation and legal costs to 30,000 inhabitants of Abidjan in Ivory Coast, for "flu-like symptoms" they might have suffered following the dumping. The oil traders continue to deny that the waste could have caused serious or fatal injuries.

The use of "super-injunctions", under which commercial corporations claim the right to keep secret the fact that they have been to court, has been growing. Anonymity is also increasingly being granted to individual litigants.

Last week, an anonymity order was overturned at the supreme court under which Mohammed al-Ghabra, an alleged al-Qaida financier named in official UN and Treasury publications, was to be known only as G. A further pending supreme court case involving an MI5 officer's memoirs is currently only known as "A v B".

Alan Rusbridger, the editor of the Guardian, said yesterday: "I'm very pleased that common sense has prevailed and that Carter-Ruck are now prepared to vary their draconian injunction to allow reporting of parliament. It is time that judges stopped granting 'super-injunctions' which are so absolute and wide-ranging that nothing about them can be reported at all."

Carter-Ruck, whose partner Adam Tudor has been representing Trafigura, issued a press release last night conceding: "The Order would indeed have prevented the Guardian from reporting on the Parliamentary Question which had been tabled for later this week." But the firm said the Guardian's reporting on the issue had been "highly misleading".

The firm added: "There is no question of Trafigura seeking to 'gag' the media from reporting Parliamentary proceedings, and the parties have now agreed to

6-7»

Continued on page 2 »

> It is scandalous that a law firm acting on behalf of a wealthy trading company should have thought, for a moment, that it could gag media organisations from reporting parliamentary business.
> These are lawyers who seem to have lost sight of the fact that people risked their liberty and their lives to fight for the right to report what their elected representatives say and do.
> It is little wonder that some social media websites went into virtual meltdown yesterday at the arrogant effrontery involved.
> **Leader comment, page 32 »**

Dear leader
Sven in line to manage North Korea

The former England coach Sven-Goran Eriksson is close to agreeing a deal to take charge of North Korea at next summer's World Cup Photograph: Clevs/Hugo Dixon

Recruited by MI5: the name's Mussolini. Benito Mussolini

Tom Kington Rome

History remembers Benito Mussolini as a founder member of the original Axis of Evil, the Italian dictator who ruled his country with fear and forged a disastrous alliance with Nazi Germany. But yesterday a previously unknown area of Il Duce's CV came to light: his brief career as a British agent.

Archived documents have revealed that Mussolini got his start in politics in 1917 with the help of a £100 weekly wage from MI5.

For the British intelligence agency, it must have seemed like a good investment. Mussolini, then a 34-year-old journalist, was not just willing to ensure Italy continued to fight alongside the allies in the first world war by publishing propaganda in his paper. He was also willing to send in the boys to "persuade" peace protesters to stay at home.

Mussolini's payments were authorised by Sir Samuel Hoare, an MP and MI5's man in Rome, who ran a staff of 100 British intelligence officers in Italy at the time.

Mussolini was paid £100 a week by MI5 to keep Italy in the first world war; he sent veterans to Milan to beat up peace protesters

Cambridge historian Peter Martland, who discovered details of the deal struck with the future dictator, said: "Britain's least reliable ally in the war at the time was Italy after revolutionary Russia's pullout from the conflict. Mussolini was paid £100 a week from the autumn of 1917 for at least a year to keep up the pro-war campaigning – equivalent to about £6,000 a week today."

Hoare, later to become Lord Templewood, mentioned the recruitment in memoirs in 1954, but Martland stumbled on details of the payments for the first time while scouring Hoare's papers.

As well as keeping the presses rolling at Il Popolo d'Italia, the newspaper he edited, Mussolini also told Hoare he would send Italian army veterans to beat up peace protesters in Milan, a dry run for his fascist blackshirt units.

"The last thing Britain wanted were pro-peace strikes bringing the factories in Milan to a halt. It was a lot of money to pay a man who was a journalist at the time, but compared to the £4m Britain was spending on the war every day, it was petty cash," said Martland.

"I have no evidence to prove it, but I suspect that Mussolini, who was a noted womaniser, also spent a good deal of the money on his mistresses."

After the armistice, Mussolini began his rise to power, assisted by electoral fraud and blackshirt violence, establishing a fascist dictorship by the mid-1920s.

Continued on page 3 »

2009

Social work is the polar opposite of my last job in I.T. This is so much more compassionate.
Personally, after so many years I find my capacity for compassion has a tendency to freeze.
Have you tried turning it off and turning it on again?
OPEN
CLOSI DOW

Well, there's a lesson to be learnt here, isn't there? No matter how much excitement 3 inches of snow might inspire, a fully grown adult and a child's toboggan don't mix, eh Brian.
Very possibly, Clare...
Yeah, well, you should have got out of the way, shouldn't you.
...except you were the one who was on it!

This bloke you've invited along: Put bluntly, Brian, what is he going to bring to the team?
He's a senior cardiologist.
Excellent!
Nice one!
Welcome aboard!

2009

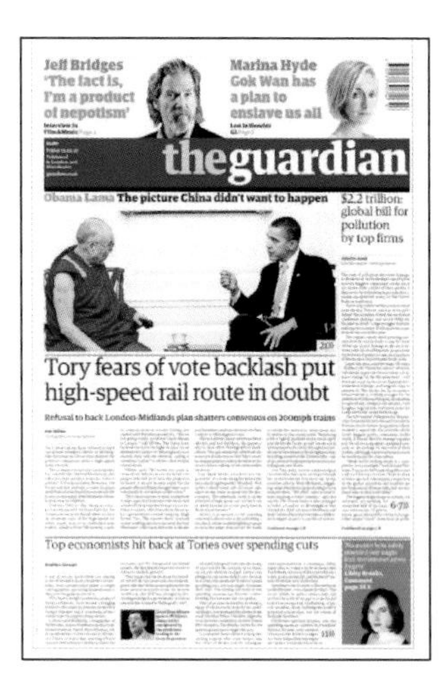
Jeff Bridges
'The fact is, I'm a product of nepotism'

Marina Hyde
Gok Wan has a plan to enslave us all

theguardian

The picture China didn't want to happen

$2.2 trillion: global bill for pollution by top firms

Tory fears of vote backlash put high-speed rail route in doubt

Top economists hit back at Tories over spending cuts

Souvenir issue Gary Younge Jonathan Freedland Naomi Wolf

theguardian

Let the remaking of America begin today

FREE Spanish phrasebook

theguardian

Revealed: Murdoch's £1m bill for hiding dirty tricks

- Tory PR chief under fire over tabloid hacking
- Politicians and celebrities among victims

Amid G8's rubble and aftershocks, Brown is in his element

How well did your school do?

England make it five out of five

theguardian

Race to save summit deal as man dies in City protest

France and Germany draw lines in sand on regulation

'Bottles were thrown ... we had to move him'

Never mind the stimulus, who sat next to the president?

FREE Spanish phrasebook

theguardian

Three inquiries into hacking claims as new victims emerge

- MPs summon Murdoch chiefs over dirty tricks
- Targeted public figures consider suing tabloid
- Scotland Yard refuses to reopen tapping probe

Ferguson and Shearer calls were hacked

Doves exclusive On the road with Britain's hottest band

theguardian

Flu – global threat raised

- Pandemic level up from 3 to 4
- First British cases confirmed
- Mexican death toll surges to 149

'Apparently we're on high alert. Nobody alerted me'

Countess's breakfast ruined as butler does porridge

theguardian

Labour to junk Blair's flagship school reform

Farrah Fawcett 1947-2009

Tory anger at Cameron order to pay back claims

Headteachers to get more powers as era of centralised control ends

HAPPY INTERNATIONAL WOMEN'S DAY

2009

The police cannot operate without public support. Which is why we have invited an audience of community leaders here today...

...to consult on the design of a new police uniform which, we believe, meets the rigourous demands of modern law enforcement yet retains elements of the old "If you want to know the time, ask a policeman" sensibility.

So, what do you think?

It's dead! It's dead! The office plant is dead! How can we hope to look after people when we can't even take care of a plant?!
Sorry, Mr. Hobbs. You were saying...?

Well, who would have guessed that The Guardian's "wild swimming" book would be so popular?

2009

OK, who wants to start the conversation? What does anyone think about the water cooler being taken away?

Thank goodness! At last those two have stopped moaning about having to carry the banner....
NO TO THE CUTS
PROTEST AGAINST THE CUTS
NO MORE CUTS
SOCIAL WORKERS AGAINST THE CUTS!

Just this evening I had to upbraid Brian for not using gender neutral words, take him to task on the misogyny inherent in one of his statements and pull him up for making a sexist assumption.
Ah well, a woman's work is never done!

2009

Good grief, Megan! How can you work at your desk when it's so untidy?
Easily, it turns out.
A messy desk is actually a very efficient filing system. One's subconscious automatically prioritises important papers by keeping them close at hand, pushing less essential documents further away. I just read an article about it.
What did I do with the **** thing!

Nice tan, Ray.
Thanks. I just got back from a week's package holiday to Tenerife.
I have to say that I have never seen so many morbidly obese bodies around a swimming pool.
Depressing.
At first. But we needed the shade.

To be honest, I think I was expecting something a bit more sophisticated.
MEDIA TECHNIQUE TRAINING DAY
THIS WAY UP
CRISPS 25 PKTS.

2009

Honestly, Mrs. Harris, you'd be amazed at the number of parents who try and use these social work visits as 'impromptu child care....Mrs. Harris?... Mrs. Harris?....
22

Sorry, kids, but no. First, because its a celebration of sectarianism. Second, because it is essentially street begging and third.....
Penny for the guy
...because that is Mr. Fletcher from the Narcolepsy Support Group. Get that hat and mask off now!
Penny for the guy

OK, Mr. Hobbs, that's the window open.
And now I think we should address the issue of your personal hygiene which, I feel, is becoming critical.
Very critical.

2009

There! What did I tell you? Male horses don't have nipples.
Flaming 'smart phones' really have killed the art of the pub argument.

Did you know that there's an International Men's Day?
Really? When is that?
EVERY ****ING DAY OF THE ****ING YEAR!
Walked into that one.

Christmas is meant to be a time for reconciliation, so I have put aside a lifetime of your carping, disparaging remarks and constant criticism and bought you this gift. Happy Christmas, Mum.
Oh, Clare, I don't know what to say.
So let's start with the wrapping. Typically slipshod. You've swathed the thing in sellotape, suggesting you did it in a hurry. Cheap paper, already beginning to tear. Vulgar design, garish colours...

Sarah Palin She's running! (Probably)

This section Page 27

Can Lucy Mangan break the world sprout-eating record?

G2 Page 4

PLUS How Guernsey resisted the Nazis This section Page 22

£1.00
Thursday 18.11.10
Published in London and Manchester
guardian.co.uk

theguardian

The John Lewis state starts here

Public sector workers urged to set up cooperatives even in areas like probation

Patrick Wintour
Political editor

Public sector workers are being urged to set up John Lewis-style co-operatives, offering everything from probation services to tax collection, in what is being billed as potentially one of the biggest transformations of state provision since the privatisations of the 80s.

The Cabinet Office minister Francis Maude said yesterday that he envisaged mutuals developing in NHS trusts, Sure Start centres, children's services, welfare provision and the civil service. He even said they could be formed in the Inland Revenue.

The aim was to liberate public sector workers and "introduce radical shifts in ownership, accountability and financing", he said. "Every government department and every local council will be expected to put in place a right to provide, with the ultimate decision to go ahead resting with the relevant minister."

But the scale of the government's ambitions for public service reform raised fresh concerns that the programme could lead to creeping privatisation.

Peter Holbrook, chief executive of the Social Enterprise Coalition, welcomed the announcement but said: "Without the necessary safeguards there is a danger that the mutuals could be demutualised and sold off to the private sector, reminiscent of what happened to British building societies in the 1980s. It would be criminal to see that happen to our public services. All mutuals need to be asset-locked to ensure that they operate for the benefit of the public, forever."

Ministers are open-minded about the form such mutuals and co-operatives will take: some could be independent of the state, some could be joint ventures with the state and others would include users of the service, such as tenants.

The new "right to provide" provision will be coupled with a new community "right to challenge": local people or employees will be able to demand the right to run a service where they believe they could run it better than failing local authority management. A localism bill is likely to be published next week.

Maude's proposals represent a big extension of an existing right to request to provide services in the NHS, which was set up by the last Labour government. That has seen a total of 38 social enterprises established providing services worth £900m.

Union leaders accused the coalition of putting dogma before delivery. Tony Woodley, the Unite joint general secretary, said: "There is no appetite from the public sector workforce or the public generally for these so-called co-operatives. It is insulting to think that these DIY co-operatives, set up on the cheap, can replace a well-established and joined-up public sector.

"To think that cancer treatment can be equated with the values of the retail sector beggers belief. And to keep repeating the words 'John Lewis' as the reasoning for these changes is just mangling and perverting the English language. You go to John Lewis to buy a sofa or a fridge, not to have chemotherapy."

Maude insisted that experience showed mutuals were successful because they gave employees an emotional stake in the organisation. Mutuals would "challenge traditional public service structures and unleash the pent-up ideas and innovation that has been stifled by bureaucracy".

Setting aside £10m in extra funding to help with startup costs, he announced a green paper on commissioning to make it easier to win contracts and said the "big society" bank could be drawn upon to extend mutuals in the public sector.

A stumbling block to the spread of mutuals in the public sector could be fears of job insecurity or loss of state-supported pension rights. Maude acknowledged that if public sector staff bid to run a service, they might also find themselves subject to EU law requiring there to be a competitive tendering process.

Cornwall hit by floods PM promises help

Flash floods in Cornwall yesterday blocked train routes, closed schools and destroyed homes Photograph: Ben Birchall/PA

Court says News of the World journalists who ordered phone hack must be named

Nick Davies

The private investigator at the centre of the phone-hacking scandal has been ordered by a high court judge to reveal who instructed him to engage in the illegal interception of voicemail messages of public figures.

Glenn Mulcaire, who was jailed in January 2007 for intercepting the voicemail of eight people, had asked the court to rule that he should not have to answer questions because it might incriminate him.

But in the high court yesterday Mr Justice Mann ruled that he must answer a list of questions about who instructed him to hack into the mobile phones of the celebrity publicist Max Clifford and his assistant, Nicola Phillips.

Mulcaire, who was employed by the News of the World at the time of his offences, is to be asked specifically whether he received instructions from the news editor of the paper, Ian Edmondson.

The judgment opens the door to the eventual disclosure of evidence that could have a powerful effect on News International, Scotland Yard, the Press Complaints Commission and the prime minister's media adviser, Andy Coulson, all of whom have claimed that Mulcaire acted without any official sanction from the News of the World.

The judge also ordered Scotland Yard to disclose paperwork that it has held since it raided Mulcaire's home and office in August 2005 which refers to Nicola Phillips or her mobile phone numbers.

At his trial in January 2007 Mulcaire admitted hacking into mobile phone messages left on Clifford's phone. When Clifford sued the News of the World last year for breach of privacy, Scotland Yard was ordered to disclose paperwork that was believed to identify a senior journalist who had ordered the hacking. However, Clifford withdrew his action in March before the disclosure was completed after the News of the World agreed to pay him more than £1m.

At the time of the hacking, in the spring of 2006, Phillips was working in Clifford's office. Following Clifford's legal action, she received information that she had also been a victim of Mulcaire's activity and started her own legal action against Mulcaire and the News of the World.

Lawyers acting for Mulcaire argued that he should not have to answer questions about the hacking of Phillips or any other alleged victim because this might tend to incriminate him. Mr Justice Mann agreed that Mulcaire might face further prosecu-

Continued on page 2 »

The Fab One: Susan Boyle now as successful as the Beatles

Helen Pidd

Less than two years ago she was, as the Los Angeles Times rather indelicately put it, "just another 47-year-old Scottish virgin", a wild-haired eccentric whose biggest audience to date had been the congregation of her parish church.

Fast forward 19 months and Susan Boyle has been watched at least 400 million times on YouTube, appeared on Oprah and even sung for the pope (sort of: he made a break for the popemobile before she really got going at Glasgow's Bellahouston Park this September).

To that list of achievements we can now add being as popular as the Beatles. Unlike numerous overhyped musicians over the years, Boyle has never claimed to want to be as big as McCartney and co – she fancied herself as the new Elaine Page.

But she has managed it anyway, by having the No 1 album in the US and UK at the same time for the second time in a year. Only the Monkees and the Beatles have managed the same feat, in 1967 and 1969 respectively. Boyle is the first ever woman to do it, her record company, Sony, said.

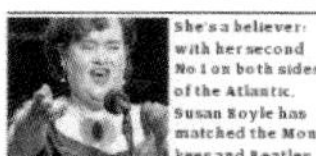

She's a believer: with her second No 1 on both sides of the Atlantic, Susan Boyle has matched the Monkees and Beatles

Her album The Gift reached No 1 in the UK on Sunday, and took the top spot across the Atlantic yesterday. It comes after her debut album I Dreamed a Dream achieved the same success following its release last year.

Reacting to the news, Boyle said: "I've never felt happier in all my life. This is an amazing result and one I never expected."

Boyle was catapulted from obscurity to global stardom after appearing on last year's Britain's Got Talent contest. The singer, from Blackburn in West Lothian, became an international star after her performance of I Dreamed a Dream from the musical Les Misérables stunned the audience and judges on the ITV1 show.

Britain's Got Talent judge Simon Cowell said: "I'm thrilled for Susan. She has once again defied the odds. She is my superwoman."

The star – who still lives with her cat, Pebbles, in Blackburn – suffered a series of problems as she buckled under the pressure of becoming a worldwide phenomenon. But it didn't hurt record sales. In 2009 I Dreamed a Dream became the fastest-selling debut album in the history of the charts and – with more than 10m copies sold – the biggest-selling album in the world in the last year.

Boyle's reign at the top of the UK album charts will be brief, however. Take That's new album, Progress, came out on Monday and, after selling 235,000 copies on the day of release, seems certain to topple her from the top spot.

2010

I mean, the very fact that you've scheduled my supervision at the end of the day suggests to me that you don't take it seriously.
Clare?
Go on, go on, I'm listening.

So, you were saying how British people should take a leaf out of the French's book when it comes to street protests.

...and finally there's a note from management suggesting we incorporate more humour into our work practices.

Swing's the thing
Will this trick win
us the Ashes?
Sport Pages 1 and 7
Silvio
Berlusconi
Why is this
man still in
power?
G2 Cover story
PLUS
Zoe Williams
on the Palin
reality show
G2, Page 2
£1.00
Tuesday 16.11.10
Published
in London and
Manchester
guardian.co.uk
theguardian

Irish told: take EU bailout or trigger crisis

Dublin warned it has 24 hours to make decision as EU emergency talks loom

Henry McDonald
Elena Moya
Larry Elliott

An increasingly isolated Irish government was coming under mounting pressure tonight to seek an EU or International Monetary Fund bailout within 24 hours amid fears that contagion from its crippled banking sector might spread through the weaker eurozone countries.

Portugal, Spain, the European central bank and opposition parties urged Brian Cowen's coalition government to remove the threat of a second crisis in six months by putting a firewall between Ireland and its 15 partners in the single currency.

With finance ministers from the eurozone due to hold emergency talks tomorrow night, financial markets were expecting Dublin to finalise negotiations with the EU over the terms of a deal to allow Ireland to rescue banks laid low by the collapse of the country's construction boom.

"The Irish problem is spreading, but it could get more volatile," said Ashok Shah, chief investment officer at London Capital, a fund management firm. "They have to get this bailout, they have a period of time before it gets impossible, before nasty things happen. The longer they leave it, the more difficult it will get."

Portugal has seen its borrowing costs rocket along with Ireland's as speculation has grown that it too may have to consider a bailout. Its finance minister, Fernando Teixeira dos Santos, told the Wall Street Journal his country had been hit by a contagion effect caused by fears about Ireland's ability to pay its debts.

"I would not want to lecture the Irish government on that," he said. "I want to believe they will decide to do what is most appropriate for Ireland and the euro. I want to believe they have the vision to take the right decision."

The Bank of Spain governor, Miguel Angel Fernández Ordóñez, a member of the European Central Bank's governing council, told a banking conference in Madrid he expected an "appropriate reaction" by Ireland to calm the markets. He later told reporters: "The situation in the markets has been negative due in some part to the lack of a decision by Ireland. It's not up to me to make a decision on Ireland, it's Ireland that should take the decision at the right moment." Ewald Nowotny, another ECB governing council member, said in a radio interview the EU wanted a "quick, good solution to Ireland, so that there will be no spillover" to other heavily indebted countries such as Portugal and Spain.

Weekend reports that Ireland was holding bailout talks with the EU helped ease pressure on Irish borrowing costs today, with the yield on benchmark 10-year Irish bonds easing to 8.3% from a peak of over 9% last week. The premium that investors demand to hold Irish 10-year bonds over benchmark German bonds (known as the spread) also fell to 545 basis points, down from a record 652 basis points last Thursday.

Analysts warned, however, that the selling would quickly resume if Ireland tried to go it alone. "The expectation of a bailout for Ireland helped its spreads to recover from last week's capitulation," said Gavan Nolan, a credit analyst at Markit. "It's good to talk." Despite Ireland's insistence that it doesn't need to be rescued, investors say the country needs support, given the fragility of its moribund banking system, and the high borrowing costs limiting the capacity of companies to raise funds.

Ireland's Europe minister, Dick Roche, said rumours that it was on the verge of seeking a bailout could be "very, very dangerous".

He conceded: "There is continuous talk going on backwards and forwards about the level of our debt but the suggestion that that constitutes going to 22»

Larry Elliott, page 28»
Leader comment, page 34»

A man threatened gala goers in Stuttgart yesterday (top). CCTV camera footage captured a male dressed as Captain America engaged in combat with the attacker (bottom)

Bizarre attack on German museum

Rhys Pugh
Crime Correspondent

Events took a brutal and disturbing turn in Stuttgart last night, as a man dressed in a strange costume consisting of an elaborate robe and helmet, first attacked the head of security for the Stuttgart Natural History Museum, and then displayed extraordinary talent as a magician, as he delivered a monologue to terrified benefactors.

The museum was celebrating its third centenary, when the man referred to as 'Loki' attacked. Bystanders reported witnessing a staff-like weapon, which fired a blue light, and claimed the man was able to move from location to location in the blink of an eye, as well as change the appearance of his clothing as if by magic.

In an even more odd twist, the scene was attended by someone dressed as the famous WWII American hero Captain America, soon joined by billionaire Tony Stark's Iron Man, and an apparently unmarked aircraft, before emergency services could make it on the scene.

The attack was reportedly part of a robbery. German Police declined to comment on the item or items stolen, but confirmed that 'Loki' was working with a team, believed to be mercenaries.

The attacker was taken by the US team, onboard the aircraft, and is reportedly in the custody of a classified international anti-terrorism taskforce.

Seven were killed in the attack, all members of the Museum's private security staff. The SMNH Director also declined comment, instead issuing a statement via a representative, offering condolences to the families of those injured or killed in the assault.

Focus has turned to the Americans' involvement in subduing the attacker, with questions raised about the jurisdiction of Iron Man, who is still considered a vigilante by most governments. Also under scrutiny is the identity of the stars-and-stripes clad man, whose movement and actions seem to suggest military training of the highest order.

The US Secretary of Defense Robert Gates, was unavailable for comment on the matter. The aircraft is believed to be an experimental transport jet, currently undergoing development by the US Air Force and Stark Industries. Tony Stark

Continued on page 13»

Diners vanish in a puff of smoke - leaving £570 unpaid billl

Esther Addley

They seemed like any other well-off young London couple dining out last Wednesday. The man and woman, both smartly dressed, arrived for their booked table for two at the Michelin-starred restaurant L'Autre Pied in Marylebone, before each ordering three courses from the menu, along with a bottle of pink Larmandier champagne at £124 and another of 1997 Bollinger that cost £285.

But after helping them on with their coats to nip outside for a cigarette, the waiting staff soon discovered that they were no ordinary diners. Some minutes later, with a plum tart and millefeuille uneaten at the table, it became clear the couple had no intention of returning – or of paying a bill totalling £572.78.

What may make the case more intriguing is that the name in which the pair booked the table, Lupin, echoes that of the fictional Arsene Lupin – a stylish Gallic gentleman thief whose adversaries, in a series of novels by Maurice LeBlanc, are invariably portrayed as rather worse

The Metropolitan police are investigating the case of a couple, left, who left a restaurant without paying their £572 bill

portrayed as rather worse villains than him. The Metropolitan police confirmed they were investigating.

"In two decades we have never had anything like this," Leonora Popaj, the restaurant's general manager, told the Guardian. The couple had not seemed unusual or suspicious, she said, and the bill was not particularly lavish by the restaurant's standards "They looked like a very genuine, very lovely couple. Their bill was an average spend. Nothing was out of place or unusual."

CCTV footage of the pair, indeed, showed nothing peculiar: both are believed to be in their 30s; the man, described by the restaurant as about 6ft tall, had a light beard and was wearing blue jeans and a jumper; his companion, wearing a black sleeveless dress with a scarf, had long dark hair .

It was only while viewing the footage, said Popaj, that she noticed the woman wasn't carrying a handbag – not in itself damning, perhaps, but which certainly facilitated their speedy departure.

It is understood that similar incidents involving other top restaurants are being looked at by police.

As for the suggestion that "Lupin" may have been chosen as some kind of joke, Popaj said: "It makes me very angry. What upsets me most is that they have this mentality that this [amount] is nothing for this level of restaurant.

"They are forgetting that they are really attacking the waiters, who don't have an enormous income."

2010

Oh no, Brian! How many times? Light colours hold shadows, which accentuate curves, which make your belly look even fatter.

You're wearing a size too small! Do you really want people to see these puppies jiggle about every time you move?

And the round collar emphasises your double chin. A V-neck would draw the eye away. This is all basic Trinnie and Susannah.

Anyway, have a good game of football and I'll see you at home later.

I'm what's known in the gay community as a 'bear'. That's to say, a large, hirsuit homosexual man. And sometimes I feel elated about my body shape, but other times the pressure to conform to a more acceptable gay physical stereotype makes me really depressed. Do you know what I'm saying?
I think so.
You're a bi-polar bear.

It's not the costume, Megan. It is a striking and appropriate costume to go to an 'anti-cuts' march in.
NO TO THE CUTS
It's your taking a short cut through the Care Home For The Elderly that's the problem.

FREE G2 calendar Inside today

With pictures by readers, plus words by Lionel Shriver, Fay Weldon and Simon Armitage

£1.00 (FR €3.20)
Friday 17.12.10
Published in London and Manchester
guardian.co.uk

theguardian

India accused of systematic use of torture

Cables show US was secretly briefed on abuse of civilians in Kashmir

Jason Burke Delhi

US officials had evidence of widespread torture by Indian police and security forces and were secretly briefed by Red Cross staff about the systematic abuse of detainees in Kashmir, according to leaked diplomatic cables released last night.

The dispatches, obtained by website WikiLeaks, reveal that US diplomats in Delhi were briefed in 2005 by the International Committee of the Red Cross (ICRC) about the use of electrocution, beatings, sexual humiliation against hundreds of detainees.

Other cables show that as recently as 2007 American diplomats were concerned about widespread human rights abuses by Indian security forces, who they said relied on torture for confessions.

The revelations will be intensely embarrassing for Delhi, which takes pride in its status as the world's biggest democracy, and come at a time of heightened sensitivity in Kashmir after renewed protests and violence this year.

Other cables released last night reveal that:

- The Dalai Lama has told US officials that combating climate change is more urgent than finding a political solution in Tibet, which "can wait five to 10 years".
- Rahul Gandhi, the crown prince of Indian politics, believes Hindu extremists pose a greater threat to his country than Muslim militants, according to the American ambassador to India.
- Five doctors were coerced by the Sri Lankan government to recant on casualty figures they gave to journalists in the last months of island's brutal civil war.

The most highly charged despatch is likely to be an April 2005 cable from the US embassy in Delhi which reports that the ICRC had become frustrated with the Indian government which, they said, had not acted to halt the "continued ill-treatment of detainees".

The embassy reported the ICRC concluded that India "condones torture" and that the torture victims were civilians as militants were routinely killed.

The ICRC has a long-standing policy of engaging directly with governments and avoiding the media, so the briefing remained secret.

An insurgency pitting separatist and Islamist militants – many supported by Pakistan – against security services raged in Kashmir throughout the 1990s and into the early years of this decade.

It claimed tens of thousands of lives, including large numbers of civilians who were targeted by both militants and security forces.

The ICRC staff told the US diplomats they had made 177 visits to detention centres in Jammu and Kashmir and elsewhere in India between 2002 and 2004, and had met 1,491 detainees. They had been able to interview 1,296 privately.

In 852 cases, the detainees reported ill-treatment, the ICRC said. A total of 171 described being beaten and 681 said they had been subjected to one or more of six forms of torture.

These included 498 on which electricity had been used, 381 who had been suspended from the ceiling, 294 who had

The US embassy cables

muscles crushed in their legs by prison personnel sitting on a bar placed across their thighs, 181 whose legs had been stretched by being "split 180 degrees", 234 tortured with water and 302 "sexual" cases, the ICRC were reported to have told the Americans.

"Numbers add up to more than 681, as many detainees were subjected to more than one form of IT [ill-treatment]," the cable said.

The ICRC said all branches of the Indian security forces used these forms of ill-treatment and torture, adding: "The abuse always takes place in the presence of officers and ... detainees were rarely militants (they are routinely killed), but persons connected to or believed to have information about the insurgency."

The cable said the situation in Kashmir was "much better" as security forces no longer roused entire villages in the middle of the night and detained inhabitants indiscriminately, and there was "more

6-7»

Continued on page 2 »

Assange free for now, but judge says he is likely to be extradited

Julian Assange left the high court last night after Mr Justice Ouseley imposed tough new bail conditions Photograph: Graeme Robertson for the Guardian

Vikram Dodd
Crime correspondent

The WikiLeaks founder Julian Assange walked free after nine days in jail last night when a high court judge released him on bail. However, the judge warned him that he is almost certain to be extradited to Sweden to face sex assault allegations.

The court refused an attempt by the Crown Prosecution Service, acting on behalf of the Swedish authorities, to stop Assange being freed but imposed tougher bail conditions than previously outlined by a lower court, which meant his lawyers had to scramble to meet them before he was returned to prison for another night.

Finally Assange emerged on to the steps of the high court at 5.46pm, as snow began to fall, to make a defiant statement and to thank his supporters. "I hope to continue my work and to continue to protest my innocence in this matter and to reveal, as we get it, as we have not yet, the evidence from these allegations," he said.

As well as the prospect of a trial in Sweden over allegations of sexual crimes involving two women, there is a growing consensus among US constitutional lawyers and other legal experts that Assange will be indicted by Washington. After his release he said that even if he were indicted in the US, the spilling of state secrets would continue. He said that WikiLeaks was a "resilient organisation" that could "withstand decapitation attacks".

Last week City of Westminster magistrates remanded Assange in custody because they said he posed too high a danger of absconding after Sweden requested his arrest and extradition on the sexual assault allegations. On Tuesday his lawyers won a reversal of that decision, with a judge granting him bail on tough conditions – but the CPS appealed.

Yesterday at the high court Mr Justice Ouseley rejected the CPS argument that there were no conditions a judge could impose that would stop Assange from fleeing justice. He ordered the CPS to pay costs but imposed tough new conditions on Assange.

His bail will see him stay at Ellingham Hall, Norfolk, owned by Vaughan Smith, a former army captain, who was approved to provide surety at Tuesday's hearing along with the restaurant designer Sarah Saunders. While at the mansion, Assange must observe a curfew and be tagged. He will have to report daily to a police station and £200,000 in security, raised by his supporters, has been paid into the court.

But there are no restrictions now on his access to the internet or communications, meaning he is much more able to defend himself and WikiLeaks from the US anger caused by its recent publication of confidential documents.

The legal victory for Assange yesterday

4-5»

Continued on page 2 »

Cuts will put 200,000 children in poverty, says thinktank

Randeep Ramesh
Social affairs editor

The government's radical programme to slash spending will see the first rise in absolute child poverty for 15 years, with almost 200,000 children pushed into penury, according to an analysis by the Institute of Fiscal Studies.

Tax changes introduced by the coalition government will, the leading independent fiscal thinktank finds, increase absolute poverty by 200,000 children and 200,000 working-age adults in 2012-13.

Cuts to housing benefit alone will force a further 100,000 children into poverty.

In the next three years the IFS says average incomes are forecast to stagnate and this, coupled with deep cuts in welfare, will see a rise in relative poverty for children and working-age adults of 800,000 and a rise in absolute poverty for the same group of 900,000.

The institute directly challenges the government's claim that the impact of the budget would have no effect on child poverty.

Sally Copley, head of UK policy at Save the Children, said: "George Osborne promised in his spending review that child poverty would not get worse over the next two years. These new figures show the government will meet this commitment.

"But standing still on child poverty is never good enough and the prospect of it actually rising after 2012 is totally unacceptable."

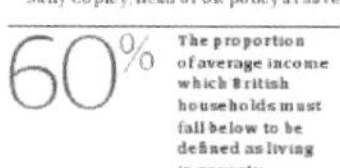

The proportion of average income which British households must fall below to be defined as living in poverty

Absolute poverty, set at 60% of 2010's average income, is used to set legally binding targets in the landmark Child Poverty Act passed this year with cross-party support.

Robert Joyce, a research economist and an author of the report, said: "We find that the coalition government's measures act to increase poverty among these groups slightly in 2012-13, and more clearly in 2013-14. Meeting the legally binding child poverty targets in 2020 would require the biggest fall in relative child poverty after 2013-14 since at least 1961."

Campaigners said the work sounded "an alarm on a future crisis".

Chris Goulden, poverty policy manager at the Joseph Rowntree Trust, which commissioned the research, said that the rise in inequality and impoverishment were mainly caused by pegging benefits to rates less than inflation, freezing child benefit, and the slew of changes to the housing benefits system which affects 4.6m households.

"It is a reversal of fortune for the poor. The coalition have said that the increases

Continued on page 2 »

2010

Marty Feldman. Remember him? wasn't he terrific.
what on earth made you think of Marty Feldman?
Do you know, I haven't the faintest idea.
The Guardian
The Guardian

OK, Clare, you were right, I was wrong. The tomato throwing festival is the next village.
SPAIN

So, Graham, 50 eh! Bit of a milestone, I'd imagine.
But then perceptions of age have changed so drastically in recent years.
Where once society regarded 50 as almost ancient...
... now you can be as young as you feel. Happy Birthday.

2010

Gordon Ramsay, Yotam Ottolenghi, Ruth Rogers, Tom Aikens, Thomasina Miers, Anjum Anand, Marcus Wareing

theguardian

Stick with me and we'll change Britain for ever, Clegg tells party

Last of the bank bosses bales out - with a £14m payoff

Syrup, lemon and water - the Naomi Campbell diet

Here's one I broke earlier - Turner Prize shortlist

theguardian

Trust me, I'm Nick How the also-ran stole the show

Blair: don't vote tactically, back party you believe in

A very pedestrian protest: day Dorset village beat the lorries

Hang out the bunting! Lost in Showbiz looks forward to its wedding invite

I'll be back ... Arnie on life after California

theguardian

Britain plc: state's reliance on private firms revealed

A 'humiliating' day for Ireland as IMF arrives in town

FREE 12-page election pullout

Your complete guide to the night

theguardian

Cameron eyes the prize

No ride of history, but he seemed a decent chap

Goodbye Gordon turns into the I'm Not Dead Yet tour

Euro surge Monty's men hit back to take Ryder Cup lead

Arlene Phillips Why I'm still haunted by Strictly

theguardian

Osborne: cuts must be fast and deep to avoid a decade of debt

UK and US alerts raise fears of al-Qaida offensive in Europe

G2 goes to Glastonbury

Backstage with ... Dizzee Rascal, Shakira and the Flaming Lips

My hero! Feminist Julie Bindel eyes Snoop Dogg

theguardian

Coalition begins welfare crackdown

Echoes of '66 - but it's all over now for England's golden generation

Union delays strike ballot as acrimony deepens at BA

theguardian

Tories demand keys to No 10 as Lib Dem challenge falters

Antique political system is left creaking under the strain

FREE Audiobook download Matter by Iain M Banks

theguardian

MPs seek fresh phone hacking investigation

This photo of Reza Khan shocked the world. The Guardian found him Page 33

North Sea safety risks of Gulf spill rig firm

Looking for Tony Blair's book? Try the crime section

World Cup 2010 Sorry Socceroos thrashed by Germany

Charlie Brooker Sometimes I behave like a minor royal

theguardian

Huge disparity in NHS death rates revealed

So, Mr Green, why don't you lie back and tell me all about that tricky ball?

New forecasts show UK's finances worse than predicted

2010

Actually, Megan, the wording I suggested was "Say no to local council cuts", but how you've got it is a lot punchier.

It is the issue nobody dare address, it is the health crisis nobody dare tackle, it is the epidemic nobody acknowledges. Obesity is 'The elephant in the room!'
So to speak.

I tell you, Megan, these two make a mockery of the whole idea that young people and the elderly have nothing in common. As soon as I introduced Wayne to Gladys the generation gap between them immediately disappeared!
FU

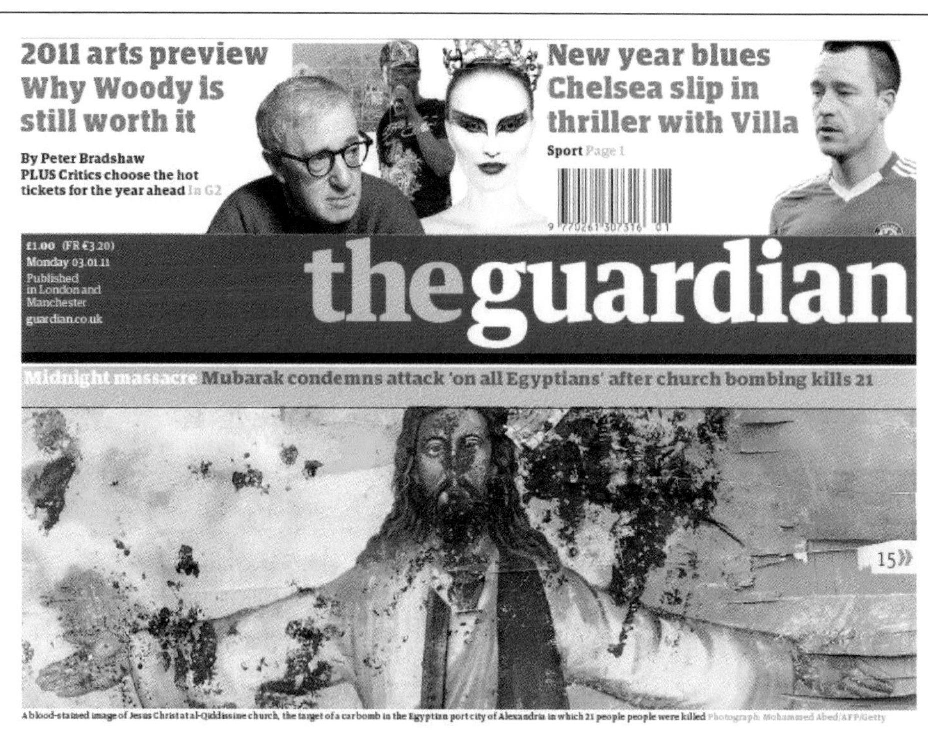

2011 arts preview
Why Woody is still worth it
By Peter Bradshaw
PLUS Critics choose the hot tickets for the year ahead In G2
New year blues
Chelsea slip in thriller with Villa
Sport Page 1
9 770261 307316 01
£1.00 (FR €3.20)
Monday 03.01.11
Published in London and Manchester
guardian.co.uk
theguardian
Midnight massacre Mubarak condemns attack 'on all Egyptians' after church bombing kills 21
15»

A blood-stained image of Jesus Christ at al-Qiddissine church, the target of a car bomb in the Egyptian port city of Alexandria in which 21 people people were killed Photograph: Mohammed Abed/AFP/Getty

Welfare bill soars as coalition counts cost of austerity drive

Slowdown in economic growth makes reducing deficit harder, says watchdog

Allegra Stratton and Julia Kollewe

Rising unemployment will cost the government £1.5bn more than expected in welfare benefits, according to official forecasts that reveal the hidden cost of the coalition's austerity drive.

As big increases in VAT are due to bite from midnight, analysis from the Office for Budget Responsibility shows slowing economic growth will make it harder to reduce the deficit by forcing more people to seek state support.

The Treasury watchdog calculates the government will have to pay out £700m more in unemployment benefit than previously forecast. Similarly, a higher number claiming jobseeker's allowance as well as falling into lower wage brackets will see the government needing to pay out another £700m more in housing assistance over the next four years.

Though the OBR data, released last month, confirms the government is still making substantial savings from its changes to both benefits, the shadow work and pensions secretary, Douglas Alexander, said the fresh assessment suggested it was government strategy that was leaving these higher numbers exposed.

He said: "The growing cost of the risk the government is running with the economic recovery is now emerging. The result of policies which undermine growth and jobs is a longer dole queue and a higher welfare bill."

The new higher official cost of supporting those claiming unemployment benefit comes as some economists warn of unemployment rising from 7.5 to 8.4% at the end of the year. Many are braced for the first squeeze on the economy when VAT is increased at midnight tonight.

The Labour leader, Ed Miliband, will hit the campaign trail in the Oldham East and Saddleworth byelection seeking to make the VAT rise a central issue, saying it is the "wrong tax, wrong time". Labour will put up posters the Liberal Democrats ran before the general election warning of the "Tory VAT bombshell" and said a Conservative government would make the average British family pay £389 extra in VAT a year was a reason to vote Lib Dem.

In a speech, Miliband will say that families will pay £7.50 a week because of the Lib Dems' "broken promise". This week Lib Dem heavy-hitters will hit the campaign trail as well with the party leader, Nick Clegg, in the seat on Wednesday; the party president, Tim Farron, today; three ministers tomorrow; the former leader Charles Kennedy on Thursday and deputy leader Simon Hughes on Friday. The election is on 13 January.

In his speech Miliband will say: "Today we start to see the Tory-led agenda move from Downing Street to your street." 6-7»

Continued on page 2 »

Inside

- VAT rise means Britons think twice about buying big-ticket items, while charities warn that the neediest will miss out on welfare grants pages 6-7 »
- Douglas Alexander: Labour has to be credible on the cuts as well as angry page 22 »
- It's like 1980 all over again – but still the right hankers for a true Thatcherite PM, says Jackie Ashley page 23 »

Prison riot just the start as cuts bite, says union

Owen Bowcott

More riots in Britain's prisons are inevitable because of staff shortages and misguided attempts to ease overcrowding, the prison officers' leader warned last night.

The comments by Steve Gillan, general secretary of the Prison Officers Association (POA), came as the prisons minister, Crispin Blunt, announced two separate investigations into the New Year's Day riot at Ford open prison, where inmates in balaclavas torched buildings in protest at a clampdown on illegal drinking.

Gillan said people who should be in high-security jails were being moved into open prisons before they are ready for rehabilitation to relieve pressure on other parts of the service. "More riots are inevitable," he told the Guardian. "We are concerned about the number of assaults on prison officers ... there will be more prison riots to come with these budget cuts. We are facing a real risk of other prisoners copycatting those sorts of riots."

He threatened to initiate legal action to ensure that the safety of "prison officers, inmates and the general public" is not put at risk through government cuts.

Continued on page 2 »

Students could boost marks by showing 'corporate skills'

Jessica Shepherd
Education correspondent

Some UK universities are considering awarding students in all subjects extra marks to their degrees if they can show "corporate skills" or experience in the jobs market, the Guardian has learned.

Undergraduates on all courses could earn credits for showing they possess the ability to run a workshop or make a good presentation, under the University of Leicester's plans. University College London's career unit is in discussions with senior managers over how to accredit employment skills, and Durham University is considering giving marks for work experience. Workplace skills courses have been a compulsory part of vocationally-oriented undergraduate degrees, such as engineering, for several years.

But awarding credits to an English literature student for these skills is thought to be a new step.

Supporters of the courses argue that a growing number of students will soon pick a degree based on whether they think it will prepare them for the jobs market.

University College London is holding talks with senior managers about ways to accredit students who gain workplace skills

This is largely because graduates will soon have to pay back up to £9,000 in tuition for each year of their degree – up from the current £3,290 a year.

Paul Jackson, director of student support and development at the University of Leicester, said his institution was "looking closely at how to embed corporate skills into the curriculum at the undergraduate stage". He said university managers were discussing whether students should be able to complete their courses without taking a corporate skills course.

"There is no difference between academic skills and employment skills," he said. "We are looking for students who can apply things in a new context."

Prof Anthony Forster, pro-vice-chancellor for education at Durham University, said Durham was reviewing its curriculum and exploring ways to "allow academic credit to be awarded for student employment or short-term community and work-based placements that have involved the application or development of academic knowledge and skills".

Karen Barnard, head of careers at UCL, said some degree courses already ran workplace skills courses, but students tended not to be awarded credits for attending them. She said she was "looking at some form of skills accreditation" with Prof Michael Worton, one of the vice-provosts.

In addition, the university's council, which advises on how the institution

Continued on page 2 »

2011

These kids have so little, Clare. Your taking them to the legendary Stamford Bridge to watch the superstars of Chelsea will boost their self-worth so much.
That's what I thought.
John Terry was awesome!
Ashley Cole was brilliant.
Didier Drogba played best.
Of course there's bound to be an element of trauma when they grow up and realise it was actually Brentford, but lets worry about that when it happens.
Which one was Torres?
He must have been the rubbish one.

This country is entering difficult times, Megan. We social workers must redouble our efforts on behalf of society's unwanted, unloved and misunderstood.
I thought that was us.
OSING
OWN
LITTER

OK, before we start can I just apologise for slamming the door behind me...
POST TRAUMATIC STRESS SUPPORT GROUP

Xavi Hernandez
The world's best footballer
A rare interview **In Sport**

★★★★★
PJ Harvey's new album
Film&Music Page 11

£1.00 (FR €3.20)
Friday 11.02.11
Published in London and Manchester
guardian.co.uk

the guardian

Egypt's hope turns to fury as Mubarak clings to power

Massive protest expected today after president hands over some powers - but remains in office

Chris McGreal Cairo

President Hosni Mubarak dashed the hopes of hundreds of thousands of Egyptians celebrating what they expected would be his resignation speech last night by defiantly telling them he would not bow to domestic or foreign pressure to quit.

Mubarak said he would hand some powers to his vice-president, Omar Suleiman, but would remain in overall control until September to oversee what he called an orderly transition to an elected government. He repeated a pledge not to seek re-election.

He also said that there would be no going back on a commitment of long-term political reform after the two weeks of growing protests to demand his resignation. However, he ominously referred to the army playing a role in ensuring an orderly transfer of power.

The president's defiant tone angered the crowds packed in to Cairo's Tahrir Square, the epicentre of protests against Mubarak's 30-year rule, and may have set the stage for an ugly confrontation at the mass demonstrations called for yesterday across Egypt. Last night, many of the protesters waved their shoes, a traditional sign of contempt, and chanted: "He must leave", and shouted "Mubarak you are finished".

Egypt's opposition leaders immediately said they would escalate the protests which in recent days have spread to include strikes that have shut down the public transport system, some hospitals and factories.

Mubarak said he would transfer some powers to Suleiman to prove that the demands of protesters for political change will be met but did not specify which ones. But he rejected foreign pressure, notably from the US, to immediately take major steps toward democratic rule.

"I have spent most of my life in defence of our homeland," said Mubarak. "I have never succumbed to any international pressure. I have my dignity intact."

In the hours before Mubarak's speech, thousands of pro-democracy activists poured in to Tahrir Square for an impromptu victory party in expectation that the president was about to quit after 30 years in power.

The prime minister, Ahmed Shafiq, and other senior politicians said they expected him to announce he would step down as the political crisis continued to deepen.

The mood of optimism was reinforced when General Hassan al-Roueini, the military commander for Cairo, told the crowd: "All your demands will be met today".

Hossam Badrawi, the new secretary general of the ruling National Democratic party, was quoted in the state press as saying he had requested Mubarak to transfer his powers to Suleiman, who had appeared to be effectively running the country in recent days.

But behind the scenes, a political struggle appeared to be under way over the terms of Mubarak's departure. The military's role was not immediately clear but the Muslim Brotherhood, a leading political force although banned, said it appeared the army had taken over behind the scenes. "It looks like a military coup," one of the group's leaders, Essam al-Erian, told Reuters. "I feel worry and anxiety. The problem is not with the president, it is with the regime."

The huge crowds served as a warning that the popular pressure for change is not likely to ease.

Besides Mubarak's resignation, opposition activists have been demanding an immediate lifting of the country's 30-year-old state of emergency, which has been used to lock up the government's opponents without trial. They have also pressing for parliament, elected in a tainted ballot last year, to be dissolved.

Some opposition leaders have said that they would accept an interim administration, controlled by civilians with a military presence, for up to a year to make constitutional changes to permit free elections and also to allow for the creation of new political parties and to give them a chance to become rooted.

Despite his defiance, Mubarak's position is increasingly threatened by the spread-

4-5»

Continued on page 4 »

Demonstrators in Tahrir Square last night. President Mubarak had seemed on the verge of giving in to demands to resign Photograph: Goran Tomasevic/Reuters

They do. Do you? Vote reform is hitched to royal wedding

Patrick Wintour
Allegra Stratton

The yes campaign in the referendum on introducing the alternative vote for Westminster elections is planning to capitalise on the royal wedding, six days earlier, by arguing that it is "a time to be optimistic and say yes".

Campaigners for change have been struggling with the impact of Prince William's wedding to Kate Middleton on 29 April, before the referendum on 5 May. That week also includes a bank holiday. But now they think they have a solution: proclaim it the season for saying yes.

"We will put all the arguments, but around the wedding it will be a coming-into-summer, more optimistic, more of a yes mood," a campaign source said. "The no camp will throw everything at us - that is the nature of a no campaign, it will be 'if in doubt vote no'."

Both campaigns recognise media obsession with the wedding will leave them struggling to capture voters' attention. Some estimates suggest turnout will be as low as 35%.

Campaigners were concerned Prince William and Kate Middleton's wedding would distract voters from the AV referendum

The referendum will ask voters whether they want to change from a first-past-the-post system to one where candidates are marked in order of preference. Yes campaigners say it is a modest but important upgrade of our electoral system that will make MPs more accountable and end the damaging culture of safe seats.

Private polling undertaken for the yes campaign by ICM in November showed 59%-41% support for AV among those expressing an intention to vote. The poll covered nearly 8,500 people, one of the largest in Britain, and showed support strong across all age groups except those aged over 65. Support was strongest among AB higher income voters.

A YouGov tracker poll this week saw the two camps neck and neck: 39% said they would vote to keep FPTP and 38% would vote to switch to AV.

Last September, YouGov was showing a consistent lead for the no campaign as large as nine points. The decline in the no vote may reflect the recent slide in the Conservatives' poll rating within the coalition.

It is expected that Nick Clegg and David Cameron will set out the respective cases for and against AV very soon after the bill introducing the referendum gains royal assent, probably next Wednesday. Cameron and the Conservatives want to keep FPTP, but Clegg and the Liberal Democrats will back AV. The two men are trying to ensure that the contest does not fracture the coalition.

22-23»

2011

Did you know that bees are a barometer of what people are doing to the environment? A healthy bee population is a healthy world!
Which makes their drastic decline in numbers a cause for concern that we ignore at our peril!
Ok, point taken. Now can I swat them?
Certainly not.

There wasn't room in the flat to keep all of my various protest placards, so I came up with this handy, easy to use, 'all purpose' alternative.
SAY NO
SAY YES

Have you ever had sex with multiple partners?
No.
Have you ever had anal or oral sex with a man?
No.
GIVE BLOOD
Have you ever taken illegal drugs?
No.
Do you have any body piercings
No
GIVE BLOOD
Do you have any tattooes?
No.
Have you ever travelled to a tropical destination?
No.
GIVE BLOOD
Wow, you're boring.
GIVE BLOOD
For actual questions go to www.blood.co.uk

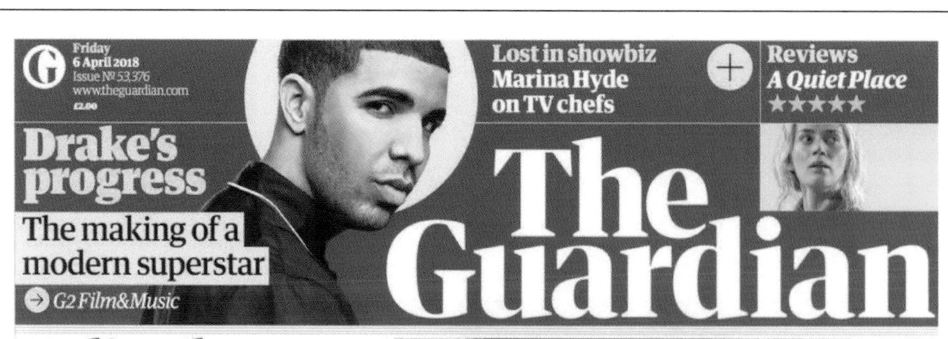

Friday
6 April 2018
Issue № 53,376
www.theguardian.com
£2.00
Drake's progress
The making of a modern superstar
G2 Film&Music
Lost in showbiz
Marina Hyde on TV chefs
Reviews
A Quiet Place
★★★★★
The Guardian

Police 'have lost control of the streets'

Former senior Met officer condemns budget cuts and lack of leadership in London

Vikram Dodd and Damien Gayle

A former senior police officer has said Scotland Yard appears to have lost control of London's streets, and has accused the Met leadership of a "deafening" silence as the capital's murder toll so far this year has passed 50.

After two murders in Hackney, east London, Victor Olisa, the Met's former head of diversity and head of policing in Tottenham, said he feared the violence could get worse. He said budget cuts and new demands on police were taking officers off the street and away from gathering intelligence.

"Communities are saying we don't see the police around any more," he told the Guardian. "It appears to people I have spoken to as though the police have lost control of public spaces and the streets."

Olisa said Met chiefs should have been more visible after this week's rise in violence. "The silence from senior officers in the Met is deafening," he said. "They should say we need more information from the public, this is what we are doing, this is what the results are."

The Metropolitan police commander, Cressida Dick, yesterday attempted to take control of the crisis by launching a new taskforce of 120 officers and telling the public: "You will see us being even more proactive out on the streets."

But Olisa said that wider cuts were making police officers' jobs harder. "You don't have as many officers available to patrol or spend time in public spaces as you did five years ago," he said. "There is less time to build conversation lines, so you can get information back."

The retired officer was speaking as investigations began into the two latest killings. An 18-year-old collapsed in the street after being stabbed, and a man aged 53 died after a betting shop fight. The teenager was named as Israel Ogunsola. The two deaths took the suspected murder toll in London to more than 50 in three months. Last night reports emerged that two more people were in hospital after a stabbing in east London.

Olisa's intervention was the latest in a week of fierce exchanges over the factors behind the increase in violence in London this year. 12 →

▲ *Israel Ogunsola, who was 18, died in the street after being stabbed*

Yulia Skripal makes her first statement since the Salisbury nerve agent attack *Page 6 →*

Exclusive

Ex-Trump aide backed 'black ops' in Ukraine

Luke Harding

Donald Trump's former campaign manager Paul Manafort authorised a secret media operation on behalf of a Ukrainian president, featuring "black ops", "placed" articles in the Wall Street Journal and anonymous briefings against Hillary Clinton.

The project, to boost the reputation of Ukraine's then leader, Viktor Yanukovych, was part of a multimillion-dollar lobbying effort by Manafort on behalf of the Kiev government, emails and documents reveal.

The strategies included:

- Proposing to rewrite Wikipedia entries to smear a key opponent of the then Ukrainian president.
- Setting up a fake thinktank in Vienna to disseminate pro-Yanukovych views.
- A social media blitz that was "aimed at targeted audiences in Europe and the US".
- Briefing journalists from the far-rightwing Breitbart website to attack Clinton, then US secretary of state.

The strategy anticipates efforts by the Kremlin and its troll factory to use Twitter and Facebook to discredit Clinton and help Trump win the 2016 US election. The material seen by the Guardian dates from 2011 to 2013.

Robert Mueller, the special counsel investigating claims of collusion between the Trump campaign and Russia, has indicted Manafort on multiple counts. He is accused of laundering profits from his lobbying work in Ukraine, carried out over a decade for Yanukovych and his political party.

Mueller also accuses Manafort of hiring retired European politicians to lobby on behalf of Yanukovych, and paying them more than €2m (£1.7m) via offshore accounts.

The documents reveal another surreptitious operation to influence international opinion.

In 2010 Yanukovych 18 →

2011

I was arrested whilst looting from the Spiritual Awareness bookshop.
What were you doing in there?

Well I'd already looted all the trainers, electrical gear and consumer goods I could carry, but when I got it all home I still felt strangely empty...

And I'm sitting on the sofa when I suddenly realise that my 40 year old, non-smoking, teetotal, fitness fanatic husband isn't watching East Enders with me, because he's dead. I've struggled to make sense of it ever since.

Have you tried iPlayer?

The thing is....
You heard me, Megan.
Its just that...
My mind is made up.
But.....

For crying out loud! Which part of "The resource allocation system minus the client contribution must equal the 'indicative budget" do you not understand?!!!!!

Superinjunctions Jemima Khan's 'nightmare' on Twitter
This section Page 3

The way we eat now How our diet defines us
G2 Cover story

PLUS Hughes, Harry or Hiddink for the Bridge?
In Sport

£1.00 (FR €3.20)
Tuesday 10.05.11
Published in London and Manchester
guardian.co.uk

newspaper of the year
the guardian

Extra places at university for rich students

Exclusive Reserving space for wealthy could improve access, say ministers

Jeevan Vasagar
Education editor

Teenagers from the wealthiest families would be able to pay for extra places at the most competitive universities under government proposals that could allow institutions to charge some British students the same high fees as overseas undergraduates.

Candidates who take up the extra places would not be eligible for publicly funded loans to pay tuition fees or living costs, limiting this option to all but the most privileged households who could pay fees up front.

Under the plans, the extra students may be charged as much as international undergraduates. At the most competitive universities, these students face fees ranging from £12,000 a year for arts subjects to £18,000 for sciences and more than £28,000 for medicine. Applicants would be required to meet the course entry requirements.

The changes would give more students the chance to attend their first choice of university. At present, the government sets a quota of undergraduate places that English universities are allowed to offer each year.

Employers and charities will also be encouraged to sponsor "off-quota" places under the plans to be outlined in a higher education white paper in the summer.

Ministers argue that the creation of extra places will boost social mobility by freeing up more publicly subsidised places for undergraduates from poorer homes.

But the proposals are likely to be criticised as a means for the wealthiest to "buy places" at a time when the government is to cut 10,000 publicly funded places.

The universities minister, David Willetts, told the Guardian: "There are various important issues that need to be addressed around off-quota places, but I start from the view that an increase in the total number of higher education places could aid social mobility.

"There would need to be arrangements to make sure any such system was fair and worked in the interests of students as well as institutions. But it is not clear what the benefit is of the current rules, which, for example, limit the ability of charities or social enterprises to sponsor students.

"We are inviting ideas on the whole concept and we will listen very carefully to all the responses we receive."

The proposal is most likely to be taken up by highly selective institutions, which turn away thousands of qualified candidates a year. Oxford accepted slightly more than 3,000 British and EU undergraduates out of about 17,000 who applied for the current academic year.

That demand is due to intensify as the latest application figures show the number of candidates for this autumn has risen by 2.1% to about 633,000 – another record high.

The places may not be covered by access agreements, under which universities are required to outline how they will improve their proportion of students from state schools and deprived backgrounds.

Under one version of the scheme, universities might operate a "needs-blind" admissions process, which assesses all candidates regardless of ability to pay, but then offers places off-quota to candidates from the most privileged homes.

The expansion of places will put greater pressure on less popular universities. Ministers have warned that undersubscribed institutions could have government-funded places withdrawn.

In a speech last month, the business secretary, Vince Cable, said: "Institutions could very well find themselves in trouble if students can't see value. In circumstances where places are unfilled, we might withdraw those places, and institutions should not assume they will easily get them back."

This is more likely to happen if more sought-after universities are free to expand in response to student demand.

The government is also keen to encourage more corporate sponsorship of univer-

Continued on page 2 »

Universities like Cambridge turn away thousands of qualified candidates each year

Cable and Huhne clash over carbon emissions

Allegra Stratton
Political correspondent

The business secretary, Vince Cable, has clashed with his Lib Dem cabinet colleague Chris Huhne by telling him he will not support new carbon reduction targets recommended by the government's independent climate change advisory body.

David Cameron will decide next week whether to accept the proposals of the Committee on Climate Change (CCC) for a fourth carbon budget covering the years 2023 to 2027, championed by Huhne, the energy secretary.

Three carbon budgets were set in 2008 but now the UK must agree a fourth as the government attempts to cut greenhouse gas emissions by 80% by 2050, compared with 1990 levels.

In a letter leaked to the Guardian, Cable tells his party leader, Nick Clegg, and the chancellor, George Osborne, he is "unable to give clearance to the proposal as it stands" and calls for an urgent cabinet meeting.

In his letter, dated 19 April, Cable says the proposed carbon budget is not "cost effective" and asks for a Treasury impact analysis to be made available to all involved in the decision.

He writes: "Agreeing too aggressive a level risks burdening the UK economy, which would be detrimental to UK, undermining the UK's competitiveness and our attractiveness as a place to do business.

"I have a number of concerns about supporting the CCC's recommended level at this time. It is important that we strike the right balance between our pursuit to decarbonise the UK economy whilst ensuring that UK economic growth and employment is sustained."

His argument rests on a concern that Huhne's plan relies on the securing of a cap on emissions trading across Europe that may not materialise. If this were not achieved, the UK would be left having to reduce carbon emissions unilaterally, which would risk putting industry at a disadvantage compared with outside competitors and "could lead to significant fiscal costs".

Instead, Cable argues for a weaker carbon target. "This level keeps us on course to meet our 2050 target and entails a steeper reduction in emissions than the previous government set for carbon budg-

Continued on page 2 »

Calls for inquiry into migrant deaths in Mediterranean

Jack Shenker

Europe's paramount human rights body, the Council of Europe, has called for an inquiry into the deaths of 61 migrants in the Mediterranean, claiming an apparent failure of military units to rescue them marked a "dark day" for the continent.

Mevlüt Çavusoglu, president of the council's parliamentary assembly, demanded an "immediate and comprehensive inquiry" into the fate of the migrants' boat which ran into trouble in late March en route to the Italian island of Lampedusa.

Yesterday, the Guardian reported that the boat encountered a number of European military units including a helicopter and an aircraft carrier after losing fuel and drifting, but no rescue attempt was made and most of the 72 people on board eventually died of thirst and hunger.

"If this grave accusation is true – that, despite the alarm being raised, and despite the fact that this boat, fleeing Libya, had been located by armed forces operating in the Mediterranean, no attempt was made to rescue the 72 passengers aboard, then it is a dark day for Europe as a whole," Çavusoglu declared. "I call for an immediate and comprehensive inquiry into the circumstances of the deaths of the 61 people who perished – one by one – of starvation and thirst while Europe looked on," he added.

An Italian Red Cross worker on the island of Lampedusa holds a baby rescued from a refugee vessel

Çavusoglu's intervention came as news emerged of another migrant boat which sank last Friday, according to the UN's refugee agency. Up to 600 were on board the overcrowded vessel as it fled the Libyan capital, Tripoli.

Witnesses who left on another boat shortly afterwards reported seeing remnants of the ship and the bodies of passengers in the sea. The International Organisation for Migration, which has staff on Lampedusa, said it had spoken to a Somali woman who lost her four-month-old baby in the tragedy and said that it was unclear how many passengers had managed to swim to safety.

The UNHCR has insisted that more communication is needed between coastguards, military and commercial ships to minimise migrant deaths at sea.

"We need to take heed of a situation that is very much evolving. We have to cooperate much more closely," said a spokesperson, Laura Boldrini, adding that ships should not wait for a problem to arise before attempting to help migrant boats. "Rescue should be automatic, without waiting for the boat to break apart or the engine to stop running," she said.

Continued on page 2 »

2011

Well its good to see every branch of the arts protesting against the cuts.

Honestly clare, if you think your profession is demoralized you should try teaching. The latest proposal is raising the retirement age to sixty-eight!
Any older and it'll be us asking their permission to go to the toilet.
COLLINS JUNIOR SCHOOL

You want me to stop playing "Tiger Feet"!
Yes, because it tacitly endorses the poaching of an endangered species and the use of their paws as ingredients in herbal medicines.
KIDZ DISCO WITH WACKY WALTER
This is political correctness gone Mud!
KIDZ DISCO WITH WACKY WALTER

Decca Aitkenhead Suzanne Moore Joris Luyendijk Zoe Williams Lucy Mangan

Thursday 26.04.12
Published in London
and Manchester
£1.20 (IR €1.20)

guardian.co.uk

Breakneck Beethoven
Barenboim's Proms sprint, in g2

Madeleine McCann 'may still be alive'
Yard calls for new investigation, page 3

Chelsea: brutal or beautiful?
Di Matteo's tactical masterclass, in Sport

Just like 1975: UK back into recession

● Osborne warns Britain faces long struggle ahead ● Labour says 'double dip' made in Downing Street

Larry Elliott
Economics editor

The government's five weeks of turmoil since George Osborne's badly received budget took a fresh turn for the worse yesterday when the latest set of growth figures showed Britain plunging into its first double-dip recession since 1975.

On a day that saw David Cameron under pressure to sack the culture secretary, Jeremy Hunt, over his handling of News Corp's attempt to mount a full takeover of BSkyB, the chancellor admitted Britain faced a long struggle to pull out of the deepest recession and the weakest recovery of the postwar era.

In a BBC interview, the chancellor said: "I've never disguised the fact that Britain faces a very difficult economic situation. We have these debts, we have this debt crisis; these debts were built up over many, many years." He added that if he had a magic wand he would wave it. Instead, he said, "we've got to work our way through the problems that have been built up".

News that the economy contracted 0.2% in the first three months of 2012 surprised the City, which had been confident the UK had avoided two quarters of falling output - the definition of a recession. The return to recession so soon after the last one ended in 2009 makes it a "double-dip".

Although some analysts said the official data painted too pessimistic a picture of the economy and would probably be revised up, there were fears that the loss of output caused by the Queen's diamond jubilee bank holiday could result in a third quarter of declining activity.

Labour seized on the news and accused the government of a recession made in Downing Street. The shadow chancellor, Ed Balls, said: "David Cameron and George Osborne complacently boasted their austerity plan had taken our economy out of the danger zone, but their failed policies have plunged us back into recession.

"We consistently warned that their austerity plan was self-defeating and that cutting spending and raising taxes too far and too fast would badly backfire. David Cameron and George Osborne arrogantly and complacently dismissed people who warned of the risk of a double-dip recession and the country is now paying a very heavy price. Their economic credibility is now in tatters."

Responding to news that a big fall in construction output and a smaller decline in manufacturing production had caused the economy to shrink for the fourth quarter in the last six, the prime minister told MPs: "These are very, very disappointing figures. I don't seek to excuse them, I don't seek to try and explain them away."

With local elections and the key London mayoral fight looming next month, Osborne made it clear that there would be no U-turn from the government on its deficit-reduction strategy and said his approach was supported by business groups and multilateral bodies such as the International Monetary Fund.

The chancellor fears that backsliding would be punished by the financial markets, and he is relying on the Bank of England to boost activity.

"It is made much harder when so much of the rest of Europe is in recession or head-

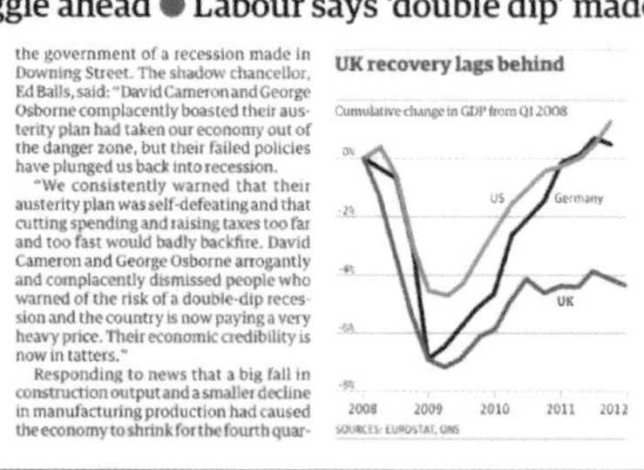

14-15 »

Continued on page 15 »

Hunt loses adviser in defence of BSkyB role

Patrick Wintour
Dan Sabbagh
Shiv Malik

The culture secretary, Jeremy Hunt, is willing to hand over texts, phone records and private emails in an effort to prove he was unaware that his disgraced special adviser had acted without his authority by providing a stream of commercially confidential information to News Corporation during its bid to take full control of BSkyB.

Hunt's special adviser Adam Smith fell on his sword yesterday an hour before prime minister's questions, admitting that he had allowed the perception to develop that the Murdochs' News Corp had "too close a relationship with the culture department".

Hunt refused to resign, saying he had acted with scrupulous impartiality, and insisted he had been unaware of "the volume and tone" of Smith's contacts with News Corp. He said his special adviser had "overstepped the mark unintentionally".

Hunt insisted he had acted in an impartial way, pointing out that on four separate occasions he taken the independent advice of his media regulators about the bid, even though these decisions ran counter to the commercial interests of News Corp.

Although Hunt survived a torrid day, he still suffered a series of blows, leaving his political career hanging in the balance, possibly for months:

● The stockmarket watchdog the Financial Services Authority is understood to be investigating whether Smith's emails to News Corp amounted to a breach of market abuse rules.

● Lord Justice Leveson rejected Hunt's request to bring forward his evidence to the inquiry, meaning he will not give evidence until mid-May at the earliest, leaving open the possibility that the minister will dangle for several weeks.

● Labour demanded that David Cameron instruct his independent adviser on the ministerial code to investigate at least

Continued on page 8 »

4-9 »

Rupert Murdoch leaving for his appearance before the Leveson inquiry yesterday with his wife, Wendi, and son Lachlan Photograph: Andrew Winning/Reuters

Myth, memory and Murdoch's imagination

The version of history told by News Corp's chairman at Leveson bears no relation to what happened, writes **Harold Evans**

Rupert Murdoch has apparently lost a great deal of his power of memory, but nature has compensated by endowing him with a vivid imagination. He can surely deploy his new gift in the service of Fox movies. There is the great scene he pitched to Lord Justice Leveson yesterday where the editor of the Times enters left, closes the door behind him and begs: "Look, tell me what you want to say, what do you want me to say, and it need not leave this room and I'll say it." And our hero proprietor, so famously fastidious about such matters, has to tell Uriah Heep: "That is not my job."

And thus, children, was how Mr KR Murdoch honoured the promises of editorial independence that enabled him to avoid the Monopolies and Mergers Commission over his bid for Times Newspapers in 1981. As the editor in question, I am not able to compete with Murdoch in fabrication – he has had a lifetime of experience – but I do happen to have retained my memory of the year editing the Times, made notes, kept documents and even had the effrontery to write a whole bestselling book about it in 1983, called Good Times, Bad Times.

It has gone unchallenged for 30 years in its detailed account of precisely how Murdoch did break all five of the crucial pledges, did press for adopting his right-wing views, did want to know why we

Continued on page 9 »

2012

That was hard. Really hard. And do you want to know the hardest part? Getting out of the front door. But it's good to set yourself a challenge in the new year. Achieving it is really empowering.
The Guardian
8TH SERIES FOR

OK, Brian. So you've taken the christmas tree to the recycling point. Now give it a rest.
The Guardian
8TH SERIES FOR

Dammit, all I want is to get home after a hard day's work, but instead I'm stuck in gridlock! I swear, if it gets worse...

...I'm going to consider taking the car.
SPORT

Look, Ms. Barker! I got a text that says "our records indicate you may be entitled to £3,350 for the accident you had"!
Its spam, Tom. They're just phishing for a response.

Oh. I suppose £3,350 is rather a lot of money for a pair of underpants.

Hadley Freeman Mike Selvey Polly Toynbee Vernon Bogdanor Hannah Betts

Tuesday 24.07.12
Published in London
and Manchester
£1.20

India: no place to be a woman
Helen Pidd in g2

From headlines to punchlines
People in the news at the fringe, page 13

Tate Modern's ★★★★★ storyteller
Adrian Searle on Tino Sehgal, page 9

G4S staff 'cheat' on tests to run x-ray scanners at Games

Recruits given several chances to pass exams on bomb detection – but just 20 minutes' training on machines

Nick Hopkins

The credibility of the Olympic security operation being run by G4S is called into further question today by claims that scores of trainees are being allowed to "cheat" their way through tests for the x-ray machines that detect homemade bombs and other weapons.

Trainees who fail the test are being given repeated opportunities to get the right answers to the same questions, and are also being allowed to confer with others during the exams under the noses of instructors, a source has told the Guardian.

Recruits are being given only 20 minutes' practice on the real machines that will be used at the Olympic venues to stop visitors bringing in dangerous materials, or possibly an IED (improvised explosive device).

G4S insisted it has followed industry standards and that the tests were designed and approved by the Olympic organisers, Locog. It said it was not "uncommon or wrong" for trainees to repeat tests.

But the Guardian has been told that concern about the proper staffing of the x-ray machines was raised at the government's Cobra meeting yesterday, which involved senior ministers and Olympic Games officials.

With the Olympic opening ceremony just three days away, police and armed forces have now been asked to "scope out" whether they can undertake more x-ray duties, and run the CCTV monitors too, if G4S cannot supply the numbers needed to operate the machines.

Gaps in the security operation have been emerging ever since G4S admitted almost a fortnight ago that it could not provide its full quota of 10,000 fully trained security guards. The firm hopes to provide 7,000.

The Ministry of Defence has mobilised an extra 3,500 personnel, and put another 1,200 on notice to deploy in 48 hours, but it is still unclear exactly where they will be needed and deployed.

Yesterday Locog was left looking for 500 extra staff at the St James's Park stadium in Newcastle for an Olympic football match on Thursday. The organisers are likely to turn to the army and the police for help.

G4S was tasked with recruiting and training teams for the x-ray machines, which include the key job of "screener" – who has to look at the x-ray image of a bag and decide whether there is anything untoward inside.

Almost all the training undertaken by G4S recruits involves computer simulations, with only a small period set aside to work on the machines themselves.

Trainees have to pass seven tests, or modules, and in each module they are shown images of 25 suspect bags. They can only pass if they have a pass rate of 75% or more.

But because the test is a multiple choice with only three possible answers, if a trainee gets it wrong first time, it is much easier next time round.

"Only two people out of a group of 40 passed the exam first time," said one G4S trainee. "Those who failed were allowed to retake the exact same modules, endlessly repeating them until they scraped through.

We were allowed to do the modules again and again, looking at the exact same bags, so by process of elimination you can pass the modules. You could retake the test as many times as you liked before the end of the day at 5pm."

The source said the trainees were all talking to each other during the exam to help them get the right answers.

"There were two invigilators but no attempt was made to stop people cheating. There was a general hum in the room with people talking to each other. By the end of the day, the majority of the people in the class, more than three quarters, had passed." This chimes with the experience of other trainees who have also contacted the Guardian.

The source, who has written a column for the Guardian about these experiences, said the training had not prepared recruits for working in these specialist roles.

"I don't think the training has properly prepared people for working as 'screeners' on the x-ray machines. It is a really difficult job, and it is also mundane, which makes it more difficult. It is extraordinary that you are only given 20 minutes on the

Continued on page 2 »

4-7»

Hoy takes the flag

Sir Chris Hoy will carry the British flag and lead out Team GB at the Olympics opening ceremony on Friday, after the cyclist was the overwhelming choice of fellow athletes in a vote. 'It's the stuff of dreams,' said the four-times gold medal winner, who added that Bradley Wiggins' triumph in the Tour de France would inspire a new generation of cyclists

Sport, back page »

Cinema shootings suspect in court

3»

James Holmes, accused of shooting dead 12 people in a cinema, appeared in court for the first time yesterday in Colorado Photograph: RJ Sangosti/Getty Images

Coulson and Brooks to learn if they face hacking charges

Josh Halliday and Vikram Dodd

Andy Coulson, the former communications director to the prime minister, is among 11 former News of the World journalists who will be told today if they are to face charges in connection with the phone-hacking scandal.

The Crown Prosecution Service is due to announce its first charging decisions since Scotland Yard reopened its investigation last year and launched Operation Weeting.

The CPS has received files from the Metropolitan police's Weeting team covering 13 individuals, including 11 journalists from the now defunct Sunday tabloid and the private investigator Glenn Mulcaire.

Those under CPS examination have not officially been identified by name, although journalists who have been arrested and remain on police bail include Coulson and Rebekah Brooks, both former editors of the paper. Neville Thurlbeck, its former chief reporter, confirmed he was among those whose files had been passed to the CPS.

Prosecutors have been working on the basis of a "broad interpretation" of the Regulation of Investigatory Powers Act (Ripa), which covers phone hacking, the director of public prosecutions, Keir Starmer, told the Guardian earlier this month. This would mean it was not absolutely necessary for the purposes of bringing a criminal prosecution for a voicemail message to have been hacked into, by, or on behalf of the NoW before it had been heard by its intended recipient.

There had previously been disagreement between the CPS and the Met over whether a criminal offence had been committed if a voicemail message had already been heard by the person for whom it was left.

The Met said yesterday it believes there are 4,775 potential victims of phone hacking, of which 2,615 have been notified. Deputy assistant commissioner Sue Akers told the Leveson inquiry that the Met had notified more than 702 people who are "likely" to have been victims.

Akers also said Operation Elveden, the Met's investigation into alleged illegal payments by journalists to police, has gone beyond News International to include payments from Trinity Mirror and Express Newspapers.

Yesterday it emerged that Patricia Bernal, the mother of Clare Bernal who was murdered by a former boyfriend while working at Harvey Nichols, is suing News International after being told by the Met that her phone was targeted hours after her daughter died in 2005.

8»

Andy Coulson, the PM's former communications director, is among a list of 11 ex-NoW journalists facing possible charges

'Swelling class sizes, squeezed hospitals, fewer benefits and massive job cuts – but the prospect of 10 years of national privation has caused barely a ripple'

Aditya Chakrabortty in g2

2012

Machu Pichu, yes, very nice if you like crowds, but for me a more authentic South American high-altitude experience is climbing the Sierra Nevada de Santa Marta in Columbia, stunning views and so quiet I thought I felt my spirit about to leave my body and take wing like a condor but it turned out to be amoebic dysentry, like in Laos...
Travel broadens the mouth....

It's when the Olympics 'feel-good factor' finally runs out that worries me...

I'm sorry, Brian, but I totally refute this notion you have that I "make you feel bad about yourself".
My words and behaviour don't do that. Any bad or negative feelings you may have are already within yourself. Do you spot the distinction?
I'm not sure I do...
Oh, come on, dimmo. It's not rocket science.

2012

Polly Toynbee Simon Jenkins Ai Weiwei Martin Kettle Mark Lawson Dan Sabbagh

Friday 22.06.12
Published in London
and Manchester
£1.20

the guardian
guardian.co.uk

In G2 Film&Music

Dizzie Rascal on aliens, fame and moving to Miami
Amazing Spider-Man director Marc Webb on reinventing the superhero
PLUS Peter Bradshaw's verdict on The Five-Year Engagement ★★★
and Alexis Petridis on Go Kart Mozart ★★★★

Italian PM: we have a week to save eurozone

● No room for failure in talks – Monti
● 'Ever more integration is needed'

John Hooper Rome

Italy's prime minister, Mario Monti, has warned of the apocalyptic consequences of failure at next week's summit of EU leaders, outlining a potential death spiral whose consequences would become more political than economic.

The Italian leader is to hold talks today with Chancellor Angela Merkel of Germany, the French president, François Hollande, and Spain's prime minister, Mariano Rajoy, in the hope that the single currency's big four countries can pave the way for a breakthrough at next week's meeting.

Speaking to the Guardian and a group of leading European newspapers, Monti said that, without a successful outcome at the summit, "there would be progressively greater speculative attacks on individual countries, with harassment of the weaker countries". The attacks would be focused not only on those who had failed to respect EU guidelines, but also on those like Italy, which he said had abided by the rules "but which carry with them from the past a high debt".

Monti warned: "A large part of Europe would find itself having to continue to put up with very high interest rates that would then impact on the states and also indirectly on firms. This is the direct opposite of what is needed for economic growth."

Outlining the result of a failure at the talks, Monti said that, faced with creeping economic paralysis, "the frustration of the public towards Europe would grow", creating a vicious circle. "To emerge in good shape from this crisis of the eurozone and the European economy, ever more integration is needed," said Monti. Yet, if the summit failed to resolve the problems quickly, "public opinion, but also that of the governments and parliament... will turn against that greater integration".

Monti said he could see the beginnings of the process "even in the Italian parliament, which has traditionally been pro-European and no longer is".

He made his remarks hours after his predecessor, Silvio Berlusconi, acknowledged that his party had bled support because of its backing for the Monti government's unpopular budgetary measures and spoke openly for the first time of the electoral advantage it could derive from torpedoing Monti's non-party cabinet of technocrats.

Monti signalled that the key eurozone leaders were working on a plan designed to halt the spread of debt contagion while satisfying Germany's refusal to sanction financial irresponsibility. The plan, he said, was one of the "absolutely necessary" outcomes of next week's summit.

The first outcome, he said, would be a clear sign of the eurozone's willingness to integrate further "in such a way that Europeans know where they're going... [and] the markets are convinced that,

Eurozone crisis »
● Mario Monti interview, page 20
● Greece gets a cabinet, page 21
● Spain reveals potential price of its banking crisis, page 28

having given birth to the euro, the will [of the member states] to make it indissoluble and irrevocable is there and will be strengthened by other steps towards integration".

He warned: "There may not be – indeed, there will not be – a fully-fledged, detailed blueprint, but there will some strong elements and a short road – I hope short, a few months – to get from there to the overall project."

Other minimum requirements were "a fuller banking union, with advances in terms of integrated, and if possible unified, supervision"; "a European deposit guarantee" system; and the plan that will be on the table on Friday for "new market-friendly policy mechanisms" to help out countries under attack – provided they had complied with EU demands for fiscal discipline.

Yesterday figures indicating that the eurozone is slipping into recession height-

Continued on page 2 »

Bet in the wet Ladies' Day at Ascot

A couple at Royal Ascot yesterday on a wet Ladies' Day, the fashion highlight of the five-day race meeting. Sport, page 39 » Photograph: Peter Macdiarmid/Getty

Change rules on migrant workers, says Miliband

Patrick Wintour
Political editor

Ed Miliband today signals a change in Labour's immigration policy by disclosing he wants to change the economic rules to do more to help people already living and working in Britain.

In an interview with the Guardian, he concedes that immigration is being discussed in "every kitchen" and that the Labour party has been too quick to dismisses the concerns of ordinary people as "prejudice".

He says the government should strengthen the law so that employment agencies cannot – even informally – favour foreign workers.

"In sectors where there is a problem, every medium and large employer that has more than 25% foreign workers – double the average share of migrants in the population – should have to notify Jobcentre Plus."

Miliband said he wanted to reframe the debate on immigration by pledging to reform a "brutish labour market" that encourages the excessive use of low-paid immigrants and allows British companies to shirk their responsibilities to train workers. But he distanced himself from remarks made by the former prime minister Gordon Brown, suggesting that it would be wrong to promise too much. "We cannot tell people things we cannot deliver. We cannot say 'British jobs for British workers'."

He admitted the Labour government allowed too many immigrants from eastern Europe into the country by lifting controls on EU accession countries such as Poland too quickly, but denied his party lied about immigration, as claimed by his former adviser Lord Glasman.

Miliband argued that immigration should be seen as a class issue, since the evidence shows lower-paid workers and the unskilled suffer disproportionately, especially from the impact of cheap eastern European labour. He said he was entering the debate on immigration in the context of his call for a more responsible capitalism.

"There has been a collision of a large amount of immigration from eastern Europe and a UK labour market that is frankly too often nasty, brutish and short-term," he said.

As part of a policy review, Miliband

Continued on page 7 »

Vindicated: the last man Britain sentenced to hang

Evidence of waterboarding by the British army was produced in the battle to clear Liam Holden's name, writes **Ian Cobain**

Liam Holden was 19 years old when he became the last person in the United Kingdom to be sentenced to hang. After deliberating for just 90 minutes, at the end of a murder trial that had lasted four days, the jury returned a guilty verdict and the judge told him: "You will suffer death in the manner authorised by law."

Holden was led down the steps from the dock at Belfast's City Commission, handcuffed to a prison officer, and escorted along the underground tunnel that led to Crumlin Road jail on the opposite side of the road. There he was taken straight to C wing – to the condemned man's cell.

This was larger than most cells, and airy. Holden was permitted a black and white television and two bottles of beer a day: luxuries no other prisoner was granted. He shared the cell with two-man teams of prison officers who watched him around the clock. One officer – a Roman Catholic, like Holden – delighted in telling him that it wouldn't be long before they broke his neck.

In the event, Holden's neck wasn't broken. His sentence was commuted to life imprisonment, and shortly afterwards capital punishment was abolished in Northern Ireland, bringing it into line with the rest of the UK. It was 1973, the Troubles were at their savage worst, and hanging a man, Willie Whitelaw, the Northern Ireland secretary, later

Liam Holden was convicted of killing Private Frank Bell in 1972 – a verdict based on his confession made after interrogation

explained, "would only succeed in promoting the mayhem and killings".

But Holden did spend the next 17 years behind bars.

Now, almost four decades later, his murder conviction has been quashed by the court of appeal in Belfast, and exposed as a miscarriage of justice: one that would have been allowed to stand, had the hangman done his work.

In its attempts to establish Holden's innocence, his defence team explored some of the darker aspects of British counter-insurgency operations in the 50s and 60s, and the manner in which troops interrogated their prisoners

Continued on page 8 »

2012

Mr. McNally, is there anything the matter?
Far from it! I have just spent my last £1 on a scratch card and I've only won the £1 million jackpot!
I can't believe it! After all the worries, the setbacks, the strain! After a lifetime of personal and financial ill fortune. You know, my wife left me last week because she said I was so unlucky!
Well who's the unlucky one now, Glynis?!!!

So, before we were interrupted, I believe Megan was about to tell us why we should discourage kids performing parkour on the roof of the building.

Has anybody seen my sellotape dispenser?
GOOD LUCK NINA AND GOODBYE!

Damian McBride Felicity Cloake Jonathan Freedland Jenny Colgan John Crace

Thursday 28.06.12
Published in London
and Manchester
£1.20

9 770261 307545 26

the guardian
guardian.co.uk

Christopher Eccleston
'TV has the best scripts', in g2

Watson a Wimbledon winner
Sport, page 38

Nora Ephron, an American hero
Hadley Freeman, in g2

Handshake of history Queen meets former IRA chief

3»

The Queen and Martin McGuinness, now Northern Ireland deputy first minister, shake hands yesterday at a theatre in Belfast Photograph: Paul Faith/WPA/Getty

Barclays fined £290m as bid to manipulate rates exposed

Diamond forfeits bonus over bank's 'serious, widespread' breaches of City rules

Jill Treanor
City editor

The boss of Barclays, Bob Diamond, was under mounting pressure last night after the bank was hit with fines of £290m for its "serious, widespread" role in trying to manipulate the price of crucial interest rates that affect the cost of borrowing for millions of customers around the world.

There were calls for Diamond to step down after the Financial Services Authority slapped a £59.5m fine on the bank - the largest ever levied by the City regulator - forcing him and other top executives to forgo any bonuses for 2012.

The FSA - and authorities in the US which hit Barclays with penalties of £230m - described repeated breaches of rules dating back to 2005. They involved "a significant number of employees", including senior managers, and called into question the integrity of the markets.

The FSA published embarrassing email exchanges in which Barclays staff were offered bottles of Bollinger champagne as payment for favours or their names printed in "golden letters". The emails demonstrated how traders manipulated the price of key interest rates in an attempt to make greater profits.

The regulators, including the US department of justice and the Commodity Futures Trading Commission, said Barclays had also taken steps to fix the rates as the bank was concerned about its public image during the 2008 financial crisis.

Andrew Tyrie, the MP who chairs the Treasury select committee, described Barclays' activities as "inexcusable". The shadow Treasury minister Chris Leslie asked whether there should be a criminal investigation.

The fines come as Diamond - who has earned almost £100m from Barclays since 2006 and was at the time running the division where the misconduct took place - has been trumpeting the bank's commitment to acting as a "good citizen", despite the bank's run-in with HM Revenue & Customs over a £500m tax avoidance scheme and a row with shareholders over his £17m pay packet this year.

Barclays said Diamond and his three close lieutenants - the head of investment banking, Rich Ricci; chief operating officer, Jerry del Missier, and finance director, Chris Lucas - would forfeit their bonuses this year as a result of the attempted manipulation. But they will still be in line for multi-million pound share payouts.

25»

The penalties levied on Barclays are part of an international investigation involving a number of banks -

Continued on page 3 »

Public services data bonanza - but it won't all be for free

Juliette Jowit
Political correspondent

Hundreds of pieces of government data about public services - ranging from the success of different GPs treating patients with cancer to where British aid money is spent - are to be published for the first time, ministers will announce today.

The plans for releasing statistics from every government department over the next year will be published alongside the open data white paper, which is expected to commit government in future to a general presumption in favour of publishing public sector data, and take further steps toward extending the policy to all organisations which deliver public services, including private contractors.

However, the white paper from the Cabinet Office will also announce a review of charging for information requested under the Freedom of Information Act (FoI) - a move that will anger campaigners for greater openness about government activities.

The document will also be scrutinised by critics who want ministers to expand the openness agenda beyond public services, to include issues such as corporate links to the state, and the use of natural resources.

Today's white paper follows previous decisions by the coalition government to release data about central government such as civil servants on higher pay grades, and 9,000 pieces of government data about the public sector such as crime maps and statistics for GP performance.

In the government's white paper consultation last summer, the cabinet office minister Francis Maude predicted opening up more government data would improve public services by improving scrutiny and encouraging excellence, give people "real choice", cut the costs of FoI requests, and "re-establish individual responsibility".

Maude is also expected to announce that more effort will go into making the data easy to use and reuse, so that individuals and companies can use it to create new applications or websites - and potentially make money from it.

As part of that agenda, the official data website, data.gov.uk, has been revamped with help from, among others, worldwide web inventor Sir Tim Berners-Lee.

Continued on page 8 »

Minister takes on twin tycoons in Sark row

Simon Bowers and Helen Pidd

The justice minister, Lord McNally, has said he told the billionaire Barclay brothers that the UK would not let them turn the tiny Channel island of Sark into a "company town" as a poisonous row between the tycoon twins and local people threatens to break the island's antiquated system of government.

The unprecedented government intervention comes after 15 years of sporadic feuding in Britain's smallest crown dependency jurisdiction which has pitched many of Sark's 600 inhabitants against the reclusive businessmen Sir Frederick and Sir David Barclay, who live in both Monaco and a castle they have built on the 32-hectare (80-acre) island of Brecqhou, 200 metres west of Sark.

McNally, who conducted a tour of the crown dependencies this month, took the unusual step of holding an open town hall meeting in Sark. He said he heard from some Sarkees grateful for jobs and investment the Barclays had brought to the island. But the justice minister said others had raised concerns with the ministry about the behaviour of senior Barclay representatives on Sark, mainly their chief lieutenant on the island, Kevin Delaney.

Asked if he felt Delaney's actions were intimidatory, McNally said: "I invite you to look at the Sark Newsletter [a weekly mailshot to almost all households produced by Delaney]. I deplore the tone of the newsletter because I don't think it's constructive to the mood of tolerance I'd like to see on the island ... A number

The intervention comes after 15 years of sporadic feuding in Britain's smallest crown dependency jurisdiction

of people have said to me that it was the sustained nature of attacks in the Sark Newsletter that made them withdraw from public life."

Those featured in the newsletter include the island's postmistress and its doctor. The latter resigned in February and calls the newsletter a "dangerous propaganda sheet". Some of those who fight back against attacks in print claim that they then receive menacing legal letters from lawyers.

McNally, the minister responsible for managing the UK's relationships with the crown dependencies, told the Guardian: "One of the things that I've got to keep in mind is if Sark was in the hands of a single company or a set of individuals, would that be a threat to governance? I do not think the British government could simply accept such a state of affairs.

"The Barclays have never said that they plan to take over Sark, but I do not believe it would be compliant with our responsibilities [to ensure] good governance to allow Sark to become a company town. And I've said this to the Barclays."

The minister's views sparked an angry response from the twins. Through their lawyer they said: "Lord McNally is poorly informed and has consistently and blindly sided with [Sark's] establishment without, apparently, ever asking himself what sort of political system he is supporting. It is, quite frankly, bizarre that the UK government should spend so

14-15»

Continued on page 2 »

2012

OK, Frank, I've thrown my 'emotion cards' on the floor. Pick up a card that best expresses how you feel.
'Unhappy'. And why do you feel unhappy?
UNHAPPY
Because I have OCD and can't stand the mess you've made on the floor.

The thing is, Ted, I'm not sure if everything that works for Native american warriors necessarily works for Mens' Group.

I see they're celebrating Joan Of Arc's 600th birthday in France.
Excuse me...
I am French. And I find your refusal to call her by her French name, Jeanne D'Arc, is indicative of the English arrogance and Imperialism that she fought against.
It's political correctness gone merde....

Arianna Huffington
'I'm stepping off a train and onto a jet'
G2 Page 10

End of the affair?
Berlusconi to go on trial
This section Page 16-17

£1.00 (FR €3.20)
Wednesday 16.02.11
Published in London and Manchester
guardian.co.uk

theguardian

Defector who triggered war on Iraq admits: 'I lied about WMD'

Former chemical engineer tells Guardian he fabricated key 'eyewitness' testimony

Martin Chulov
Helen Pidd Karlsruhe

Our source was an eyewitness ... he was present during biological agent production runs
Colin Powell, February 2003
I had the chance to fabricate something to topple the regime
Rafid Ahmed Alwan al-Janabi, February 2011

The defector who convinced the White House that Iraq had a secret biological weapons programme has admitted for the first time that he lied about his story, then watched in shock as it was used to justify the war.

Rafid Ahmed Alwan al-Janabi, codenamed Curveball by German and American intelligence officials who dealt with his claims, has told the Guardian he fabricated tales of mobile biological weapons trucks and clandestine factories in an attempt to bring down the Saddam Hussein regime, from which he had fled in 1995.

"Maybe I was right, maybe I was not right," he said. "They gave me this chance. I had the chance to fabricate something to topple the regime. I and my sons are proud of that and we are proud that we were the reason to give Iraq the margin of democracy."

The admission comes just after the eighth anniversary of Colin Powell's speech to the United Nations in which the then-US secretary of state relied heavily on lies that Janabi had told the German secret service, the BND. It also follows the release of former defence secretary Donald Rumsfeld's memoirs, in which he admitted Iraq had no weapons of mass destruction programme.

The careers of both men were seriously damaged by their use of Janabi's claims, which the defector now says could have been - and were - discredited well before Powell's landmark speech to the UN on 5 February 2003.

Janabi is an elusive exile from his country and has never before told the full story of how he duped the world's most powerful country into believing Saddam had weapons of mass destruction. In a series of meetings with the Guardian in Germany, where he has been granted asylum, he said he had told a German official, who he identified as Dr Paul, about mobile bioweapons trucks throughout 2000.

He said the BND had identified him as a Baghdad-trained chemical engineer and approached him shortly after 13 March of that year, looking for inside information about Saddam's Iraq.

"I had a problem with the Saddam regime," he said. "I wanted to get rid of him and now I had this chance."

He portrays the BND as gullible and so eager to tease details from him that they gave him a copy of Perry's Chemical Engineering Handbook to help communicate. He still has the book in his small, rented flat in Karlsruhe, south-west Germany.

"They were asking me about pumps for filtration, how to make detergent after the reaction," he said. "Any engineer who studied in this field can explain or answer any question they asked."

Janabi claimed he was first exposed as a liar as early as mid-2000, when the BND travelled to a Gulf city, believed to be Dubai, to speak with his former boss at the Military Industries Commission in Iraq, Dr Bassil Latif.

The Guardian has learned separately that British intelligence officials were at that meeting, investigating a claim made by Janabi that Latif's son, who was studying in Britain, was procuring weapons for Saddam.

That claim was proven false, and Latif strongly denied Janabi's claim of mobile bioweapons trucks and another allegation that 12 people had died during an accident at a secret bioweapons facility in south-east Baghdad.

The German officials returned to confront him with Latif's version. "He says, 'There are no trucks,' and I say, 'OK, when [Latif says] there no trucks then [there are none].'" Janabi recalled.

He said the BND did not contact him again until May 2002. But he said it soon became clear that he was still being taken seriously. The meetings continued through 2002 and it became clear to Janabi that a case for war was being constructed.

Janabi said he was comfortable with what he did, despite the chaos of the past eight years and the civilian death toll in Iraq, which stands at more than 100,000.

"I tell you something when I hear anybody - not just in Iraq but in any war - [is] killed. I am very sad. But give me another solution. Can you give me another solution? Believe me, there was no other way to bring about freedom to Iraq. There were no other possibilities."

Meanwhile US intelligence officials have been picking over Janabi's confession. The former CIA chief in Europe, Tyler Drumheller, said the emergence of the truth "makes me feel better". "I think there are still a number of people who still thought there was something in that. Even now," said Drumheller.

Richard Perle, who chaired the Pentagon's advisory board at the time of the invasion, said: "It's the job of intelligence agencies to distinguish between defectors who claim to have something to say and defectors who are lying and they obviously didn't do their job. The Germans didn't, and we didn't."

Stephen Biddle, an Iraq expert at the Council on Foreign Relations, said Janabi's admission undermined accusations that the Bush administration had lied. "The source did actually tell them those things. But it does support the idea that they didn't do due diligence on checking out the information in part because they were being told what they wanted to hear."

4-5 »

Women's refuge chief returns OBE in protest over cuts

Amelia Gentleman

The head of a leading women's refuge is handing back the OBE she received for services to disadvantaged women because she believes government cuts will leave her unable to provide proper support to vulnerable women.

Denise Marshall, chief executive of Eaves charity, which specialises in helping women who have been victims of violence and those who have been trafficked into prostitution, said the level of funding cuts to support organisations such as hers meant they would soon be unable to function properly.

National and local government funding decisions have hit women's support services hard. Preliminary research by the national charity Women's Aid shows that more than half of all domestic violence services still do not know whether they will have enough money to remain fully open after March.

Marshall told the Guardian: "I received the OBE in 2007 specifically for providing services to disadvantaged women. It was great to get it; it felt like recognition for the work the organisation has done. But recently it has been keeping me awake at night. I feel like it would be dishonourable and wrong to keep it. I'm facing a future where I can't give women who come to my organisation the services they deserve - I won't be able to provide the services for which I got the OBE."

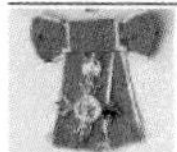

Denise Marshall won this OBE for services to disadvantaged women. She says cuts will stop her providing proper support

Marshall is worried about what the cuts will mean. "We will see situations where women are in danger as a result of the cuts. There are disasters waiting to happen."

Like many charity directors, Marshall is unclear whether government grants will continue to fund all the projects she runs in the new financial year. She has been asked by the Ministry of Justice to reapply for funding for the scheme she runs for trafficked women, the Poppy Project - but with a projected reduction in funding of up to 75% for each victim. "They want a bargain basement service," she said.

She has declined to submit a tender to provide services at a radically reduced level, and has pulled out of tendering to continue to provide refuge services in Kensington and Chelsea, west London, at similarly reduced rates.

"I'm not prepared to bid for a service that did not enable women to get the quality of service that is essential," she said. "If you run a refuge where you don't have the support staff it just becomes a production line, where you move people on as quickly as possible to meet the targets. You're not helping women to escape the broader

Continued on page 2 »

2013

Brian, please! Don't just turn around and go to sleep. For me the lovemaking isn't over because the sex has finished. I still have needs.
Sorry, Clare, that was selfish of me. What is it you want?
I quite fancy an omelette.

No subject should be off limits to Men's Group, but if there is any repeat of this behaviour I shall have to ban all further discussion of 'Great British Bake Off'.

Apart from that, Mr. Bell, how are you finding the anger Management course?

2013

Inside: unique 16-page supplement including Mikhail Gorbachev, Shirley Williams, Lech Walesa, Carol Thatcher, Nigel Lawson and Nancy Reagan

Tuesday 09.04.13
Published in London and Manchester
£1.40

the guardian

"She became harder than hard"

Hugo Young on Margaret Thatcher, 1925 - 2013

Days before he died in 2003 Young, Guardian columnist and Thatcher biographer, wrote an epitaph for the prime minister who changed Britain for ever

The first time I met Margaret Thatcher, I swear she was wearing gloves. But without any question, sitting behind her desk, she was wearing a hat.

Being a woman is undoubtedly one of the features, possibly the most potent, that makes her ascent to power memorable.

The woman, however, changed. The gender remained, its artefacts deployed with calculation. But it was overlaid by the supposedly masculine virtues, sometimes more manly than the men could ever assemble. She became harder than hard. Sent Bobby Sands to an Irish hero's grave without a blink. Faced down trade union leaders after her early years - apprentice years, when Jim Callaghan's Britain was falling apart - in which the commonest fear was that the little lady would not be able to deal with them across the table.

Thatcher became a supremely self-confident leader. No gloves, or hats, except for royalty or at funerals, but feet on the table, whisky glass at hand, into the small hours of solitude, for want of male cronies in the masculine world she dominated for all her 11 years in power.

I think by far her greatest virtue, in retrospect, is how little she cared if people liked her. Britain was battered out of the somnolent conservatism that had held back progress and, arguably, prosperity. This is what we mean by the Thatcher revolution, imposing on Britain, for better or for worse, some of the liberalisation that the major continental economies know, 20 years later, they still need. I think on balance, it was for the better, and so, plainly did Thatcher's chief successor, Tony Blair. If a leader's record is to be measured by the willingness of the other side to decide it cannot turn back the clock, then Thatcher bulks big in history.

But this didn't come without a price. Thatcher left a dark legacy that, like her successes, has still not disappeared behind the historical horizon. What happened at the hands of this woman's indifference to sentiment and good sense in the early 1980s brought unnecessary calamity to the lives of several million people who lost their jobs. It led to riots that nobody needed. More insidiously, it fathered a mood of tolerated harshness. Materialistic individualism was blessed as a virtue, the driver of national success. Everything was justified as long as it made money - and this, too, is still with us.

2-15

Read the full text on pages 2-3 »

2013

I tell you, Megan, there are few sights less edifying than people celebrating the death of a fellow human being, however much despised.
Round the back? Of course, round the back!
SPARROWHAWK FAMILY CENTRE

I campaign to protect badgers from the cull in my own spare time. To suggest it could somehow compromise my professionalism here at work is ludicrous.
What?

Seriously, Megan, what kind of signal do you think this will send out to the clients?
SPEECH IMPEDIMENT SUPPORT GROUP

Exclusive

Revealed: how US secretly collects private data from AOL, Apple, Facebook, Google, Microsoft, Paltalk, Skype, Yahoo and YouTube

theguardian
guardian.co.uk

Files prove existence of undercover operation codenamed Prism

Glenn Greenwald
Ewen MacAskill

The National Security Agency has obtained direct access to the systems of Google, Facebook, Apple and other American internet giants, according to a top secret document obtained by the Guardian.

The NSA access is part of a previously undisclosed programme called PRISM, which allows them to collect material including search history, the content of emails, file transfers and live chats, the document says.

The Guardian has verified the authenticity of the document, a 41-slide Powerpoint presentation – classified as Top Secret with no distribution to foreign allies – which was apparently used to train intelligence operatives on the capabilities of the programme. The document claims "collection directly from the servers" of major US service providers.

Although the presentation claims the programme is run with the assistance of the companies, all those who responded to a Guardian request for comment yesterday denied any knowledge of any such programme.

In a statement, Google said: "Google cares deeply about the security of our users' data. We disclose user data to government in accordance with the law, and we review all such requests carefully. From time to time, people allege that we have created a government 'back door' into our systems, but Google does not have a 'back door' for the government to access private user data."

The NSA access was enabled by changes to US surveillance law introduced under George Bush and renewed under Barack Obama in December 2012.

The programme facilitates extensive, in-depth surveillance on both live communications and stored information. The law allows for the targeting of any customers of participating firms who live outside the US, or those Americans whose communications include people outside the US.

It also opens the possibility of communications made entirely within the US being collected without warrants.

Disclosure of the PRISM programme follows a leak to the Guardian on Wednesday of a top secret court order compelling telecoms provider Verizon to turn over the telephone records of millions of US customers.

The participation of the internet companies in PRISM will add to the debate, ignited by the Verizon revelation, about the scale of surveillance by the intelligence services. Unlike the collection of those call records, this surveillance can include the content of communications and not just the metadata.

Some of the world's largest internet brands are claimed to be part of the information-sharing programme since its introduction in 2007. Microsoft, which is currently running an advertising campaign with the slogan: "Your privacy is our priority", was the first, with collection beginning in December 2007.

It was followed by Yahoo in 2008; Google, Facebook and Paltalk in 2009; YouTube in 2010; Skype and AOL in 2011; and finally Apple, which joined the program in 2012. The programme is continuing to expand, with other providers due to come online.

Collectively, the companies cover the vast majority of online email, search, video and communications networks.

The extent and nature of the data collected from each company varies.

Companies are legally obliged to comply with requests for users' communications under US law, but the PRISM programme allows the intelligence services direct access to the companies' servers. The NSA document notes the operations have "assistance of communications providers in the US".

The revelation also supports concerns raised by several US senators during the renewal of the Fisa Amendments Act in December 2012, who warned about the scale of surveillance the law might enable, and shortcomings in the safeguards it introduces. When the FAA was first enacted, defenders of the statute argued that a significant check on abuse would be the NSA's inability to obtain electronic communications without the consent of the telecom and internet companies that control the data. But the PRISM programme renders that consent unnecessary, as it allows the agency to directly and unilaterally seize the communications off the companies' servers.

The logo for PRISM, the secret US operation which was used to harvest data from the country's internet giants

A chart prepared by the NSA, contained within the top secret document obtained by the Guardian, underscores the breadth of the data it is able to obtain: email, video and voice chat, videos, photos, voice-over-IP (for example, Skype) chats, file transfers, social networking details, and more.

4-5»

Continued on page 4 »

Friday 07.06.13
Published in London and Manchester
£1.40

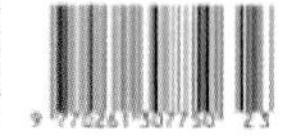

2013

I heard what you lads said to that elderly woman and I found it offensive, disrespectful and unacceptable!
But she's totally hogging it!

How interesting! So you also have a client who has serious issues around abandonment! Let's discuss it later.

Nothing to do with me. I thought they were with you.

2013

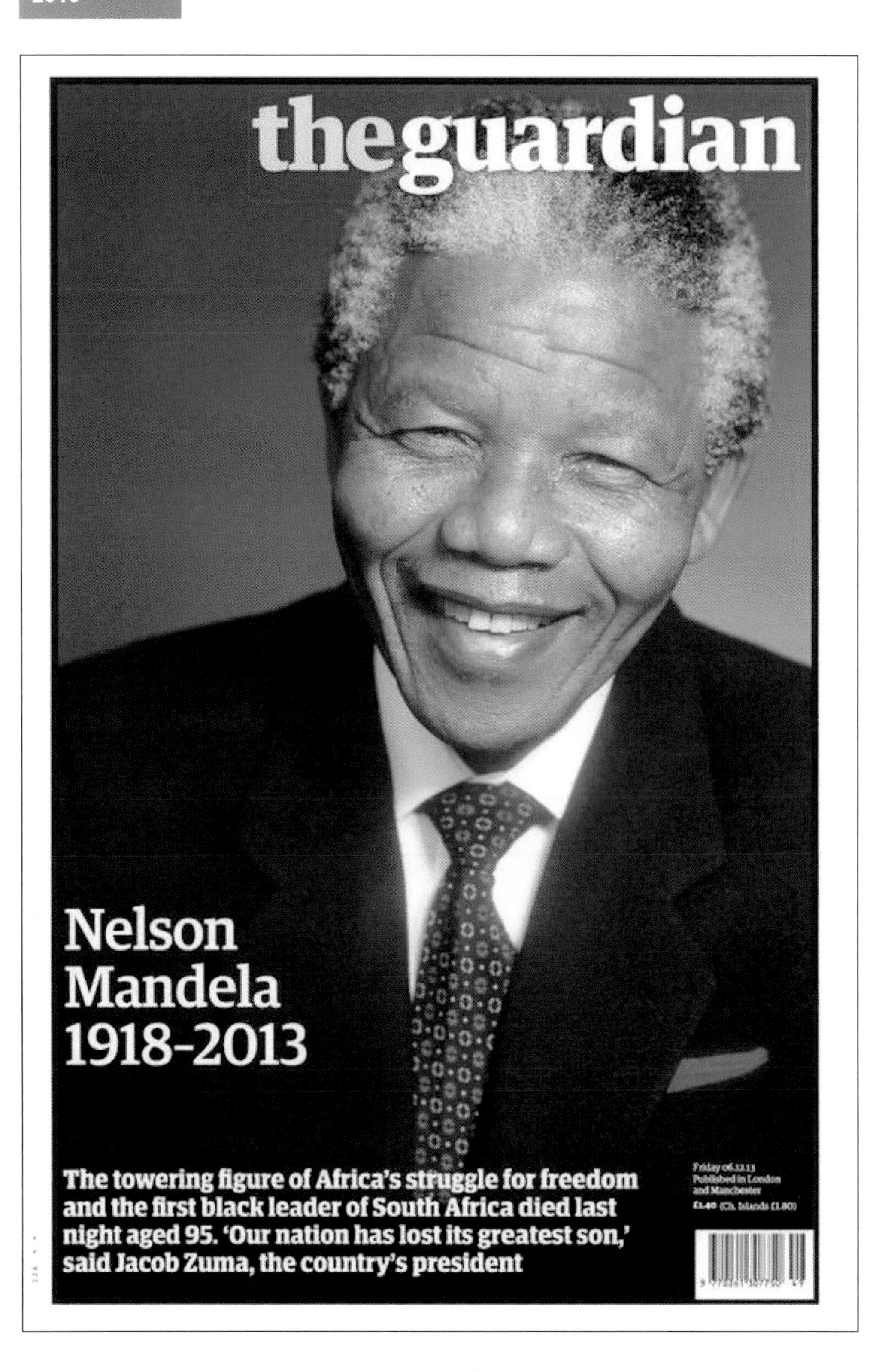

the guardian

Nelson Mandela 1918-2013

The towering figure of Africa's struggle for freedom and the first black leader of South Africa died last night aged 95. 'Our nation has lost its greatest son,' said Jacob Zuma, the country's president

Friday 06.12.13
Published in London and Manchester
£1.40 (Ch. Islands £1.80)

2013

Dammit! No matter how you dress this up it reeks of AGEISM! Pure, simple and totally unacceptable in the context of a community resource!
Sorry, but like I said, the stability penguins are strictly for the use of under 8's.
Get out of the way, would you love?

Why shouldn't you Trick or Treat as a 'Psycho in a straight-jacket'? First, because it reinforces a negative stereotype of people with mental illness. Second...
... because you've got nothing to hold your sweets with.

GAY MEN'S CHOIR
FAG HAG ORCHESTRA

The secret world of Isis brides

Special report g2

g2

"This was one of the strangest first nights I can remember'
Michael Billington

this section

£1.80 (Ch. Islands £2.20)
Thursday 25.06.15
Published in London and Manchester
theguardian.com

Winner of the Pulitzer prize 2014

theguardian

Exclusive How Clegg offered to resign as Lib Dem leader a year before the election, fought off a ham-fisted coup, and was told ...

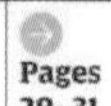

Pages 29-31

'You've got to carry this burden to the end'

Patrick Wintour and Nicholas Watt

Nick Clegg discussed resigning as Liberal Democrat leader in the wake of the party's humiliating reverses in the European and local elections in 2014, asking colleagues if he had become a barrier to the party's message being heard.

In a sign of the immense toll after four years in coalition, the former deputy prime minister experienced what his mentor and former Lib Dem leader Lord Ashdown described as the "darkest of the dark nights of the soul" and consulted senior colleagues about whether he should go.

Clegg made numerous phone calls to discuss his position a year before the general election in which his party was reduced from 56 seats to eight. He told one colleague: "If I believe - and I am very close to thinking it - I am the problem and not the solution, I have to stand to one side".

One senior Lib Dem who spoke to Clegg at the time said: "I told him, 'You don't have that luxury - this is your burden now, you have to carry it through to the election. Whether you believe that or not, it's tough titty. You can't now put this down until the election. You can do it after the election if you want, but you can't do it now."

Clegg was talked out of quitting by Lord Ashdown, his most likely successor Tim Farron, and almost all of his closest advisers, and was told to stay in post and fight to defend the cause of liberalism at the election in a year's time.

Farron was clear that Clegg should hang on. Farron, who is standing for the Lib Dem leadership after Clegg finally resigned on the day after the general election, said: "I just thought this could end up in a bloodbath and we're far better off sticking with the captain who has done nothing to deserve this."

Farron, who spoke to Clegg two days after the 2014 elections, recalled: "Nick was just distraught about everything and we knew the Euro [results] were going to come the day after, and he felt personally every single loss."

Ashdown said Clegg soon recovered. "It was astonishing the speed from which he moved from the darkest of the dark nights of the soul to utterly on form, utterly clear about what he was doing."

The revelation of the near resignation of Clegg and a subsequent attempt to force him out comes as part of a Guardian investigation into the collapse of the party that was in government just over a month ago. The Guardian report also reveals:

- The extent to which the former business secretary Vince Cable was fully aware of a plot to oust Clegg in the wake of the 2014 elections.
- The party's director of communications, Steve Lotinga, bluffed Cable on a ministerial visit in China to confirm that the business secretary's friend Lord Oakeshott was behind polls showing the party was heading for defeat in 2015.
- The former cabinet minister Ed Davey praises Clegg for strong leadership in difficult circumstances but criticised the party's "blancmange" manifesto.
- The leadership was rocked by the leaking by an aide to the former Scotland secretary Alistair Carmichael of a private civil service note which claimed that Nicola Sturgeon favoured David Cameron over

Continued on page 2 →

The Lib Dems' crushing defeat in the 2014 elections led Nick Clegg to consider his position Photograph: Murdo MacLeod

UK faces call to explain role in US drone killing in Yemen

Alice Ross and James Ball

The British intelligence agency GCHQ is facing fresh calls to reveal the extent of its involvement in the US targeted killing programme after details of a fatal drone strike in Yemen were included in a top-secret memo circulated to agency staff.

A leading barrister asked by the Guardian to review a number of classified GCHQ documents said they raised questions about British complicity in US strikes outside recognised war zones and demonstrated the need for the government to come clean about the UK's role.

The documents, provided to the Guardian by NSA whistleblower Edward Snowden and reported in partnership with the New York Times, discuss how a joint US, UK and Australian programme codenamed Overhead supported the strike in Yemen in 2012.

The files also show GCHQ and Overhead developed their ability to track the location of individuals - essential for the targeted killing programme - in Yemen and Pakistan. The legality of the US's lethal operations in both countries has been questioned by international lawyers and human rights groups.

The classified GCHQ documents revealed by the NSA whistleblower Edward Snowden discuss a joint US, UK and Australian programme

Jemima Stratford QC, who reviewed the Snowden documents for the Guardian, said: "Assuming the documents which I have seen are genuine, in my view they raise questions about the extent to which UK officials may have had knowledge of, or helped to facilitate, certain US drone strikes which were not carried out in the context of an international armed conflict.

"These documents underline why greater transparency as to UK official policies would help to ensure legality from a domestic and international law perspective."

Stratford published a legal opinion last year warning that UK intelligence support for lethal strikes outside traditional battlefields - such as Iraq and Afghanistan - was likely to be illegal. "In our view, if GCHQ transferred data to the NSA in the knowledge that it would or might be used for targeting drone strikes that transfer is probably unlawful," she wrote.

British officials and ministers follow a strict policy of refusing to confirm or deny any support to the targeted killing programme, and evidence has been so scant that legal challenges have been launched on the basis of single paragraphs in news stories.

Commenting on the new information, the Conservative MP David Davis said: "It's no good the government hiding behind its standard security line that they never comment on security matters. The phrase extrajudicial killing is a

Continued on page 12 →

2014

Twelfth Night, my arse! I'm taking the tree down when I'm good and ready, Brian, and to hell with your ridiculous superstitions.

UKIP! I ask you! Ugly, nauseating, discordant, unpleasant, loud and ill-conceived! In a word: WRONG!
And that's just their colour scheme.

Brian! Brian! Come here quickly! You've got to see this!!!
Nigel Farage isn't on TV.

2014

£1.60 (Ch. Islands £2.00)
Thursday 18.09.14
Published in London
and Manchester
theguardian.com

Newspaper of the year
Winner of the
Pulitzer prize

theguardian

Day of destiny

Scotland's **4,285,323** voters have **15 hours** to decide their country's fate

Ewen MacAskill
Travelling with a 'totally confident' Alex Salmond on the cusp of history

Close to the last
No campaign two points ahead in opinion poll on eve of vote

Guardian view
Some see a no vote as the dull choice, but it could be very different

2014

If we'd kept the book cases like I suggested you wouldn't have to show Brian how terrifically well read you are.

A HANDBAG!!!
ADOPTION SERVICES

Its an 'Emotion Ball', with different feelings written on it, and we pass it back and forth. I find it an invaluable tool to help children express themselves.

Suited, booted
The Apprentice in a fashion timewarp
g2
Rich, but super?
What history tells us about this incarnation of the über-wealthy
g2
John Lydon
'Ukip? They are a black hole for the ignorant to fall into'
g2

£1.60 (IR €1.80)
Wednesday 15.10.14
Published in London and Manchester
theguardian.com

Newspaper of the year
Winner of the Pulitzer prize

theguardian

Ebola: warning of 10,000 new cases a week

Health chief predicts rapid spread of virus with death rate running at 70%

Sarah Boseley
Health editor

The Ebola outbreak could grow to 10,000 new cases a week within two months, the World Health Organisation warned yesterday as the death toll from the virus reached 4,447 people, nearly all of them in west Africa.

Dr Bruce Aylward, the WHO assistant director general, told a news conference in Geneva that the number of new cases was likely to be between 5,000 and 10,000 a week by early December.

WHO's regular updates show that deaths have resulted from 4,447 of the 8,914 reported cases, but Aylward said that any assumption that the death rate was 50% would be wrong. He put the death rate at 70% because many deaths are not reported or recorded officially.

Where detailed investigations have been carried out, it was clear that only 30% of people were surviving, he said, adding that the figure was almost exactly the same number in the three hardest hit countries, Guinea, Liberia and Sierra Leone. "This is a high mortality disease in any circumstances but particularly in these places," said Aylward.

The grim forecast came as the first returning passengers from west Africa to London's Heathrow airport were asked to undergo temperature checks and questionnaires about their contacts with Ebola patients. The £9m screening exercise has been criticised by some experts, who say it will not pick up those who have the virus but are not yet symptomatic.

In the US, it emerged that a nurse who contracted Ebola had been given a blood transfusion from Dr John Brantly, who has recovered from the disease. The nurse, Nina Pham, was infected while caring for Thomas Duncan, who was taken ill on a visit from Liberia and died in Texas Health Presbyterian hospital, Dallas.

Brantly has donated blood for three Ebola patients, including Pham. "He's a doctor. That's what he's there to do. That's his heart," said Jeremy Blume, a spokesman for the non-profit medical mission group Samaritan's Purse, which Brantly was working for in Liberia. The WHO said plasma from people who had overcome Ebola, which contains antibodies against the virus, should be tried as a treatment, but it is hard to use outside the sophisticated healthcare settings of the west.

The UN Mission for Ebola Emergency Response, newly set up to coordinate the fight against the disease, has set targets to isolate 70% of suspected cases in west Africa and safely bury 70% of the dead within the next 60 days – described as the 70-70-60 plan.

It is a tough target, said Aylward, but if it takes 90 days rather than 60, "a lot more people will die who shouldn't and we will need that much more capacity on the ground to manage the caseload".

As the numbers continue to rise, the need for beds and health personnel to treat the sick will increase – and there is a serious shortage of trained and experienced people to lead the effort, according to Aylward.

Good training programmes are being put in place, particularly by the UK and the US, "but there is still the challenge of getting internationals on the ground who have expertise – in Ebola ideally".

For the past four weeks, about 1,000 new infections a week – including suspected, confirmed and probable cases – have come to light. Aylward said the WHO was concerned about the continued spread, especially in the capital cities of Sierra Leone, Guinea and Liberia – Freetown, Conakry and Monrovia.

"The virus is still moving geographically and escalating in the capitals," he said. Large treatment centres are taking a long time to build and staff and those that exist are full. A new strategy, which the UK is supporting in Sierra Leone, is to set up a lot of community care units with a handful of beds, where people can stay and get basic care rather than endangering their families at home, while waiting for a treatment centre bed. The units will also help people arriving

Continued on page 7 →

Power to the Chibok girls
Keys joins abduction protest

The US singer-songwriter Alicia Keys joins campaigners for Bring Back Our Girls outside the Nigerian consulate in New York yesterday on the six-month anniversary of the abduction of more than 200 schoolgirls by Boko Haram militants in the village of Chibok, Nigeria Photograph: Kathy Willens/AP

Blairs may have been terror target, court told

Ian Cobain

A man accused of plotting a terrorist attack on the streets of Britain may have been targeting the former prime minister Tony Blair and his wife, Cherie Booth, among others, the Old Bailey was told yesterday.

Erol Incedal was preparing to mount an attack that could have been against a small group of people or a single prominent person, the jury was told. Alternatively, he may have been planning an indiscriminate attack on a hotel, such as that mounted in Mumbai, India, in 2008.

Significant parts of the evidence presented in the case are being heard in secret, in what the prosecution has described as an exceptional case.

The former prime minister's home address was discovered in September last year after Incedal's black Mercedes car was pulled over for a road traffic matter and searched, said Richard Whittam QC, prosecuting. It was written on a piece of paper found inside the defendant's white Versace glasses case.

A listening device was placed in the car after the police search, and Incedal was subsequently recorded talking about the need to find an "illegal house", to avoid moving material around, the court was told. Incedal was also heard to tell his wife that he hated white people, and that he was "effed" if something had been found in his car.

Incedal, 26, a British citizen from south London, was arrested the following month when three police vehicles surrounded his Mercedes near Tower Bridge in London and armed officers shot out the vehicle's tyres. Incedal's passenger, Mounir Rarmoul-Bouhadjar, also 26 and from south London, was arrested at the same time. The court heard that after Incedal was handcuffed, arrested and asked for his address, he responded: "Are you going into my address with guns? My wife and kids are there."

Both men had SD memory cards wrapped in masking tape inside the cases of their Apple iPhones, Whittam said. On the cards were three files about bomb making. The jury heard that Rarmoul-Bouhadjar had admitted possession of the documents. He will be sentenced after Incedal's trial.

Incedal denies two terrorism charges. The first, brought under section 5(1) of the Terrorism Act 2006, states that between 1 February 2012 and 14 October 2013 he

Continued on page 3 →

Scientists treat Google Glass user for internet 'addiction'

Azeen Ghorayshi

Scientists have treated a man they believe to be the first patient with internet addiction disorder brought on by overuse of Google Glass.

The man had been using the technology for around 18 hours a day – removing it only to sleep and wash – and complained of feeling irritable and argumentative without the device. In the two months since he bought the device, he had also begun experiencing his dreams as if viewed through the device's small grey window.

The existence of internet addiction disorder linked to conventional devices such as phones and PCs is hotly debated among psychiatrists. It was not included as a clinical diagnosis in the 2013 update to the Diagnostic and Statistical Manual of Mental Disorders, the official reference guide to the field, and many researchers maintain that its effects are merely symptoms of other psychological problems.

But Dr Andrew Doan, head of addictions and resilience research at the US navy's Substance Abuse and Recovery Programme (Sarp) and co-author of the paper on the patient, published in the journal Addictive Behaviours, says people are clearly suffering from problems related to internet addiction, and it is only a matter of time before the research and treatments catch up. "People used to believe alcoholism wasn't a problem – they blamed the person or the people around them," Doan said. "It's just going to take a while for us to realise that this is real."

The man, who had been using Google Glass technology for around 18 hours a day, said he felt irritable and argumentative without the device

The patient – a 31-year-old US navy serviceman – had checked into the Sarp in September 2013 for alcoholism treatment. The facility requires patients to steer clear of addictive behaviours for 35 days – no alcohol, drugs, or cigarettes – but it also takes away all electronic devices.

Doctors noticed the patient repeatedly tapped his right temple with his index finger. He said the movement was an involuntary mimic of the motion regularly used to switch on the heads-up display on his Google Glass.

He said he was "going through withdrawal from his Google Glass", Doan explained, adding: "He said the Google Glass withdrawal was greater than the alcohol withdrawal he was experiencing."

He said the patient used Google Glass to improve his performance at work, where he was able to quicken his job of making inventories of convoy vehicles for the navy. By the time the patient checked into the facility, he was suffering from involuntary movements, cravings, memory problems and dreaming as if he was wearing the glasses. When he was not wearing them he felt irritable and argumentative.

Google declined to comment.

2014

Megan, meet my new student Emma. Emma can't hear enough of my social work anecdotes, can you Emma?
Emma?

You tell that bloke of yours that I don't pay good money for a skip just so he can sneak about and fill it with his crap when he thinks I'm not looking!
How dare you! Brian does no such thing!
ow.
SKIP HIRE

When I was a lad any elderly bloke who expressed an interest in sex was derided as a 'dirty old man'. Well now I am that bloke and, yes, I'm interested in sex!
Dammit, sex doesn't belong to the young, and I won't be dictated to by their ageist agenda. I still have physical desires, I still need erotic stimulation, I still crave the soft warmth of a woman's body!
Of course, she'd have to be at least thirty years younger, or it would be disgusting.

→ **MH370 mystery** Normcore **Le Tour**
Somerset floods **Gaza bombardment**
Isis **Kim Kardashian** Sochi Olympics
Bake Off hipster Rotherham scandal
Boko Haram Pharrell's hat **Toll road**

What happened next? Special edition g2

JK Rowling
Time to leave orphanages to Grimms' fairytales
→ journal

£1.60 (IR €1.80)
Thursday 18.12.14
Published in London and Manchester
theguardian.com

Newspaper of the year
Winner of the Pulitzer prize

theguardian

US decides to bring Cuba in from the cold

Obama and Castro pay tribute to Pope Francis for brokering historic detente

Dan Roberts Washington
Rory Carroll Los Angeles

Barack Obama and Raúl Castro thanked Pope Francis yesterday for helping broker a historic deal to begin normalising relations between the United States and Cuba, after 18 months of secret talks over prisoner releases brought a sudden end to decades of cold-war hostility.

The two presidents spoke simultaneously to confirm the surprise reversal of a long-running US policy of isolating Cuba, detailing a series of White House steps that will relax travel, commercial and diplomatic restrictions in exchange for the release of Americans and dissidents held in Havana.

Though a formal end to the US trade embargo requires legislation in Congress, both Obama and Castro said they believed such executive action was sufficient to significantly open up relations between the two countries and allow travellers and trade to flow relatively freely.

"In the most significant changes in our policy in more than 50 years, we will end an outdated approach that, for decades, has failed to advance our interests, and instead we will begin to normalise relations between our two countries," said Obama in an address from the White House cabinet room. "Through these changes, we intend to create more opportunities for the American and Cuban people, and begin a new chapter among the nations of the Americas."

President Castro, who took over from his brother Fidel in 2006, was only slightly less glowing, calling on Congress to formally lift the embargo but saying he believed Obama could substantially "modify its use".

"This decision of President Obama deserves the respect and acknowledgement of our people," said Castro in an address on Cuban television. "The progress attained in the interchange show it is possible to find solutions to many problems. As we have repeated we should learn the art of coexistence in a civilised manner with our differences."

The former defence minister welcomed the release of three Cuban intelligence agents held in the US and recalled a promise from Fidel that they would return. It was the only mention of his sibling, who retired in 2008 in poor health and remains largely out of the public eye.

Gerardo Hernández, Antonio Guerrero, and Ramón Labañino were among five Cubans jailed for spying on the US. An unnamed American spy said to have been responsible for revealing their identities and several other spy rings was also freed by the Cubans after nearly 20 years in prison, together with 53 political dissidents held by the government in Havana.

But the surprise breakthrough came principally after a phone call, said to have lasted 45 minutes to an hour, between Obama and Castro on Tuesday finalised the release of Alan Gross, a US government aid contractor held for five years in Cuba, which accused him of being a spy.

Gross, whom the US insists was released on "humanitarian grounds" unrelated to the exchange of spies, was flown back to Washington yesterday accompanied by the senators Patrick Leahy and Jeff Flake and the congressman Chris van Hollen.

As he was flown back to the US, it became clear that a far larger negotiation had been under way since private talks began in Canada in June 2013. This was supported closely by Pope Francis, who personally wrote to both leaders and hosted a crucial secret summit at the Vatican this autumn, which they credited with helping clinch the deal.

Nevertheless, the deal brought immediate and fierce criticism from Congress, where many senior figures in both sides believe Obama has struck a poor deal, with few concrete commitments toward political reform from Havana. "The White House has conceded everything and gained little in return," said the Florida senator Marco Rubio. "We are getting no commitment on freedom of the speech, elections, no binding commitment on opening up the internet or even the semblance of a transition to democracy."

The Democratic senator Bob Menendez, outgoing chair of the foreign relations committee, said: "President Obama's actions have vindicated the brutal behaviour of the Cuban government."

A full end to the US trade embargo of Cuba would require legislation in Congress, but the White House hopes that by using a series of executive actions to minimise its enforcement, it can provide a breakthrough that will encourage political reform in Cuba and soften political opposition in the US.

"I'm not expecting transformation of Cuban society overnight," said Obama "[But] we can't keep doing same thing for five decades and expect a different result." Castro, who has introduced economic reforms but retained tight political control, said Cubans had stayed loyal to the revolution and its social justice ideals despite numerous challenges and would continue to do so.

"We carry forward, given the difficulties, with the actualisation of our economic model to build a prosperous and sustainable socialism."

Pages 8-9 →

- Celebratory cigars in Havana, but protests from exiles in Miami after historic Cuba-US deal
- Headlines recall decades of hostility dating back to Fidel Castro's 1959 takeover
- The Vatican's role in hosting key talks
- Freed US prisoner who Havana had accused of spying hopes nations can 'get beyond belligerent policies'

The children of Peshawar
Families release pictures

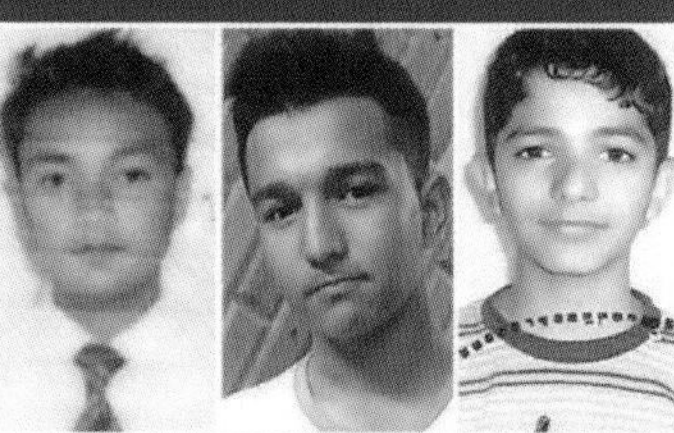

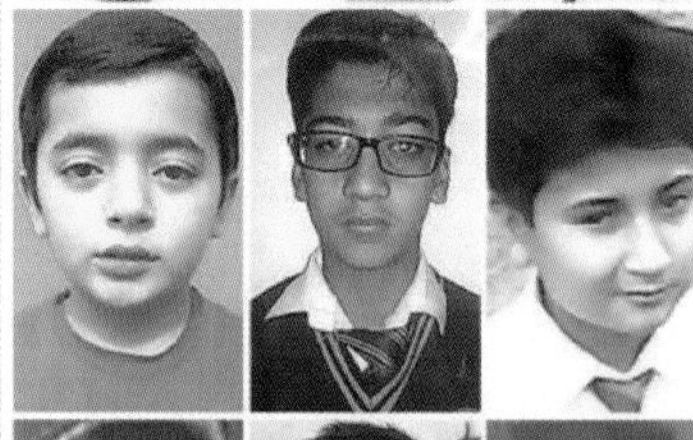

Pictures of some of the 148 victims of the Taliban attack on a school in Peshawar were released as Pakistan began three days of mourning

Mubenga jury not told of guards' racist texts

Robert Booth

An Old Bailey judge refused to allow a jury to hear about dozens of "grossly offensive and undoubtedly racist" text messages on the phones of two of the G4S security guards acquitted of killing Jimmy Mubenga because they did not have "any real relevance" to the trial.

One of the three defendants, Terrence Hughes, had 76 racist texts on his phone which abused black Africans, Asians and Muslims and were racist about immigration, but Mr Justice Spencer's decision meant that they were not put into evidence in the trial that ended on Tuesday.

A second defendant, Stuart Tribelnig, 39, also had racist texts on his phone and forwarded them to others, although they were fewer in number. One of the texts received read: "Fuck off and go home you free-loading, benefit grabbing, kid producing, violent, non-English speaking cock suckers and take those hairy faced, sandal wearing, bomb making, goat fucking, smelly rag head bastards with you."

Spencer said the texts had no bearing on the central issue of "whether the defendants deliberately held Mr Mubenga forward, head down, for a considerable period and whether [they] deliberately ignored his repeated protests that he could not breathe".

The six-week trial ended on Tuesday with the acquittal of Hughes, Tribelnig and Colin Kaler, who were accused of the manslaughter of the 46-year-old Angolan deportee.

No racist messages were found on Kaler's phone.

A coroner had previously found that Mubenga died of cardiorespiratory collapse as a result of restraint on a British Airways deportation flight in October 2010.

In legal argument during the trial, which can only now be reported, the prosecution unsuccessfully argued that the jury should know about the texts because they shed light on the guards' state of mind. But the defence lawyers said they would "release an unpredictable and uncorrectable cloud of prejudices".

Hughes's counsel had argued the texts do not prove he is racist and were a small fraction of a mass of offensive "jokes" on his phone "at the expense of almost every imaginable minority". He said there was no evidence of any ill will towards Mubenga. Tribelnig's counsel said that

Continued on page 2 →

2014

Why, Ray, this must be your new addition! There is nothing as cute as a mongrel puppy!
He's not a mongrel. He's a specialist cross-breed.
Half Beagle, half Labrador. They're called Beagradors. I paid £1,500 for him.
Really?
Fidiot.

Is that your idea of being helpful? What the hell does it mean, anyway?
I have walked around with my eyes open, my eyes have sent signals to my brain...
...So yes, in answer to your stupid sodding question, I have "LOOKED PROPERLY"!!
Here they are.
Thanks.

Ho ho ho! Merry Christmas!... ho ho ho.... Do not cross the white line....ho ho ho...children must be accompanied at all times!.... ho ho ho... I have been fully CRB checked....
SANTA'S GROTTO
THIS WAY

HSBC files

In 2003 a deal meant EU citizens with billions hidden in Swiss accounts had to stump up some tax. So HSBC began aggressively marketing a way to get round it

Fresh analysis of massive bank leak raises questions over how super-rich clients were saved a fortune in Switzerland

Pages 4-5

£1.60 (Ch. Islands £2.00)
Wednesday 11.02.15
Published in London
and Manchester
theguardian.com

Newspaper of the year
Winner of the
Pulitzer prize

theguardian

As tax officials face questions in the Commons on their dealings with HSBC, and whether they 'went easy' on the bank, files show how staff in its Swiss arm contacted clients to help them avoid tax

9 770261 307934 07

David Leigh
James Ball
Juliette Garside
David Pegg

HSBC's Swiss bankers aggressively marketed a device that would allow its clients to avoid a new tax introduced under a treaty Switzerland signed with the European Union, the HSBC files reveal.

The documents show for the first time that rather than acting as a passive party to the tax schemes of its clients, HSBC Suisse proactively contacted clients to market techniques that would have in effect sabotaged the tax treaty deal.

The bank's activities around the treaty, which related to the EU-wide European savings directive (ESD), form the core of the criminal investigations into HSBC's activities in France and Belgium, both launched due to the leaked documents.

The treaty, signed in 2003, allowed EU citizens to carry on hiding billions in anonymous Swiss accounts. But in return, Swiss banks such as HSBC's would be obliged to collect some tax from each of their secret customers.

This "withholding tax" on the income from savings interest, initially 15%, would then be handed over in bulk to Britain and other EU states, to compensate them for losses caused by anonymous tax dodgers.

But HSBC came up with a "vehicle" that enabled customers to avoid the tax by exploiting a key loophole in the treaty: ESD only applied to individuals' savings, not companies.

So the bank offered to transfer all of a customer's secret cash into a corporate account with no genuine trading activity.

This would technically belong to a shell company, set up in such secretive offshore havens as Panama or the British Virgin Islands. To be doubly sure, the company itself could, for a further price, even be registered as technically owned by an offshore trust or foundation, generally in the tiny principality of Liechtenstein, where details of the trust deed could be kept completely secret. The customer would be written in as the "beneficiary" of the trust, but not the legal owner of the company.

In return for several thousand pounds in annual fees to the bank, clients could carry on enjoying the secret fruits of their cash, tax-free. One such BVI sham entity was even wittily named Alter Ego Ltd.

According to the notes in the HSBC files, the Swiss bank's staff were remarkably explicit about the purpose of the scheme. Recording a conversation with a client, one banker noted: "ESD, for now will pay the 15%. We discussed the possibilities for not paying. She will think about it."

Scores of these "solutions" were marketed by Swiss bank managers throughout 2005, the files show.

In one case, a British businessman from Deal, in Kent, and his financial adviser turned up in Geneva in October 2005, two among many such visitors.

The English family had the equivalent of more than £1m hidden in FLAMINGO22, a numbered Swiss account. The bank now needed their signatures on a card, in order to purchase HSBC's latest tax-avoidance plan. The family signed up to the device in October 2005: "He ... asked us to transfer the ... current account balance to Future Investments and Development SA ... a Panamanian company that he, and his co-account holders, have arranged to be created in the context of ESD."

Another typical entry concerned a diamond dealer from Stoke Newington, north London. The client "will come to ZH [Zurich] on 15.06.2005 to establish a new company with Audina Treuhand and will sign new docs for a new a/c ... new BVI to be opened by Audina Treuhand as ESD solution", the bank noted.

The Liechtenstein agency, Audina, eventually set up a company called Derbe Ltd for him, not in the BVI but in Samoa, an even more obscure offshore jurisdiction. His personal account, codenamed 35666 ZZ, was emptied while Derbe Ltd by the following year held the equivalent of £770,000.

The terse leaked notes show HSBC clients passively accepting to be party to the new structures that were proposed by bankers: "Explained in details how ESD works; client accepted to establish a new offshore company for this purpose and signed all necessary documentation," one note records for a Hatton Garden jeweller with £15m.

Another example explains the structure the bank proposed for a British client: "A new Liberian company that we shall open for ESD reasons, as the client is Greek and UK resident ... transfer all assets from the named accounts to the Corp. account", it notes for a retail heiress with £8m.

'They were finding ways to get around the new rules introduced in 2005 to tackle tax evasion'
Richard Brooks

Other UK clients did much the same. "We discussed the ESD and they have decided to establish a ... Panamanian company, to establish an account and to receive these assets, and on which they will have individual signing power," one notes. "Long ESD discussion ... Client has signed a letter, to transfer assets from account to BVI company," states another.

Former tax inspector Richard Brooks said the files showed the bank was "actively encouraging them not to pay their tax bill ... finding ways to get round new rules introduced in 2005 to tackle tax evasion. It was saying, 'OK you don't have to play along with those, we've got another product for you that will allow you to carry on evading tax.'"

Other notes from the dozens of examples within the files show that clients from Greece, Spain and Israel were offered the same loophole, with companies incorporated in Liberia, Panama, the British Virgin Islands and other jurisdictions.

HSBC now faces criminal charges in Belgium and criminal investigation in France on the allegation that it "knowingly promoted serious and organised tax fraud" in connection with its ESD schemes.

The bank would not comment directly on the Guardian's evidence, but in a statement it has admitted various forms of wrongdoing occurred in its Swiss subsidiary. It said regulatory expectations had nowadays "dramatically shifted". Banks were now expected not to facilitate "any form of non-compliance with tax obligations". HSBC's current leadership, the bank said, "fully welcome and support these reforms".

The leaked files, which reveal how HSBC advised some clients on how to circumvent domestic tax authorities, were obtained through an international collaboration of news outlets, including the Guardian, the French daily Le Monde, CBS 60 Minutes, BBC Panorama and the Washington-based International Consortium of Investigative Journalists.

Sky and BT splash out £5bn for right to show live football

Owen Gibson
Chief sports correspondent

Premier League clubs are celebrating another huge windfall after competition between BT and Sky drove the overall value of TV rights to live football matches to more than £5.14bn over three seasons.

The enormous increase, to more than £10m per broadcast game - sparked by competition between the two media giants for so called "quad play" customers - immediately led to calls for more money to be redistributed to grassroots sport and for ticket prices to be slashed.

Even on a conservative estimate, the total amount raised once international rights are taken into account is likely to top £8.5bn over three years from 2016-17. The BBC has already agreed to pay £204m to retain the highlights. That would mean that even the bottom club in the Premier League would receive around £99m, while the champions would get £156m.

The deal for 168 live matches per season will come as music to the ears not only of clubs but also players and their agents. Previous increases in TV rights income have tended to lead to a commensurate increase in wages. It will also spark a renewed debate over whether the ever increasing television riches will further constrict the chances of homegrown players of making the grade and the ever growing gap between the Premier League and the Football League.

£99m **The amount likely to be earned by the club finishing bottom of the Premier League. The champions would be in line to receive £156m**

The two broadcasters will pay an average of more than £10m per match, an increase of 70% on the current £6.5m. The increase was driven by Sky's determination to hang on to the lion's share of matches, but it came at a price.

Sky has retained the rights to 26 first-pick matches, compared with 12 for BT, and it will also show Friday night football for the first time.

Having agreed to pay £897m for exclusive Champions League and Europa League action from next season in a three-year deal, BT executives were determined to retain enough Premier League broadcast rights to attract subscribers to their new paid-for offering.

Sky will pay more than £11m per game, up from the £6.6m it pays now. BT will pay £7.6m per game, up from the current £6.5m. The total income will make the Premier League the second most lucrative league in the world behind the NFL, overtaking Major League Baseball.

So important have the rights to live football become to the business plans of Sky and BT in their battle for television, broadband, mobile and phone customers that neither could afford to lose out entirely in the multi-billion pound auction.

Continued on page 6 →

2015

Brian!...You come back... to the dinner party....this instant!
No!....I won't!.. they're discussing... local schools....

Those were delicious home-made brownies, Skylark Moonbeam, but I think you should tell me what you put in them...

Because I'm Team Leader, that's why'. Now do you want to discuss the crisis in funding for office resources, or don't you?

Caitlyn Jenner

Olympic gold medal winner reveals the new her

p3

Me as 007? Absolutely

Jason Statham on why Bond needs to go big and go bad

g2

Of course, you can see Cameron as a genius

Frankie Boyle

g2

£1.80 (Ch. Islands £2.20)
Tuesday 02.06.15
Published in London and Manchester
theguardian.com

theguardian

Winner of the Pulitzer prize 2014

Shoot to kill: a US horror story

Special report
464 dead this year. 102 unarmed. Big disparity between numbers of black and white victims

Jon Swaine
Oliver Laughland
Jamiles Lartey
New York

Black Americans are more than twice as likely to be unarmed when killed during encounters with police as white people, according to a Guardian investigation, which found that 102 of 464 people killed this year in incidents with law enforcement officers were not carrying weapons.

An analysis of public records, local news reports and Guardian reporting found that 32% of black people killed by police in 2015 were unarmed, as were 25% of Hispanic and Latino people, compared with 15% of white people killed.

A database based on a five-month study of police fatalities in the US shows that police and federal law enforcement agencies are killing people at twice the rate calculated by the US government's official public record of police homicides. The database names five people whose identities have not been publicly released.

The Guardian's statistics include deaths after the police use of a Taser, deaths caused by police vehicles and deaths following altercations in police custody, as well as those killed when officers opened fire. They reveal that 29% of those killed by police, or 135 people, were black. Sixty-seven, or 14%, were Hispanic or Latino, and 234, or 50%, were white.

In total, 102 people who died during law enforcement encounters in 2015 have been unarmed. Of the 464 people counted by the Guardian, an overwhelming majority – 95% – were male.

The figures illustrate how disproportionately black Americans, who make up 13% of the country's total population according to census data, are killed by police. Steven Hawkins, the executive director of Amnesty International USA, described the racial imbalance as "startling". Hawkins said: "The disparity speaks to something that needs to be examined, to get to the bottom of why you're twice as likely to be shot if you're an unarmed black male."

Relatives of unarmed people killed by police in high-profile incidents during the past year – including Michael Brown, Eric Garner, Tony Robinson and Walter Scott – described the Guardian project as a breakthrough in the national debate over the use of deadly force by law enforcement.

"Giving this kind of data to the public is a big thing," said Erica Garner, whose father's killing by police in New York City last year led to international protests. "Other incidents like murders and robberies are counted, so why not police-involved killings? With better records, we can look at what is happening and what might need to change."

The initiative was also praised by a range of policing experts and by campaigners who are urging government authorities to make the official recording of fatalities mandatory for all 18,000 police departments and law enforcement agencies operating in the US. "It's troubling that we have no official data from the federal government," said Laurie Robinson, the co-chair of Barack Obama's taskforce on 21st century policing. "I think it's very helpful, in light of that fact, to have this kind of research undertaken."

32% The proportion of black people killed by police in the US in 2015, who were unarmed, compared with 15% who were white and unarmed

The Guardian website is publishing The Counted, a comprehensive interactive database monitoring all police killings in the US through 16 data points including age, location, gender, ethnicity, whether the person killed was armed and which policing agency was responsible. The Counted logs the precise location of each incident, providing the most detailed map of police killings published.

California, America's most populous state, has the highest total with 74 fatalities this year. However, an analysis of location data shows that Oklahoma, where 21 people have died through encounters with law enforcement, is the state with the highest rate of fatal incidents per person in 2015, at one fatality per 175,000 people over five months.

Over the weekend, Nebr- 11

Continued on page 11 →

A mother's nightmare 'I'm just a piece of paper on a desk'

Sallie Chapman's son was shot dead by police aged 18 in Virginia. Weeks later she is still in the dark about his death, reports **Jon Swaine**

At dawn on the last day of his life, William Chapman lay dozing on a battered black leather sofa. The living room television to which he'd fallen asleep buzzed beside him.

When his mother, Sallie, woke at 4.30am as she often does, she crept around her 18-year-old, checking all the windows and doors of their small slatted house in southern Virginia to get the peace of mind she needed for a couple more hours of sleep.

"And I tiptoed back into my room, because I didn't want to wake him," Sallie, 35, told the Guardian, tearful with regret that she hadn't whispered some final message.

Three hours later, William lay on the concrete of the car park of their local Walmart, to where he had raced along State Route 337 on his bike while Sallie dreamed. He had been shot dead by Stephen Rankin, a Portsmouth police officer who tried to arrest William for an alleged shoplifting incident in the store minutes earlier.

No-one told Sallie.

Later, after not hearing from her son by 7pm and learning from news reports that the man the radio said had been killed at Walmart was 18 years old, she called the police. "All that day, it just didn't feel right," she said.

A phone operator began creating a missing person's report, but William's name seemed to jolt her. Sallie was abruptly put on hold. Then a detective came on the line.

He asked for her address and said he had to visit. Sallie's stomach dropped. "Are you telling me you need to come to my house because my son is gone?" she asked. "Ma'am, I really need to come to your home," said the detective.

Five years earlier, when a police officer had arrived at their home, William was in the back seat of the squad car. He had been picked up walking to the mall along a tunnel that takes traffic underneath the Elizabeth River into downtown Norfolk, according to Sallie. "Cars and construction

Continued on page 11 →

2015

Oh my God! One second we're discussing how the banning of conkers in schools is indicative of a trend to overprotect children, the next....

I'll tell you the sort of country I want. The sort of country where women and children are respected....
where racial, sexual and cultural diversity are celebrated! Where animals are treated as friends not food!
A country where people can hold and promote whatever beliefs they choose, and where only the intolerant aren't tolerated!
First things first. Do we want 'Flight Plus Hotel' or just 'Hotel'?

So, it's unanimous! Mens' Group denounces pornography as exploitative objectification of women, and we will stop using it just as soon as anyone comes up with a viable alternative...

Marcy Borders
The tragic story of 9/11's 'Dust Lady'
g2
g2
Jeremy Corbyn couldn't be more British if he bled tea
Frankie Boyle
Giving it all away
Meet the extreme moral crusaders
the long read
£1.80 (Ch. Islands £2.20)
Tuesday 22.09.15
Published in London and Manchester
theguardian.com
theguardian

The revenge of Lord Ashcroft

Peer who had given the Tories £8m hoped for a senior job in Cameron's team after the 2010 election. When it didn't come, he went looking for revelations

Robert Booth

In January, four months before the general election, Lord Ashcroft assumed he was writing the prime minister's political epitaph. The Conservatives were heading for possible defeat and the former deputy party chairman, who helped propel David Cameron into Downing Street in 2010, told a book awards audience: "As most of you know we are writing the obit ... ah sorry David, the biography."

The billionaire Tory donor who has given his party £8m, felt strongly he had been spurned over a senior job and his joke suggested he might relish documenting Cameron's demise. But now instead of reading the last rites, Ashcroft's 592-page unofficial biography of the PM, Call Me Dave, is being published as Cameron heads triumphantly to his party's autumn conference in Manchester with a mandate for another five years in power. Rather than an obituary, Ashcroft's book bears the hallmarks of a revenge job, and a gory one at that.

Extracts published in the Daily Mail on Monday included claims the PM stuck "a private part of his anatomy" in a pig's mouth in a student initiation ceremony at Oxford's Piers Gaveston society, smoked pot and listened to Supertramp records in a student friends' room and allowed cocaine to be used at parties at his home. No 10 said it would not dignify Ashcroft's allegations by offering any comment.

Only a few years ago Ashcroft was inside Conservative Central Office using his fortune to help Cameron's party target dozens of crucial marginal seats. Today more revelations are promised about Cameron's "links to the Chipping Snorton set" in a serialisation understood to have cost the Mail over £50,000.

Ashcroft, whose company Political Holdings Limited is the majority shareholder in the book's publisher Biteback, has insisted his work would be objective and "not about settling scores". His co-author, Isabel Oakeshott, the former Sunday Times political editor, said yesterday: "If this was just a revenge job then Lord Ashcroft and I could have published it before the election and that could have caused far more damage."

But as well as the highly embarrassing claims about the prime minister, the Tory peer also sets out in the clearest terms yet his falling out with the Cameron.

He was in Gallipoli, Turkey, yesterday visiting first world war battlefields, but tweeted the foreword of his book which set out in detail how he was disappointed by Cameron's failure to offer him a significant job in government and implied that he thinks Cameron had broken his word. Ashcroft complained he was offered nothing more than a role as a junior whip in the foreign office, which he turned down.

One rival newspaper executive described the serialisation and its timing as a "declaration of war" by the paper's editor-in-chief Paul Dacre on David Cameron, who he believes is too soft on issues such as immigration and Europe. A spokesperson for the paper said it was "a hugely anticipated and important biography".

Even the authors concede the claim that has most captured public interest, about the pig, comes from only a single source. They said the claim was made by an MP who had pointed them towards another individual who supposedly had photographic evidence of the incident. However, this person never responded to their approaches. Ashcroft and Oakeshott concluded: "Perhaps it is a case of mistaken identity."

The book was begun in earnest three years into the coalition government when Ashcroft poached Oakeshott from the Sunday Times. "When this project was conceived," he said in the foreword, "it seemed possible the outcome of the 2015 election would mark the end of Cameron's tenure at Downing Street."

He gave a hint of his motivation when Cameron reshuffled his cabinet in July 2014 and William Hague stood down from his role. Ashcroft tweeted "Standing by to take over as foreign secretary."

The next day, he wrote: "No call from No 10! Ah well ... back to the biography of Cameron ... any anecdotes or stories to follow up welcome."

Oakeshott, who lives part of the time in the Cotswolds close to Cameron's constituency home, threw herself into the task. When the prime minister took part in the annual Great Brook Run, a mile-long race through a shallow stretch of the Evenlode river in January this year, she donned her running kit and followed him and his security detail through the icy water. Cameron said to her: "The things you'll do for this book." MPs and Cameron's former student friends were persuaded to talk on and off the record.

As they progressed, Ashcroft and Oakeshott gave teasing glimpses into their research. Cameron spent time in Russia before going to university and claimed when he appeared on Desert Island Discs that the KGB tried to recruit him. Was it this the writers were researching as they posed for pictures in front of the VIP terminal at Sochi International airport in Russia and outside the Moscow parliament? Either way, they seemed to be enjoying their work.

Oakeshott posted pictures inside a luxurious Moscow restaurant featuring

Continued on page 7 →

Lord Ashcroft donated millions to David Cameron's party before their relationship soured Photograph: Edward Lloyd/Alpha

PM quizzed over what he knew of tax status

Patrick Wintour and Rowena Mason

David Cameron was facing fresh questions from Labour and the SNP yesterday over allegations by the former Conservative deputy chairman Lord Ashcroft that the prime minister conspired to mislead the public before the 2010 election about his knowledge of Ashcroft's non-dom tax status.

Ashcroft, the millionaire businessman Tory donor and onetime key Cameron ally, has said he is not seeking to settle old scores, but also claimed in a long-awaited unofficial biography that Cameron took drugs at Oxford University and was involved in an initiation ceremony involving mock sex with a dead pig.

In the preface to his book Ashcroft asserts that he discussed his tax status with Cameron in 2009 in detail. He says Cameron was "fully aware of my status as a so-called non dom. Indeed we had a conversation about how we could delay revealing my tax arrangements until after the election."

But in March 2010, when Ashcroft's tax status was revealed in advance of a freedom of information disclosure, Cameron claimed to have known about it for only a month. A non-dom does not have to pay tax on overseas earnings in the UK, and Ashcroft had promised William Hague in 2000, as part of his receipt of a peerage, that he would take up "permanent residence in the UK".

The question about Cameron's knowledge of Ashcroft's tax status came after No 10 was forced to deny the most lurid allegation in the book. No 10 sources said yesterday afternoon that Cameron had not been involved in any initiation ceremonies at university and had not been a member of the decadent Piers Gaveston club at Oxford, where the initiation ceremony allegedly took place. Earlier,

Continued on page 7 →

2015

So, it's agreed. Short straw engages her in conversation giving the rest of us the chance to dash across the road and get to the next street.

Women's group? Yeah, right! Admit it, it's just an excuse to moan about me to your girlfriends.

I know that this will come as a shock to your male ego, Brian, but you are not the centre of my existence, the focus of my interest nor even the topic of my conversations.

Please moan about me.

Corbyn has taken a commanding lead in the Labour Party Leadership race! How about that!

Although I think I'd feel a lot more comfortable giving him my full and unequivocal support if he didn't stand any chance of winning.

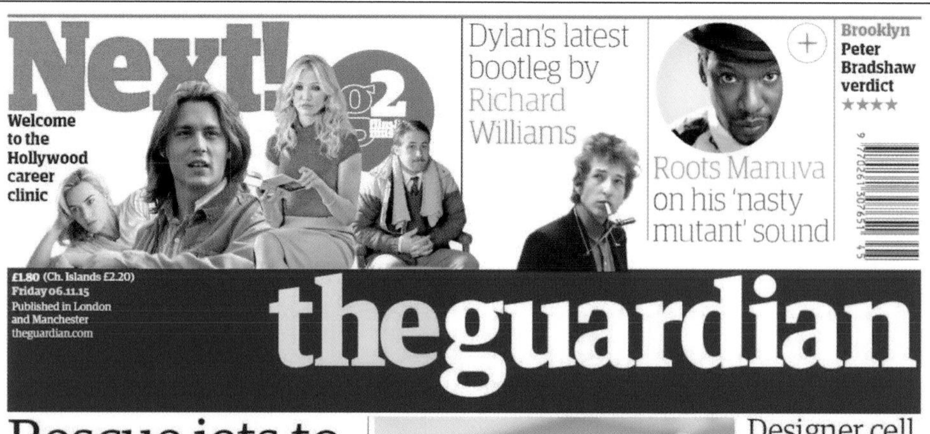
Next!
Welcome to the Hollywood career clinic
g2
Dylan's latest bootleg by Richard Williams
Roots Manuva on his 'nasty mutant' sound
Brooklyn
Peter Bradshaw verdict
★★★★

£1.80 (Ch. Islands £2.20)
Friday 06.11.15
Published in London and Manchester
theguardian.com

theguardian

Rescue jets to bring 4,000 out of Egypt

US backs British suspicion that bomb caused airliner crash

Rowena Mason
Political correspondent

Thousands of British tourists will fly back from Sharm el-Sheikh without their luggage today, after David Cameron gave the go ahead for air travel to resume with very tight security restrictions.

About 25 flights will take off from the Egyptian beach resort, clearing a backlog of up to 4,000 stranded holidaymakers, who had been due to return when the Foreign Office advised against all travel through the airport on Wednesday night.

The approval was given after a dramatic 24 hours in which Cameron decided to ground all planes because of Britain's concerns that the Russian plane that crashed over Sinai on Saturday could have been brought down by an Islamic State bomb.

The US last night appeared to back up that theory, saying "all indicators" were pointing to "an Isis attack with an explosive device in the airplane".

Cameron had earlier been warned during a 10-minute phone call with president Vladimir Putin not to jump to conclusions that the disaster was caused by terrorism.

Downing Street stressed it was a "cordial" exchange but a statement from the Kremlin said: "Vladimir Putin stressed that assessment of the causes of the crash should be based on the data that would become available in the course of the official investigation currently under way."

No 10 said there had been agreement with the Egyptian authorities on a additional security measures, including empty holds, extra screening on passengers and checks on their hand luggage.

Several airlines confirmed they would begin "rescue flights", including Thomson, Monarch and easyJet, which told passengers the luggage would be sent back by a government agency and returned by courier within the next seven days. British Airways and Thomas Cook also confirmed they will be resuming flights today.

A No 10 spokeswoman said the government was "working with the airlines to ensure there are arrangements in place to reunite passengers with their belongings as soon as possible". She said outbound flights from Britain to Sharm el-Sheikh remain suspended and the Foreign Office "continues to advise against all but essential travel by air to or from the airport".

The surprise move to suspend flights provoked diplomatic tensions with Russia and Egypt, whose president Abdel Fatah al-Sisi was coincidentally visiting Downing Street for talks. He was in the air on his way to London when Cameron took the decision without consulting Cairo.

Egypt's foreign minister called the move premature and unwarranted, but Sisi took a calmer tone yesterday, saying his country understood Britain's reasons for wanting to keep its citizens safe.

Staff at Sharm El-Sheikh airport have told the Guardian Britain had complained about lax security more than a year ago. A staff member said: "The British complained then that they weren't checking people enough. We should have done more. The security could have been improved by putting another scanner outside and updating the others."

At an appearance with Cameron, Sisi confirmed Britain raised concerns at least 10 months before the crash, but insisted the UK had been "happy" with improvements. Downing Street gave a slightly different account, saying there had been "good cooperation" and the Egyptians had responded to "some of the concerns" when UK experts were sent last year to make checks at the airport and resort where up to 20,000 Britons stay at any one time.

8 9 →

Continued on page 9 →

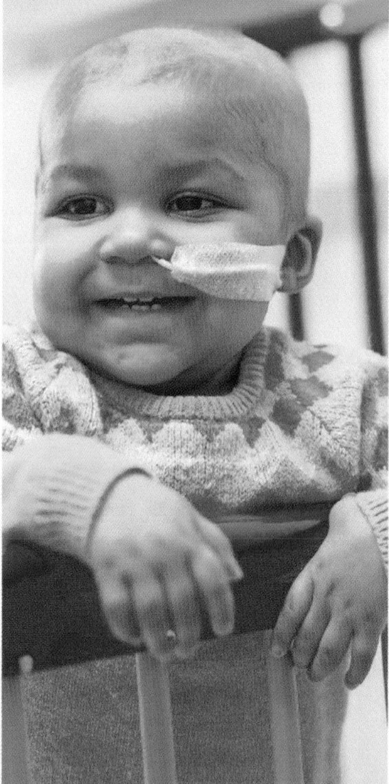
In June last year, Layla Richards was severely ill with cancer and given months to live. Now she is said to be doing well and cancer-free Photograph: Sharon Leese

Designer cell treatment of baby's cancer is world first

Ian Sample
Science editor

A baby girl with aggressive leukaemia has become the first in the world to be treated with immune cells that were genetically engineered to wipe out her cancer.

One-year-old, Layla Richards was given months to live after conventional treatments failed to eradicate the disease, but she is now cancer-free and doing well, a response one doctor described as "almost a miracle".

Specialists at Great Ormond Street hospital in London treated the girl two months ago and stressed that it could be more than a year before they know for sure whether the therapy has cured the disease or simply delayed its progression.

"We have only used this treatment on one very strong little girl, and we have to be cautious about claiming this will be a suitable treatment option for all children," said Waseem Qasim, professor of cell and gene therapy at University College London's Institute of Child Health, and a consultant immunologist at Great Ormond Street. "But this is a landmark in the use of new gene engineering technology and the effects for this child have been staggering."

Layla was born a healthy 7lb 10oz in June last year, but three months later developed a fast heartbeat, went off her milk and cried a lot. Doctors suspected nothing more than a stomach bug, but blood tests revealed she had infant acute lymphoblastic leukaemia (ALL).

Layla went into intensive care at the hospital with what doctors described as the most aggressive form of ALL they had seen. Sujith Samarasinghe, one of the doctors who cared for her, said while cure rates are generally high for the disease, only about 25% of children survive the most aggressive forms. Layla began chemotherapy the next day, then had a bone marrow transplant to replace her damaged blood cells. Despite several rounds of intensive chemotherapy, Layla still had leukaemia cells in her body when the transplant was performed, and seven weeks later the disease returned. Soon after, doctors told the family there were no

Continued on page 3 →

Most ministers not told of mass surveillance, Clegg reveals

Patrick Wintour
Political editor

Most members of the cabinet were never told that the security services had been secretly harvesting data from the phone calls, texts and emails of a huge number of British citizens since 2005, Nick Clegg has disclosed.

Clegg says he was informed of the practice by a senior Whitehall official soon after becoming David Cameron's deputy in 2010, but that "only a tiny handful" of cabinet ministers were also told - likely to include the home secretary, the foreign secretary and chancellor.

He said he was astonished to learn of the capability and asked for its necessity to be reviewed. The former deputy prime minister's revelation in the Guardian again raises concerns about the extent to which the security services felt they were entitled to use broadly drawn legislative powers to carry out intrusive surveillance and keep this information from democratically elected politicians.

The government finally admitted on Wednesday that the mass surveillance of British citizens began in 2001 after 9/11 and was stepped up in 2005, using powers under national security directions largely hidden in the 1984 Telecommunications Act. It is not known if government law officers sanctioned the use of the act in this way, but it appears the intelligence and security committee responsible for parliamentary oversight was not informed, adding to the impression of a so-called deep state operating outside the scrutiny of parliament.

Nick Clegg said he was astonished when he learned of the extent of secret data harvesting and had asked that its necessity be reviewed

Clegg writes: "When I became deputy prime minister in 2010, I was the leader of a party that had been out of government for 65 years. There were a lot things that we had to relearn, and a lot that was surprising and new. When a senior official took me aside and told me that the previous government had granted MI5 direct access to records of millions of phone calls made in the UK - a capability that only a tiny handful of senior cabinet ministers knew about - I was astonished that such a powerful capability had not been avowed to the public or to parliament and insisted that its necessity should be reviewed.

"That the existence of this previously top secret database was finally revealed in parliament by the home secretary on Wednesday, as part of a comprehensive new investigatory powers bill covering many other previously secret intelligence capabilities, speaks volumes about how far we've come in a few short years."

He also contends that when the revelations of Edward Snowden hit, "the knee-jerk response within government was

Continued on page 5 →

Writer's warning
Arundhati Roy returns award in protest at Hindu violence in India
Page 26 →

2015

You know, guys, I think it's about time we got another picture of Ian Duncan Smith.

No Clare tonight?
She's out at her Women's Group Christmas Evening. Sitting around in a circle communing with their inner goddesses, or some such bollocks, is my guess.
RIDE THE MALE CHAUVINIST PIG!

So, it's agreed. If the BDSM experience becomes actually unbearable you will use your safeword "offside".
"I scowl with frustration at myself in the mirror. Damn my hair..."
OFFSIDE! OFFSIDE!
FIFTY SHADES OF GREY

Panama Papers

Iceland

PM steps aside over claims he hid millions in offshore firm

Page 5 →

Leaked files show that Gianni Infantino signed off on deals linked to the unfolding scandal that brought down Sepp Blatter

Fifa chief elected to clean up game is dragged into corruption crisis

£1.80
Wednesday 06.04.16
Published in London and Manchester
theguardian.com

theguardian

Owen Gibson

The new head of world football has been caught up in the sport's corruption scandal because of documents that have been revealed by the Panama Papers leak.

Files seen by the Guardian will raise questions about the role Fifa's president, Gianni Infantino, played in deals concluded when he was director of legal services at Uefa, European football's governing body.

According to records, Uefa concluded offshore deals with one of the indicted figures at the heart of an alleged "World Cup of fraud" despite previously insisting it had no dealings with any of them.

The emergence of the contracts from 2003 and 2006, which were co-signed by Infantino, link Uefa for the first time to one of the companies involved in the huge unfolding scandal that has brought down former Fifa president Sepp Blatter.

Uefa has denied any wrongdoing by any of its officials or any other marketing partner. It said the contracts were all above board. Fifa has previously insisted Infantino had no dealings with any of the officials currently under investigation - or their companies.

Last night, Infantino released a statement in which he said: "I am dismayed and will not accept that my integrity is being doubted by certain areas of the media, especially given that Uefa has already disclosed in detail all facts regarding these contracts."

The disclosures are based on the leak of 11m documents from the files of the offshore financial law firm Mossack Fonseca, which were obtained by Süddeutsche Zeitung and shared by the International Consortium of Investigative Journalists with the Guardian and other news organisations.

Infantino is the Swiss-Italian former Uefa secretary general who won the race to succeed the disgraced Blatter in February. The files show that in 2006, when he worked at Uefa, the organisation sold the rights for broadcasting its club competitions in South America.

Thousand dollars
Profit Cross Trading made after buying a TV rights package from Uefa for $111,000 and selling it for $311,000

200

'Neither Team nor Uefa had any reason to believe that there was anything suspicious ...'

The rights to the Champions League, the Uefa Cup and the Super Cup were acquired by an Argentinian company called Cross Trading. Cross Trading immediately sold on to broadcaster Teleamazonas for up to three or four times the amount paid for them. The contracts covered the period from 2003-06 and from 2006-09.

Cross Trading is a subsidiary of a company called Full Play, which is owned by Hugo Jinkis. Last year, in unrelated proceedings, Jinkis was alleged by US prosecutors to have handed over millions of dollars in bribes and kickbacks to football executives to obtain and retain media and marketing rights.

Jinkis, along with his son Mariano, is under house arrest in Argentina.

Jinkis's involvement in the deals with Uefa from a decade ago are set out in the Panama Papers. Cross Trading signed a deal with Uefa's broadcasting and marketing partner, called Team. Infantino's name appears on the contract as Uefa's director of legal services.

According to the contracts, Cross Trading, which was registered in the tiny South Pacific tax haven of Niue, agreed to pay $111,000 for the exclusive rights to broadcast Champions League football in Ecuador between 2006-07 and 2008-09.

In the covering letter containing the fully executed contracts, Uefa states: "Congratulations on joining the family of broadcast partners for the 2006-2009 Uefa Champions League seasons ... we look forward to working with you!"

Ecuadorian broadcaster Teleamazonas then paid Cross Trading $311,170 for the rights to the Champions League.

Uefa insisted the TV rights deals with Cross Trading were all above board and it could not have known when they were signed in 2003 and 2006 that Jinkis would be involved in the scandal a decade later.

It said the rights were sold "pursuant to an open, competitive, tender process", and that the offer from Teleamazonas/Cross Trading was 20% higher than the next best bid.

"There is no suggestion whatsoever of any Uefa official or marketing partner taking any form of bribe or kickback, whether in relation to this tiny deal, or any other commercial transaction," it said.

Uefa added: "The TV contract in question was signed by Gianni Infantino since he was one of several Uefa directors empowered to sign contracts at the time. As you will have observed, the contract was also co- 2 7 →

Continued on page 7 →

841.2

Million pounds
The losses Fifa revealed in last month's financial report which it blamed on deserting sponsors and spiralling legal fees

Cameron feels the heat over links to father's offshore fund

Ewen MacAskill
Rowena Mason
David Pegg
Holly Watt

David Cameron was left dangerously exposed last night after repeatedly failing to provide a clear and full account about links to an offshore fund set up by his father, as the storm over the Panama Papers gathered strength in the UK and elsewhere around the world.

The prime minister and his office have now offered three partial answers about the fund set up by his father Ian Cameron, who died in 2010, which avoided ever paying tax in Britain.

The key unanswered question is whether the prime minister's family stands to gain in the future from Ian Cameron's company, Blairmore, an investment fund run from the Bahamas.

After Downing Street said on Monday that the fund was a "private matter", Cameron was asked yesterday about it by a journalist, during a visit to Birmingham. Cameron replied: "I own no shares, no offshore trusts, no offshore funds, nothing like that. And, so that, I think, is a very clear description."

He dodged the key part of the question about whether he or his family stood to benefit from the arrangement.

Having failed to satisfy reporters Downing Street issued a further statement saying Cameron's wife and children also did not benefit from offshore funds. But again the main question about the future was left unanswered.

Labour's leader, Jeremy Corbyn, who earlier in the day had called for an independent investigation, said: "Three times Downing Street has been asked to provide a full and comprehensive answer. The public has a right to know the truth.

"We need to know the full extent of the links between Britain and the web of tax avoidance and evasion revealed by the Panama Papers at all levels."

The leak of 11.5m files from the Panama-based legal firm Mossack Fonseca continued to create uproar and upheaval around the world.

The documents were leaked to the German daily Süddeutsche Zeitung, which shared them with the Washington-based International Consortium of Investigative Journalists, the Guardian, BBC and other media organisations. The latest developments include:

- The resignation of Iceland's prime minister, Sigmundur Davíð Gunnlaugsson, who quit after outrage over his family's offshore investments.
- Barack Obama's call for tax evasion to be tackled worldwide in the wake of the publication of the Panama Papers
- An announcement by the German justice minister, Heiko Maas, that Germany planned to introduce a national transparency register to make offshore companies disclose owner identity
- A statement from France's finance minister, Michel Sapin, saying Panama would again be blacklisted as an uncooperative tax haven
- A decision by Pakistan's prime minister, Nawaz Sharif, to set up an independent judicial commission to determine whether his family was involved in anything illegal through ownership of several offshore companies
- The revelation that the president of the UAE, Sheikh Khalifa bin Zayed Al Nahyan, had secretly built one of the single biggest offshore property empires in Britain, which included dozens of central London properties worth more than £1.2bn, bought through offshore companies supplied by Mossack Fonseca.

Ian Cameron
Downing Street seeks to distance the PM from revelations about his father's investment

The row embroiling Cameron picked up pace in the morning when Corbyn, responding to No 10's description that the matter was private, told reporters: "Well, it's a private matter insofar as it's a privately held interest. But it's not a private matter if tax is not being paid. So an investigation must take place, an independent investigation, unprejudiced, to decide whether or not tax has been paid."

Continued on page 7 →

12 A

2016

For crying out loud, Clare, I wish you'd stop bringing your work home with you!

Social workers' senses are more finely tuned than those of the general public....

Take this home visit: The sight others see would be one of deprivation. We'd also see the inequality that underlies it. The sound they'd hear is discord, we'd hear the cry for help beneath.

And the smell?'
Sorry, that's me. Lentil bake for lunch.

Clare! Have you heard what happened to Becca from the Elderly Client Unit? She was with a client in a wheelchair, who she left for one second..

...to press for the lift, but she forgot to put the brake on and Mr. Hobbs rolled off down the stairs, and he only stopped three flights on because he hit a party of visiting dignitaries coming up in the opposite direction!

I appreciate it, Megan but I'm afraid there are some days when nothing can cheer me up.
Well, I tried.

Panama Papers

HSBC
Former chief tried to avoid tax on house
Page 4 →

Putin
'It is a bid to destabilise Russia'
Page 4 →

Watchdog
Banks told to disclose links with law firm
Page 5 →

£1.80 (tbd/£2.20) £2.20)
Friday 08.04.16
Published in London and Manchester
theguardian.com

theguardian

Cameron finally admits: yes, I benefited from tax-avoiding offshore fund

After three days and four partial denials PM says he did have shares in his father's Panama investment fund

Robert Booth
Holly Watt
David Pegg

David Cameron has finally admitted he benefited from a Panama-based offshore trust set up by his late father. After three days of stalling and four partial statements issued by Downing Street, he confessed that he owned shares in the tax haven fund, which he sold for £31,500 just before becoming prime minister in 2010.

In a specially arranged interview with Robert Peston of ITV News he confirmed a direct link to his father's UK-tax-avoiding fund, details of which were exposed in the Panama Papers revelations in the Guardian this week.

Admitting "it has been a difficult few days", the prime minister said he had held the shares together with his wife, Samantha, from 1997 and during his time as leader of the opposition. They were sold in January 2010 for a profit of £19,000.

He paid income tax on the dividends but there was no capital gains tax payable. He said he sold up before entering No 10 "because I didn't want anyone to say you have others' agendas or vested interests".

The interview appeared unlikely to end scrutiny of Cameron's tax affairs. Labour MP John Mann, a member of the Treasury select committee, said the prime minister should resign and had "covered up and misled".

Cameron admitted he did not know whether the £300,000 he inherited from his father had benefited from tax haven status, because part of his estate was based in a unit trust in Jersey. "I obviously can't point to the source of every bit of money and Dad's not around for me to ask the questions now," he said.

It was the fifth explanation in four days given by Cameron and his aides about the benefit he and his family have enjoyed from the offshore fund. No 10 initially insisted it was a "private matter" but Cameron then said he had "no shares, no offshore trusts, no offshore funds".

His spokesman later clarified: "The prime minister, his wife and their children do not benefit from any offshore funds."

Downing Street then said there are no offshore funds or trusts they will benefit from "in future", leaving questions about the past.

In his first interview after days of stonewalling, Cameron was questioned on whether there was any conflict of interest between his father setting up the Panama-based Blairmore Investment Trust, which did not have to pay UK tax on its profits, and his professed policy to crack down on aggressive tax avoidance.

"Roles have changed, culture has changed," he said. "And I welcome that. I want to be as clear as I can about the past, about the present, about the future, because frankly, I don't have anything to hide."

Earlier Cameron had refused to take questions from the press while campaigning in Exeter for Britain to stay in the EU. A student managed to tell him: "I am very interested in what the collective EU states could do to combat tax avoidance - something you have personal experience of."

Speaking about his personal wealth, Cameron told Peston: "In all of this I've never hidden the fact that I'm a very lucky person who had wealthy parents, who gave me a great upbringing, who paid for me to go to an amazing school. I have never tried to pretend to be anything I am not. But I was keen in 2010 to sell everything - shares, all the rest of it - so I can be very transparent. I don't own any part of any company or any investment trust or anything else like that."

He also said it was a "misconception" that Blairmore was set up to avoid tax. "It wasn't," he said. "It was set up after exchange controls

Continued on page 5 →

Communist party
'Please self-inspect and delete all content related to the 'Panama Papers' leak'
Page 4 →

Looted art

Stolen by the Nazis, now hidden offshore

A Modigliani at the centre of a legal dispute is currently the property of a gallery corporated in Panama

Holly Watt
David Pegg
Juliette Garside

The law firm at the centre of the Panama Papers leak helped a New York art gallery defend itself over a claim about a Nazi-looted artwork after the original owner's descendant launched a legal battle for its return, documents reveal.

The case involves a $25m (£18m) Modigliani painting taken from Paris when the Germans marched into the city in 1940 and the role played by the law firm, Mossack Fonseca, as the family who say it is theirs fought for its return.

The story of the theft of Modigliani's 1918 work, Seated Man With a Cane, and its re-emergence combines the injustice of art seizures during the second world war with the smoke and mirrors of 21st-century offshore tax havens.

The descendant claims the painting was owned by Oscar Stettiner, a Jewish gallery owner in Paris who fled weeks before the Nazis entered the city. He managed to get his wife and children to the Dordogne but had to leave his collection behind. The artwork was taken by the Nazis, and by the time the Stettiners are thought to have started searching for it after the war, the painting had vanished.

In 2008, the Modigliani allegedly resurfaced at Sotheby's in New York. It was consigned to the auctioneers by the Helly Nahmad Gallery - run by the heir of one of the best-known art dealers in the world.

David Nahmad and his brother Ezra had built up an art-dealing dynasty that has made hundreds of millions buying and selling works by some of the world's greatest artists. David's son Helly - a playboy - spent much of his time in high-stakes poker games before he was jailed in 2014 for running an illegal gambling business from his Trump Tower apartment.

Meanwhile, Stettiner's only remaining heir, his grandson Philippe Maestracci, was convinced that the Modigliani going up for auction was his family's missing painting - and with questions raised about its provenance, the artwork failed to sell.

Maestracci then began a quest to reclaim the painting from the gallery, which fought his efforts with a surprising argument: it said it had never owned the artwork in the first place. Instead, it claimed the painting had been bought by International Art Center SA, a company set up in Panama in 1995, arguing that this meant the gallery could not be sued for the Modigliani's return in New York.

Now the Panama Papers - a cache of 11.5m documents leaked from the Panamanian law firm - raise new questions about the case. The papers mention dozens of paintings by some of the greatest artists in history. Among documents referring to works by artists ranging

Continued on page 2 →

↑ **Homme Assis (Appuyé sur une Canne)** by Amedeo Modigliani was painted in 1918 Photograph: Christie's/Corbis

18
Million pounds
Value of the work at the centre of the dispute. It disappeared from Paris in 1940

2016

Oh no, not Michael Gove again! I've seen more than enough of him recently, so would you mind handing me the remote control?
Not at all.

FAMILY FUN DAY
Look, forget who did or didn't support the anti-Sats strike and just do the face painting, OK?
CAKES
GUESS THE BEANS
SCAB
SCAB
SCAB
SCAB

Wow, Clare, have you been watching that new Scandi crime series..?
Can I stop you there, Megan.
We are in a 'Death Cafe', set up for the specific purpose of providing a space in which people can share their beliefs, feelings and experiences of society's greatest taboo.
Oh, I see.
Man, I hope I don't die before the end of that new Scandi crime series...

Glastonbury preview
g2 film&music
Coldplay
'It will be magical'
Exclusive interview
New Order
Best ever festivals
Anton Yelchin
The great Hollywood everyman
Reviews
Peter Bradshaw
Alexis Petridis
£2.00 (Ch. Islands £2.40)
Friday 24.06.16
Published in London and Manchester
theguardian.com
theguardian

Party leaders reach out to divided nation after bitter EU referendum

- Huge turnout estimated at 83% throughout UK
- Evidence that undecided voters shifted to remain
- PM to assure nation he listened to valid concerns

Anushka Asthana
Heather Stewart

David Cameron and Jeremy Corbyn are preparing to reach out today to the millions of British people who voted to leave the EU, as they seek to heal the wounds of a bitterly fought referendum that has divided the nation.

An opinion poll published at 10pm yesterday suggested that undecided voters had shifted towards backing the prime minister's call for Britain to remain a member of the European project in the final days of the battle. The YouGov poll showed remain on 52%, leave on 48%, with turnout a remarkable 83%.

The Ukip leader, Nigel Farage, also suggested in an interview that remain had "edged it".

Last night, 84 Conservative MPs, two-thirds of those who publicly backed the campaign to leave the EU, pledged their support to the prime minister, whatever the outcome of the referendum.

However, it still appeared to be a fiercely close fight that would inevitably leave millions disappointed, with commentators warning of a need to mend a fractured nation.

Early indications appeared to suggest high turnouts both in areas likely to strongly back remain and those where communities were thought to favour leave. Some voters, particularly in London, took to social media to complain that they might miss out on the opportunity to vote after severe weather conditions disrupted the transport system.

Labour's deputy leader, Tom Watson, said Cameron's first job should be to confront the anxieties of voters who had backed Brexit, however Britain votes. "Whatever the outcome, it seems to me that the country is more divided at the end of this process than at the beginning, and it's beholden on political leaders to listen to voters, and respond to the concerns they've raised.

Labour will be doing that, and we very much hope that the prime minister will do that too."

Cameron will deliver a speech this morning that will attempt to reach out across the divide and reassure the millions of people who voted against him that his government has listened to their concerns over immigration, public services and democracy. The prime minister, who had dinner with his family before spending the night in Downing street with close advisers, is hoping to hail a remain result, before making a pledge to rebuild alliances with the Conservative party's grassroots and the dozens of MPs who campaigned against him. He will also promise to take his mandate back to Europe and insist that British voters want further reform if Britain votes to remain.

In the case of Brexit, there will be calls from out campaigners for Cameron to remain in position, as he has suggested he will, in order to secure stability as negotiations for an exit from the EU begin.

Labour will also unveil a charm offensive to win back Brexit-supporting voters in the party's working-class heartlands, after the electoral battle also exposed widespread frustration about immigration, as well as jobs and living standards.

Continued on page 3 →

A voter leaves a polling station in Chelsea, west London
Photograph: Toby Melville/Reuters

EU referendum

Inside
How Britain went to the polls – and what might happen next
Pages 2-7 →

2016

'Mansplaining'? What the hell is 'mansplaining'?
Brian?
This is a sodding trap, right?
The Guardian
The Guardian

It was good of his Facebook friends to show up.

Seriously, Brian, if you are going to behave like this every time you go over a line I'm going to take that Mindfulness colouring book away.

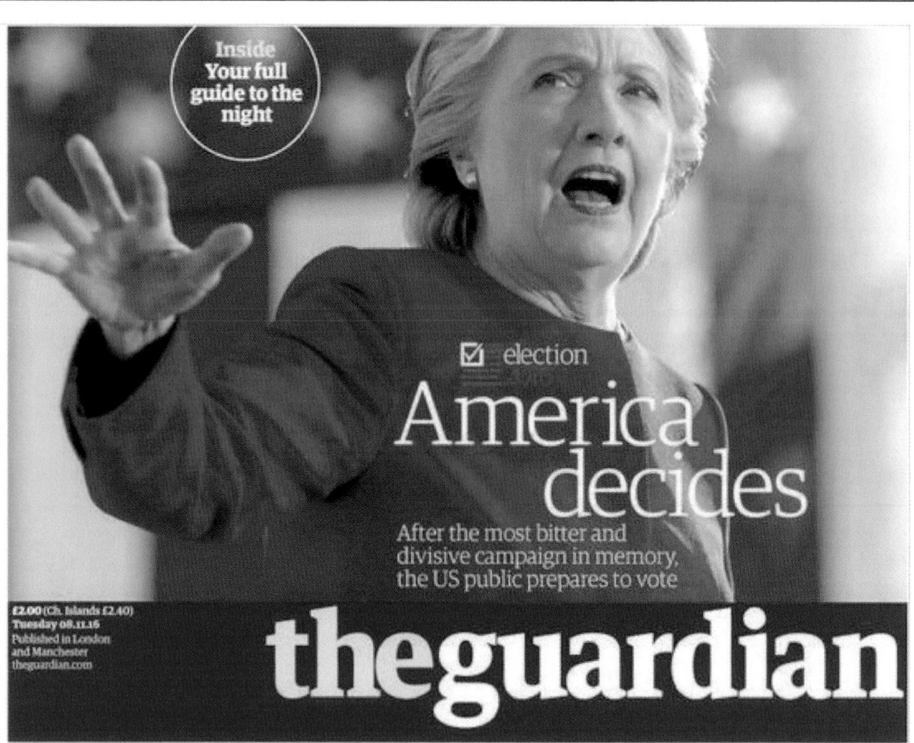

Inside
Your full guide to the night
election
2016

America decides

After the most bitter and divisive campaign in memory, the US public prepares to vote

£2.00 (Ch. Islands £2.40)
Tuesday 08.11.16
Published in London and Manchester
theguardian.com

theguardian

Presidential rivals in final push as polls give Clinton the edge

Dan Roberts New York
Ben Jacobs Florida
Sabrina Siddiqui Pennsylvania

American voters will deliver their verdict today on one of the starkest choices in political history after Hillary Clinton and Donald Trump spent the last hours of a bitter campaign focused on the country's deep economic divide.

Democrats gained a late confidence boost yesterday as a final series of national opinion polls confirmed a small but steady lead for Clinton ahead of today's election. The latest aggregate poll showed Clinton slightly widening her lead to 47.2% with Trump on 44.2%.

Early voting numbers point already to a record turnout among Latino voters stirred into action by Trump's anti-immigration rhetoric, boosting Clinton's chances.

But the continued risk of an upset that would send shockwaves around the world was underlined by state-level polling suggesting several possible paths to victory also remain for Trump. He hopes to galvanise white working class anger over jobs and trade in the traditionally Democratic rustbelt, though he also needs an almost clean sweep of battleground states such as Florida and North Carolina to win outright.

Sensing possible danger, the Clinton campaign poured last-minute resources into the industrial midwest, a region where she struggled against a similar anti-establishment surge for Bernie Sanders during the primary election season. Both Clinton and Barack Obama held afternoon rallies in Michigan and were due to finish the night on stage together in Philadelphia with Bruce Springsteen, an emblem of blue-collar angst.

Trump also headed to Michigan, where he planned to end the night, before returning to New York where he will vote today.

Both presidential candidates planned to watch tonight's election returns in New York, prompting the city to stage the largest election day police deployment in its history, officials said yesterday.

More than 5,000 police officers will be stationed in the city. "We know that the eyes of the world will be on New York City," the mayor, Bill de Blasio, said yesterday. "We have an obligation, not only to the people in the city but to this country, to make sure that tomorrow, all through the day and particularly tomorrow night, goes smoothly and goes well."

The New York Police Department plans to station uniformed officers, including some with automatic weapons and explosives-detection equipment, across Manhattan and the city's 1,205 polling stations. All of the city's bomb-sniffing police dogs will be deployed, as well as special roving teams of officers, police said.

"This is by far the largest election detail that the NYPD has ever had," said Carlos Gomez, the chief of department. "It's comparable to the detail size we have here on New Year's Eve and last year when Pope Francis visited."

At his first rally of the day yesterday, in Florida, after the FBI confirmed overnight it would not be changing its decision not to charge Clinton over her private email use, Trump told the crowd: "What's happening is a disgrace. With what's happening with our justice, our country is a laughing stock all over the world. They're laughing."

Under the crisp blue skies forecast for much of the country on election day, his opponent began her last full day of campaigning with a more personal moment: one that highlights the historic opportunity ahead of her to become the first female president and a role model for a generation of young women.

Passing beneath the plane that has carried her through the closing months of a sometimes interminable-feeling campaign, she stopped to show the scene to her two-year-old granddaughter Charlotte via her mobile phone.

"I wouldn't have worked as hard as I have over 18 months ... if I did not believe in my heart that we can do this," she later told supporters in Pittsburgh. "We don't have to accept a dark and divisive vision for America. Tomorrow you can vote for a big-hearted America."

"Our core values are being tested in this election," Clinton added. "I know a lot of people feel frustrated and left behind. There is fear and anger in our country, but anger is not a plan. We have got to start talking to each other again."

Amid continued Democratic rancour over the late role of the FBI and Trump's threat to refuse to recognise an election result he claims may be rigged, it will be a tough battle whoever wins.

The Department of Justice announced yesterday that its civil rights division plans to deploy more than 500 personnel to 67 jurisdictions in 28 states to monitor voting. There is particular concern that changes to voting rules in some states such as North Carolina may have deliberately

Continued on page 5 →

Latest poll

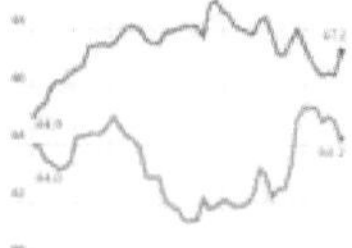

Facing the crowds: Republican presidential candidate Donald Trump holds a mask of himself at a campaign rally in Sarasota, Florida Photograph: Carlo Allegri/Reuters

Anxiety is palpable as election day dawns

Sabrina Siddiqui

Hillary Clinton's gaze was fixed on her phone as she emerged from her motorcade at the Westchester County airport. "Do you see the big plane?" she asked, turning the camera towards the 737 she was about to board for the final day of her campaign.

She was speaking to her granddaughter, Charlotte, through FaceTime. "I love you," the Democratic candidate said as she signed off.

It was a peaceful start to an otherwise frenetic day. Clinton was set to blitz four cities in three battleground states to deliver her closing argument to voters, who will determine whether she breaks "that highest, hardest glass ceiling", becoming the first female president in America's 240-year history.

Clinton arrived at the airport 40 miles north of New York City just as 55 members of the press had gathered at the wing of the plane for a group photo. Some had trailed the former secretary of state nearly every day for two years.

The Democratic nominee appeared relaxed on a day of many "lasts": her last visits to a trio of states – Pennsylvania, Michigan and North Carolina – as a presidential candidate; her last voyage in the campaign plane; her last opportunity to sum up her argument.

Sensing their chance to quiz the candidate, also perhaps one last time, the press corps swiftly surrounded her the moment the photos were snapped.

Continued on page 4 →

2016

Brian! I just had this terrifying nightmare that Donald Trump became President of the U.S.A!!
Actually, Honey...
...You're still asleep! Happy Halloween!
Really? Well this still isn't as scary as you becoming President.

This is ridiculous. We can't keep adjusting the settings every time he comes on the news....

I mean, its ridiculous. Teenagers have to go somewhere, so they go wherever their mates are..
But all of a sudden hanging together has become 'gang culture' and the newspapers and TV see 'gangs' on every corner
Yeah!
Yeah!
You're saying its absurd to believe that every collection of young people is intent on crime.
Completely.
Although, as it happens, we are. Give us your ****ing purse.

The new culture war How Hollywood took on Trump

→ all in g2

Mushroom or mullet? 10 ways to tuck in stylishly

Mark Gatiss Gay rights and the Sherlock backlash

£2.00 (IR €2.50)
Wednesday 01.02.17
Published in London and Manchester
theguardian.com

£1.60 for subscribers page 40→

theguardian

UK faces return to inequality of Thatcher years

Thinktank says inflation, welfare cuts and pay squeeze will punish poorest

Larry Elliott
Economics editor
Katie Allen

Pressure on the government to help struggling Britons has intensified after a leading thinktank warned that falling living standards for the poor threatened to bring the biggest rise in inequality since Margaret Thatcher was prime minister.

The Resolution Foundation said Theresa May would need to make good on her pledge to support "just about managing" households as it released a report showing that rising inflation and an end to recent strong jobs growth would hit the least well-off hardest.

Its warnings chime with other forecasts for a squeeze on family budgets on the back of sluggish wage growth, welfare cuts, rising global oil prices and the pound's sharp fall since the Brexit vote.

The drop in sterling has made imports more expensive and there are already signs that this is being passed on to consumers, with inflation hitting its highest level for more than two years in December.

The Resolution Foundation's study found that the current parliament would be the worst for living standards for the poorest half of households since comparable records began in the 1960s and the worst for inequality since the early years of Thatcher's 1979-90 tenure in No 10.

Since its sharp increase in the early 1980s - a period of high unemployment, factory closures and a cut in the top rate of income tax from 83% to 60% - inequality has broadly remained flat.

But the Resolution Foundation forecast that between 2015 and the next general election in 2020 incomes for the poorest half of households would fall by 2%.

That compares with a rise of 4% during the last parliament and 1% between 2005 and 2010 - the period that included the deepest recession since the 1930s.

Torsten Bell, director of the Resolution Foundation, said: "Britain has enjoyed a welcome mini-boom in living standards in recent years. But that boom is slowing rapidly as inflation rises, productivity flatlines and employment growth slows. The squeeze in the wake of the financial crisis tended to hit richer households the most. But this time around it's low and middle income families with kids who are set to be worst affected.

"This could leave Britain with the worst of both worlds on living standards - the weak income growth of the last parliament and rising inequality from the time Margaret Thatcher was in Downing Street.

"The prime minister's focus on supporting just managing families is absolutely right if we are to avoid the next few years being like the 1980s without the feelgood factor."

The prediction that inequality is set to start rising again is based on the thinktank's forecast that while incomes will fall for the poorer half of households they will rise by around 5% for the richest fifth over the next four years.

It blamed the upcoming living standards squeeze on a combination of stagnating pay, rising inflation and the rollout of more than £12bn of welfare cuts.

It emphasised that the pound's weakness since the Brexit vote and other economic factors such as flat productivity growth were only part of the picture.

The unequal nature of the squeeze would be the result of government policy on tax and benefits.

"The vote to leave the EU does not, thus far, appear to have impacted on the macroeconomy or employment, but it has hastened the end of ultra-low inflation and increased how far it is likely to rise in the next few years as the increase in import costs associated with the fall in sterling feeds through into higher consumer prices and lower living standards growth," the report said.

"But, in some ways regardless of the average level of household income growth, Britain is also actively choosing to increase inequality. Despite welcome policies such as the national living wage, the plans the prime minister has inherited are likely to

Continued on page 7 →

Kenneth Clarke
'Today's Tory party would amaze even Enoch Powell'

Kenneth Clarke delivers a passionate defence of the EU in his Commons speech yesterday. Article 50 debate, pages 6-7 →

Opposition to Trump's travel ban grows

Lauren Gambino
Sabrina Siddiqui
David Smith Washington

Opposition to Donald Trump's ban on travel from seven Muslim-majority countries continued to mount yesterday with some of the most successful business executives in the US, including Amazon's founder, Jeff Bezos, pledging to join the fight against the divisive executive order.

As the president prepared last night to unveil his pick to fill the vacancy in the US supreme court, opponents escalated their tactics to thwart his administration, with Democrats boycotting votes on two of Trump's cabinet nominees. There was also sharp criticism of the decision to fire the acting attorney general, Sally Yates, on Monday for refusing to endorse the president's travel ban. In an email to employees, Bezos said the company would be putting its legal and lobbying efforts behind the fight against the ban signed by the president on Friday.

"We're a nation of immigrants whose diverse backgrounds, ideas and points of view have helped us build and invent as a nation for over 240 years," Bezos said in an internal email to employees.

The company is supporting the attorney general for Washington state, where Amazon has its headquarters, in his lawsuit against Trump - the first confirmed legal action from a state against one of the new administration's policies.

Fellow Washington state-based companies Microsoft and Expedia are supporting the suit, which was filed on Monday.

Yesterday morning Senate Democrats delayed the consideration of Tom Price, Trump's pick for health secretary, and Steven Mnuchin, his choice for treasury secretary. Democrats refused to attend votes on the committees tasked with reviewing the two nominees, who rank among Trump's more controversial selections, saying Price and Mnuchin had misled them in their confirmation hearings.

Democrats demanded that Price, a congressman from Georgia, and Mnuchin, a former 16 17 →

Continued on page 16 →

'As the truck bomb exploded, it felt as if the ground lifted'

Ghaith Abdul-Ahad finds the Iraqi army fighting its way into Mosul - and trying to win over once-hostile civilians in Isis's stronghold

Rasoul, a 26-year-old radio operator, stood in a narrow street in east Mosul a mile from the frontline, peering into the early morning light as the armoured truck packed with explosives crawled towards him.

The other soldiers around him fired a volley of bullets that ricocheted harmlessly off its thick steel armour before they ran away. But Rasoul, still wrapped in his wool sleeping cloak, stood his ground, shouting warnings to anyone who could hear. He darted and hid in a side street when it was just metres away. The counter-terrorism force's Mosul brigade had made its temporary headquarters in the small residential street just a few days earlier.

As the truck bomb exploded, it felt as if the ground was lifted into the air and fell back down again. The force of the blast flattened two houses, damaged several more and incinerated four of the unit's vehicles.

Across the street from where Rasoul had stood, two officers had been asleep in the back room of a two-storey house as the family who lived there rested elsewhere. Suffocating smoke and dust filled the air; only the back room had weathered the blast. One of the officers moaned, while the other made wails that mixed his pain with the word "Allah".

The family survived, but civilians elsewhere on the street bore the brunt of the attack.

Since last October, when the assault to prise Mosul from the grip of Islamic State began, the fight between Iraqi forces and the jihadi group, which captured Mosul in June 2014, has taken place on a battlefield inhabited by civilians. Iraqi forces have now claimed to be largely in control of east Mosul, but in the west of the city an estimated 750,000 people are still living under the control of Isis.

As the dust from the bomb settled, civilians began trickling out on to the

Continued on page 20 →

Time Lady
Could this be the face of the new Doctor Who?
Page 9 →

2017

Damn! Damn! Damn! Flaming Damn!
Sorry, but it took me absolutely ages to put together this 'End Of Life' care package.

For crying out loud, Men's Group! If Simon doesn't want to tell us the name of his painter/decorator he doesn't have to!

Sorry to just stop you in the street but I wanted to say 'well done' to some young people. Dismissed as apathetic and uninterested, it was the 'Youth Vote' that had most influence on the election
Wow! There's been an election!

Kim Wall
Remembering the fearless journalist
→ all in g2

Quiche lorraine
Best and worst in the supermarket

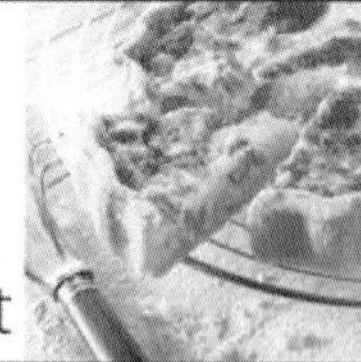

+ Meet the aromantics
Rejecting true love

9 770261 307842 41

£2.00
Thursday 12.10.17
Published in London and Manchester
theguardian.com

£1.60 for subscribers page 26 →

theguardian

Time to tax the rich to help the poor, says IMF

Report demolishes argument against increasing burden on the richest 1%

Larry Elliott Washington
Heather Stewart

Higher income tax rates for the rich would help reduce inequality without having an adverse impact on growth, the International Monetary Fund has said.

The Washington-based IMF used its influential half-yearly fiscal monitor yesterday to demolish the argument that economic growth would suffer if governments in advanced western countries forced the top 1% of earners to pay more tax.

It said tax theory suggested there should be "significantly higher" rates for those on higher incomes but the argument against doing so was that hitting the rich would be bad for growth.

But the institution said: "Empirical results do not support this argument." The IMF added that different types of wealth taxes might also be considered.

Labour seized on the report, calling for higher taxes on the rich and citing the IMF's intervention as evidence of the need for a fairer tax system. In its election manifesto, Labour proposed a 45% tax band on those earning more than £80,000 and a 50% rate for those on more than £123,000.

John McDonnell, the shadow chancellor, said: "The IMF support the argument we made in the general election for a fairer tax system. There is no evidence to support those who scaremonger about the effects of making the rich pay fairer tax."

He added: "Not only have the Tories slashed the top rate of tax, they still plan billions in tax giveaways to the super-rich and big corporations over this parliament."

Despite claims from ministers that Labour's tax plans would be politically and economically damaging, McDonnell believes higher taxes for the rich would be workable and popular.

"With every day that passes, the case for a change of direction at the Treasury grows. Instead of engaging in infighting in his own party the chancellor should listen to Labour's calls for fairer taxes and increased investment, so we will build an economy for the many not the few."

Theresa May has repeatedly attacked Labour's approach as extreme, claiming in prime minister's questions yesterday that the Labour leader, Jeremy Corbyn, and McDonnell are on "planet Venezuela".

But the prime minister conceded at a fringe meeting at her party's conference in Manchester that public opinion appeared to be more favourable to some of Labour's economic ideas than Conservative strategists had assumed in the run-up to June's general election.

"We thought there was a political consensus," she said. "Jeremy Corbyn changed that."

With Philip Hammond due to deliver his budget next month, it is unclear whether the government will press ahead with promised tax cuts for higher earners, including plans to increase the higher rate threshold for income tax to £50,000.

The fiscal monitor does not mention any country by name and does not specify at what level governments should set the new higher rate for top earners.

But the report stressed that cutting tax for the top 1% had gone too far - a strong hint that the IMF has doubts about the pro-rich tax plan proposed by Donald Trump for the US.

Instead, the IMF said higher tax for the rich was necessary to arrest rising income inequality - the argument used by McDonnell and Corbyn.

The fiscal monitor said most advanced economies in the west had experienced a sizeable increase in income inequality in the past three decades, driven primarily by the growing income of the top 1%.

Traditionally, governments have sought to make their societies less unequal by levying higher income tax rates on the rich and using the proceeds to help those less well off either directly or through public services.

But the IMF found that income tax systems had become markedly less progressive in the 1980s and 1990s and had remained stable since then, even though growing inequality raised the need for a more progressive approach.

Continued on page 2 →

'Weinstein jumped on me. I had to defend myself'

Exclusive

Léa Seydoux, star of the film Spectre, recalls the night she met Harvey Weinstein - and discovered his ugly side

I meet men like Harvey Weinstein all the time. I have starred in many films over the last 10 years and have been lucky enough to win awards at festivals like Cannes. Cinema is my life. And I know all the ways in which the film industry treats women with contempt.

When I first met Harvey Weinstein, it didn't take me long to figure him out. We were at a fashion show. He was charming, funny, smart - but very domineering. He wanted to meet me for drinks and insisted we had to make an appointment that night. This was never going to be about work. He had other intentions - I could see that clearly.

We met in the lobby of his hotel. His assistant, a young woman, was there. Throughout the evening, he flirted and stared at me as if I was a piece of meat. He acted as if he were considering me for a role. But I knew that was bullshit. I knew it, because I could see it in his eyes. He had a lecherous look. He was using his power to get sex.

He invited me to come to his hotel room for a drink. We went up together. It was hard to say no because he's so powerful. Soon, his assistant left and it was just the two of us. That's the moment where he started losing control.

We were talking on the sofa when he suddenly jumped on me and tried to kiss me. I had to defend myself. He's big and fat, so I had to be forceful to resist him. I left his room, thoroughly disgusted. I wasn't afraid of him, though. Because I knew what kind of man he was all along.

Since that night in his hotel room, I've seen him on many other occasions. We are in the same industry, so its impossible to avoid him. I've seen how he operates; the way he looks for an opening. The way he tests women to see what he can get away with.

He also doesn't take no for an answer. I once went with him to a restaurant and when he couldn't get a table he got angry and said, "Do you know who I am? I am Harvey Weinstein." That's the kind of man he is.

I've been at dinners with him where he's bragged openly about Hollywood actresses he has slept with. He's also said misogynistic things to me over the years. "You'd be better if you lost weight," he said. That shocked me.

One night, I saw him in London for the Baftas. He was hitting on a young woman. Another time, at the Met Life ball, I saw him trying to convince a young woman to sleep with him. Everyone could see what he was doing.

That's the most disgusting thing. Everyone knew what Harvey was up to and no one did anything. It's unbelievable that he's been able to act like this for decades and still keep his career. That's only possible because he has a huge amount of power.

Continued on page 9 →

Grenfell Tower: only 10 families permanently rehoused

Robert Booth and Kevin Rawlinson

Only 10 of the households made homeless by the Grenfell Tower fire in west London have been permanently rehoused four months after the blaze, the communities minister has told MPs.

Sajid Javid revealed yesterday that officials are trying to rehouse 203 households in total after the fire in June that claimed about 80 lives. That is more than the 151 homes that were lost in the tower and in neighbouring Grenfell Walk, because many households have chosen to split and be rehoused separately, he said.

Just over half of the households - 111 - have accepted offers of either temporary or permanent accommodation. Of those, 44 have moved into temporary homes and 10 into permanent homes. That leaves 92 households yet to accept accommodation of any kind.

"Clearly, a large number still remain in hotels and emergency accommodation and on top of that there are also others in hotels following the tragedy who haven't lost their homes but they may have been damaged or the families traumatised," Javid said.

He said the delay was partly down to families asking for redecoration or specific furniture in their new homes, as was their right. He added that the council was aiming to ensure no one is living in hotels at Christmas, unless they want to be.

Javid said the priority in trying to get people rehoused as quickly as possible was to "listen very carefully to what each family wants, what they say their needs are and to move at their pace".

He said: "No one is being pushed in any way into reaching a decision. There are still some families, particularly the bereaved families who are not ready to make a decision and do not want to engage in the process."

Javid said there were several families who could not decide whether they wanted to be near their old home or even outside the borough. Some individuals had said they preferred to stay in hotel rooms at the moment while other families had refused several properties.

He reported that the London Borough of Kensington and Chelsea had bought 167 new permanent homes and had 130 temporary properties available. Bereaved families were being given first refusal, followed by disabled people, those with children and then the rest, in a system agreed in consultation with the survivors' group Grenfell United.

Meanwhile, survivors who feared deportation because of their uncertain immigration status are to be allowed permanent residency in the UK, the Home

Continued on page 2 →

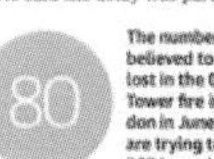

The number of lives believed to have been lost in the Grenfell Tower fire in west London in June. Officials are trying to rehouse 203 households

2017

Flaming PC Brigade can't leave anything alone! First it's a female Dr. Who next there's talk of a female James Bond. Unacceptable!
How about a female James Bond that kills people and still sleeps with women?
Yeah. I'd watch that.

CONGRATULATIONS HOWARD
25 YEARS IN HEALTH & SAFETY

Thanks for joining in with the 'Take The Knee' anti-racism protest, Brian, but you can get up now.
No I can't.

2017

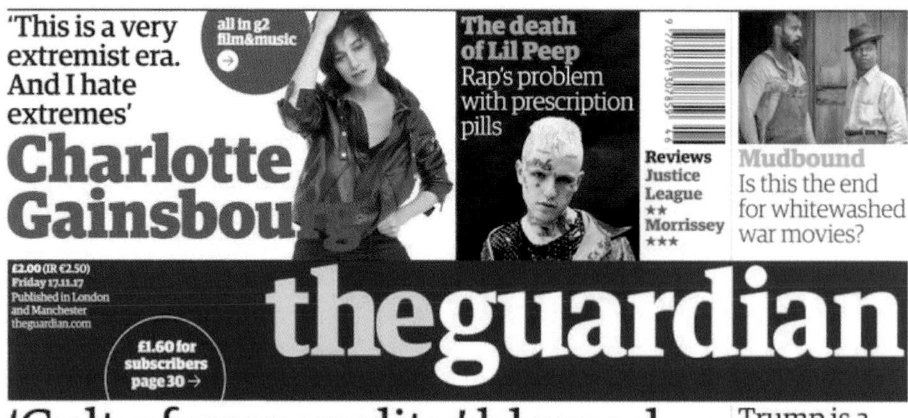

'This is a very extremist era. And I hate extremes'

Charlotte Gainsbourg

all in g2 film&music →

The death of Lil Peep
Rap's problem with prescription pills

Reviews
Justice League ★★
Morrissey ★★★

Mudbound
Is this the end for whitewashed war movies?

£2.00 (IR €2.50)
Friday 17.11.17
Published in London and Manchester
theguardian.com

£1.60 for subscribers page 30 →

theguardian

'Cult of personality' blamed as theatre apologises for Spacey

- Inquiry finds star power led to failings at Old Vic
- 20 allegations dating as far back as 1995 revealed
- Artistic director says unfair to say 'everyone knew'

Kevin Spacey is reportedly being treated at the same rehab clinic as Harvey Weinstein Photograph: Adrian Dennis/AFP/Getty

Mark Brown
Hannah Ellis-Petersen

A leading London theatre has apologised "wholeheartedly" for failing to create an environment in which people could raise concerns about Kevin Spacey after receiving 20 separate allegations of inappropriate behaviour by the star.

An inquiry into the actor-director's conduct during his 11 years at the Old Vic theatre, in south London, has concluded that his star power, which the theatre described as a "cult of personality", contributed to failings at the organisation.

The theatre said 14 of the 20 allegations against Spacey, who was its artistic director from 2004 to 2015, were so serious that it had advised complainants to take them to the police.

"The Old Vic apologises wholeheartedly to the people who told us they have been affected," the theatre's executive director, Kate Varah, said. "We've learned that it is not enough to have the right process in place. Everyone needs to feel able to speak out, no matter who they are."

The theatre has been criticised for remaining largely silent since allegations about Spacey emerged. But Varah said it had been important to properly investigate what went wrong.

"We have not slept since this came out, because we have been working incredibly hard to do this in a robust and detailed and measured and careful way," she said.

"It would have been easy for us to make a quick statement. It was not appropriate for us to do that because of the nature of the allegations."

The theatre opened a confidential complaints process after allegations against the actor emerged. It also hired the law firm Lewis Silkin to investigate.

Yesterday it said 56 people had contacted the theatre, with 20 individual allegations made of inappropriate conduct by Spacey. All were against young men over the age of 18; with 16 of them former staff. One testimony dated to 1995, 17 were from 2004-09, and two were after then. Allegations ranged from behaviour that made people feel uncomfortable to sexually inappropriate conduct. None of the allegations were of rape.

Claims against Spacey emerged last month, when he was accused of making unwanted sexual advances toward a Star Trek actor, Anthony Rapp, who said that in 1986, when he was 14, Spacey, then 26, lay on top of him and tried to "seduce" him.

Spacey said he did not recall the incident but if he did what Rapp described, it "would have been deeply inappropriate drunken behaviour".

The Old Vic said no formal complaints about Spacey were received during his tenure and that no board trustees were aware of any allegations. It found one case of a complainant telling a manager who was in the room at the time of an incident and the manager taking no further action.

The theatre's current artistic director, Matthew Warchus, said: "As somebody who worked here, in that period, and as a freelance director over the last 30 years, I've worked in pretty much every producing theatre in London ... this was in no way a toxic environment. My experience of working here was identical to every theatre I'd ever worked in.

"My big hope is that it doesn't reflect on the Old Vic as a name and a brand. It was a very, very hard situation to spot."

Asked how he felt about Spacey now, Warchus said: "This last month has cre-

Continued on page 2 →

Trump is a 'fascist kind of figure', says Stiglitz

Larry Elliott

The Nobel-prizewinning American economist Joseph Stiglitz has accused Donald Trump of fascist "tendencies", and said there was a risk that the president would push the nuclear button if prevented from getting his way.

In an interview with the Guardian, Stiglitz said Trump was a liar, a cheat, not fit to occupy the White House, and would have gone down to defeat in 2016 had Bernie Sanders rather than Hillary Clinton been the Democrat candidate.

Stiglitz, one of the world's most well known economists, who worked in the White House for Bill Clinton in the 1990s, said Trump's election victory had been the result of a failure to tackle inequality. He added that he had been fearful of the political consequences of stagnant living standards and falling life expectancy for the past six or seven years.

"I began to say if we didn't fix this problem we are going to have a political problem, and historically a Trump figure, a fascist kind of figure, arises."

Stiglitz said Trump had fascist "tendencies" but that he was held back by America's political system. "He is restrained by our institutions and every day those institutions work we feel relieved. We don't know what the bounds are and we don't know how far he would push those bounds.

"A couple of things are most disturbing - the attack on the press and the attack on the foundations of knowledge, which goes beyond the press.

"I think the other thing you have seen with some of these fascist leaders is using 'us versus them' as a way of dividing society."

Trump ran for office on a protectionist agenda and is seeking to pull out of the North American Free Trade Agreement (Nafta) between the US, Canada and Mexico, something opposed by big business.

"What I worry about is that when Trump is confronted with the reality that he can't do on Nafta what he wants to do, he will strike out like a little kid and do something dangerous, like putting his finger on a button he shouldn't be putting his finger on," Stiglitz said.

Interview, page 29 →

2017

For pity's sake, Clare, stop! The Trump state visit may never happen.

OK Workshop, let's have a bit of fun introducing ourselves! The ball goes round and when it comes to you you say your name and a fact about yourself. Here goes!
I'm Doreen and I'm visually impaired.

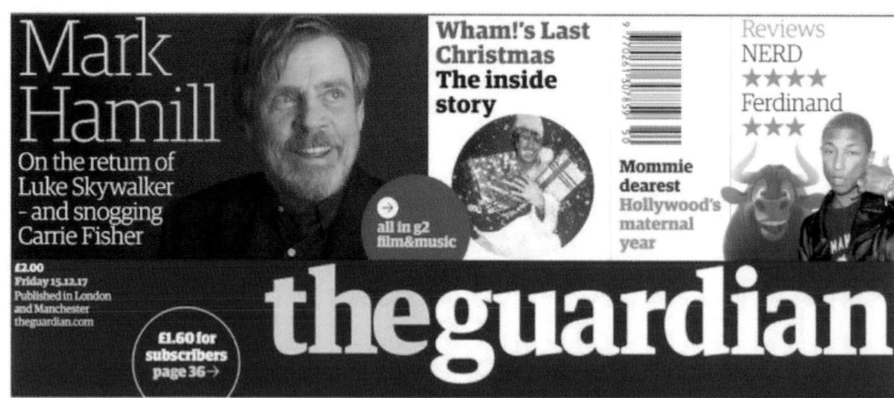

Mark Hamill
On the return of Luke Skywalker - and snogging Carrie Fisher
Wham!'s Last Christmas The inside story
all in g2 film&music
Mommie dearest Hollywood's maternal year
Reviews
NERD ★★★★
Ferdinand ★★★
£2.00
Friday 15.12.17
Published in London and Manchester
theguardian.com
£1.60 for subscribers page 36→
theguardian

Sale to Disney marks end of era for Murdoch

Tycoon reshapes media empire with disposal of film studio and Sky stake

Mark Sweney

Rupert Murdoch has begun the break-up of his global media empire, announcing a $66bn (£50bn) deal with Disney to sell assets including his Hollywood film studio and a controlling stake in Sky.

Disney is buying the bulk of Murdoch's 21st Century Fox media and entertainment business, in a significant strategic withdrawal for the Australian-born mogul after 60 years of deal-making and expansion from newspapers into film and TV.

Murdoch, as combative as ever at 86, insisted the move was not a retreat but a pivot to new business opportunities. However, he is giving up the Fox film and TV studios responsible for the box-office blockbusters Titanic and Avatar as well as hits such as The Simpsons, cable channels including FX and National Geographic, a 39% Sky stake and India's Star network.

The deal marks a significant moment in Murdoch's dynastic ambitions, as his younger son, James, chief executive of 21st Century Fox, has in effect been carved out of the line of succession after two decades with the business. The elder son, Lachlan, is left as executive heir to the remaining Murdoch empire, which includes the Fox News network, and newspapers including the Sun, Times and Wall Street Journal.

Disney's chief executive, Bob Iger, who has signed a contract extension to 2021 to oversee the takeover, said discussions were continuing about whether the 45-year-old James Murdoch might join the company after the deal was completed. If not, he is expected to leave Fox to set up his own venture, although either way the separation is viewed as an amicable one.

Claire Enders, of the media analysts Enders Analysis, said: "It is a fundamental parting of ways between James and his father, the result over a period of time of the development of many differences between them that have become accentuated. Fundamentally, Rupert believes his son has not made a great fist of running the entertainment assets. The issues of the past look to have cost James's ambitions in the present again."

The all-stock deal will result in the Murdoch family trading control of 21st Century Fox for a 4.25% stake in Disney, which has reinforced its status as the world's most powerful media brand.

"Are we retreating? Absolutely not," said Rupert Murdoch in a conference call. "Those who know me know I am a news man with a competitive spirit. Fox News is probably the strongest brand in all of television. We are pivoting at a pivotal moment." However, Lachlan Murdoch acknowledged that 21st Century Fox had hoisted the white flag in the sale to Disney, saying that "sometimes the right decisions are the hardest ones".

Assets that are not part of the 21st Century Fox sale to Disney will be spun off as a separate business, called New Fox, which will include the Fox TV network, Fox News, Fox Business, Fox Sports and regional stations in the US.

Rupert Murdoch told Sky News that in two or three years he might look to merge New Fox with News Corp, the separately listed company that owns the book publisher HarperCollins and publishes newspapers including the Sun, Times, Sunday Times and Wall Street Journal.

The deal allows Murdoch to focus on his first passion: newspapers. His global business grew from a single Adelaide paper that he took charge aged 21 in 1952, following the death of his father. "The New Fox is about returning to our roots as a lean, aggressive, challenger brand," Lachlan said.

The deal will not, for now, affect the

Continued on page 7 →

Mourners hold photographs of loved ones lost in the Grenfell fire after the service at St Paul's Photograph: WPA Pool/Getty

Six months on, the grief is as raw as ever

Harriet Sherwood
Religion correspondent

Clutching white roses and photographs of lost loved ones, the survivors and the bereaved of the Grenfell Tower fire were joined by members of the royal family, faith leaders and politicians at St Paul's Cathedral yesterday to mark six months since the catastrophe.

An hour-long national memorial service, with probably the most diverse congregation ever seen at St Paul's, saw emotions spill over, with many wiping away tears during music, prayers and a minute's silence to remember the 71 people who died and the hundreds made homeless.

More than 1,500 people gathered under the cathedral's magnificent dome, along with five senior royals: the Prince of Wales, Duchess of Cornwall, Duke and Duchess of Cambridge and Prince Harry. Theresa May was joined by the communities secretary, Sajid Javid, the Labour leader, Jeremy Corbyn, and the shadow home secretary, Diane Abbott.

The singer Adele and actor Carey Mulligan were also present, along with uniformed members of the emergency services, volunteers from the community, and children from local schools. The leader of Kensington and Chelsea council, Elizabeth Campbell, and her colleagues stayed away at the community's request.

To open the service, a Catholic priest and an imam from North Kensington carried through the congregation a banner emblazoned with the green heart of Grenfell, which has become the symbol of the community.

David Ison, the dean of St Paul's, welcomed those in the church and "all of you watching on national television, among whom are those painfully affected who could not face such a public event". The service was screened at al-Manaar mosque and St Clement's church in North Kensington.

Ison said: "In this service we come together as people of different faiths and none, as we remember before God those whose lives were lost, and pray for them

Continued on page 4 →

Grieve receives death threats after leading Tory rebellion

Anushka Asthana
Heather Stewart

The Conservative MP Dominic Grieve has received death threats after leading a parliamentary rebellion that resulted in the prime minister's first defeat on Brexit.

The former attorney general, who reported some incidents to the police, said such threats should have "no part in the political process of a democracy".

Others among the 11 Tory politicians who defied a three-line whip to secure a vote for MPs on the final Brexit deal have also been threatened. Antoinette Sandbach said she had also received "oblique" death threats, including phrases such as "you'll get what's coming to you".

A senior government official said Theresa May felt "no politician should face intimidation or threats".

Grieve told the Guardian he was disturbed by the atmosphere that had unfolded since the decision of the group to press the issue in parliament.

"The thing which continues to cause me concern is not that people will disagree vigorously with the positions we take, but that the atmosphere is so febrile that it leads firstly to people not listening to what the debate is about; secondly, suggests that any questions around Brexit amount to an intention to sabotage and, thirdly, results in some people expressing themselves in terms that at times include death threats," he said.

Anna Soubry, one of the 11 Conservatives who defied the whips on the Brexit vote, said 'bully boys' were ringing councillors in her constituency

Grieve also questioned the response of some newspapers to the vote, including a front-page story in the Daily Mail that claimed 11 Tory "self-consumed malcontents" had betrayed their leader, party and 17 million Brexit voters and had increased the "possibility of a Marxist in No 10".

He added: "The form of reporting that the Daily Mail adopts is an incitement to obscuring what the issues actually are. That then adds to the atmosphere."

Sandbach said the Mail's front page was now "lining my cat's litter tray". Asked whether any of her fellow MPs had chastised her, she said: "I haven't had any comeback on it - but I won't take lectures from people who have rebelled endless times in their careers."

Anna Soubry, another rebel, also said she was facing "bully boys" ringing local councillors in her Broxtowe constituency.

She said the issue was about reclaiming democracy - and hit back at claims that she and colleagues had enjoyed a champagne celebration after the vote. She tweeted that they were marking "taking back control" with a glass of wine, and that no champagne had been drunk. She tweeted to the Mail: "Yes. We put our country first exerting British principles of

Continued on page 13 →

Collusion, doping and the price of fish
The strange spectacle of Vladimir Putin's annual press conference
Page 30 →

2017

Got any vegan?
Got any lactose free?
Got any gluten free?
Got any sugar free?
Got any egg free?
No.
No.
No.
No.
No.
BRIC A BRAC
Cake Stall
A word to the wise, Kid: You'll not make any money around here just selling this weird shit.
RIC A RAC
Cake Stall

Brian, what are you watching?
A martial arts movie. And before you start with your tutting disapproval I want you to know that I love a martial arts movie and nothing you can say will spoil my enjoyment of it.
Not at all! For beneath the veneer of macho brutality exists a grace and athleticism which, combined with the almost fetishistic dedication to the male physique, provides a thrilling homo-eroticism absent from other film genres.
OK, you've spoilt it.

OK Workshop, let's have a bit of fun introducing ourselves! The ball goes round and when it comes to you you say your name and a fact about yourself. Here goes!
I'm Doreen and I'm visually impaired.

Ivanka Trump
The first female president of the United States?
all in g2
Fantastic figs
The only fruit for 2018
Ridley Scott
Ditching Kevin Spacey from my film was no dilemma
£2.00 (IR €2.50)
Monday 08.01.18
Published in London and Manchester
theguardian.com
theguardian

May moves to assert control with reshuffle

Education secretary said to be at risk as PM bids to reboot her government

Andrew Sparrow
Political correspondent

Theresa May will attempt to give her government a new year reboot today as she carries out what is expected to be her most wide-ranging reshuffle since her ill-fated decision to call a snap general election last summer.

The prime minister is expected to sack or move about a quarter of the cabinet in an assertion of authority that was impossible in the immediate aftermath of the loss of her Commons majority.

Justine Greening, the education secretary, was last night tipped by Conservative and government sources as the most prominent likely victim, with Sir Patrick McLoughlin, the Conservative party chairman, also widely expected to be replaced.

But Philip Hammond, the chancellor, Amber Rudd, the home secretary, Boris Johnson, the foreign secretary, and David Davis, the Brexit secretary, are all set to keep their jobs, according to government sources, in a sign that although May is in a stronger position than she was last summer, she is still wary of picking fights with potential challengers.

In October last year she gave an interview in which she openly speculated about shifting Johnson, who had been widely criticised after saying that the Libyan city of Sirte could be transformed into the new Dubai once "they clear the dead bodies" away.

The idea of moving the foreign secretary was floated again more recently, but he made it clear that he would not accept a lesser role, so the prospect of replacing him has been shelved.

May will, however, be appointing a new first secretary of state and Cabinet Office minister to replace Damian Green, who was in effect sacked before Christmas for not telling the truth about pornography being found on his office computer during a police raid in 2008.

Green was in effect deputy prime minister, standing in for May in the Commons when she was away and playing a key coordinating role in Whitehall as chair of several cabinet committees. At one stage, May was considering letting the title of first secretary of state lapse - prime ministers have often done without one in the past - and simply appointing a new Cabinet Office minister, but over the weekend government sources indicated that Green would be replaced as first secretary.

Jeremy Hunt, the health secretary, has been tipped as a possible candidate, but the NHS winter crisis would make moving him awkward and yesterday one insider close to the reshuffle process indicated that he was now out of the running for that post.

Chris Grayling, the transport secretary, has also been named as a possible candidate, but May has a history of making surprise reshuffle appointments - Johnson as foreign secretary, Gavin Williamson as defence secretary - and she may again choose someone unexpected in what is likely to be the key announcement of the reshuffle.

Although attention will focus on movements at cabinet level today, a Downing Street source said a key purpose of the reshuffle was to refresh the government at a lower level and bring on new talent. Junior ministerial appointments will be announced tomorrow and they would involve "more women and more people from diverse backgrounds" coming into the government, a source said.

May also wants to show that the government has ambitions that go beyond Brexit, the source said. To reinforce the point, she will be making her first major speech on the environment on Thursday. Other domestic priorities this year are housing, school standards and the NHS, and further May speeches on subjects other than Brexit are expected in the coming weeks.

Greening was appointed education secretary when May became prime minister in July 2016, having previously served as transport secretary and international development secretary. But she has never shared

Continued on page 7 →

Peter Preston, 1938-2018

Peter Preston, the editor of the Guardian between 1975 and 1995, has died at the age of 79. He oversaw some of the most significant moments in the newspaper's history, transforming it into a national force Photograph: Jane Bown

2018

LESBIAN VISIBILITY DAY

So, having pledged our unequivocal support to the # Me Too campaign, may I suggest we take advantage of the 'safe space' offered by Men's Group to feel pleased with ourselves.

Put bluntly, Brian, the fact you possess a penis can never justify a 'gender pay gap', no matter how small it may be.
The pay gap, Brian, the pay gap!

Wednesday
28 February 2018
Issue № 53,344
£2.00

Jumping through hoops
The weird world of retail recruitment
→ G2

Drones and cyborgs
Milan's futuristic fashion week
→ G2

Mane event
Britain's last lion tamer
→ G2

The Guardian

Chaos and disruption
Snow and ice hit UK
Page 8 →

▼ *The central London skyline is hit by a snowstorm yesterday. The UK is set to remain very cold all week*
PHOTOGRAPH: NPAS

Arctic heatwave triggers climate meltdown fears

Jonathan Watts

An alarming heatwave in the sunless winter Arctic is causing blizzards in Europe and forcing scientists to reconsider even their most pessimistic forecasts of climate change.

Although it could yet prove to be a freak event, the primary concern is that global warming is eroding the polar vortex, the powerful winds that once insulated the frozen north.

The north pole gets no sunlight until March, but an influx of warm air has pushed temperatures in Siberia up by as much as 35C above historical averages this month. Greenland has already experienced 61 hours above freezing in 2018 - more than three times as many as any previous year.

Seasoned observers have described what is happening as "crazy", "weird", and "simply shocking".

"This is an anomaly among anomalies," said Michael Mann, the director of the Earth System Science Center at Pennsylvania State University. "It is far enough outside the historical range that it is worrying - it is a suggestion that there are further surprises in store as we continue to poke the angry beast that is our climate.

"The Arctic has always been regarded as a bellwether because of the vicious circle that amplifies human-caused warming in that particular region. And it is sending out a clear warning."

Although headlines focusing on Europe's current cold weather have been jolly, the concern is that this is not a reassuring return to winters as normal, but rather a displacement of what ought to be happening farther north.

At the world's most northerly land weather station - Cape Morris Jesup on Greenland - recent temperatures have been, at times, warmer than London and Zurich, which are thousands of miles to the south. Although the peak of 6.1C on Sunday was not quite a record, on the previous two occasions (2011 and 9 →

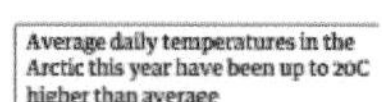

Average daily temperatures in the Arctic this year have been up to 20C higher than average

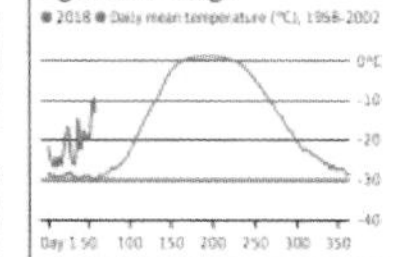

Source: Danish Meteorological Institute
Data recorded north of the 80th northern parallel

Corbyn gets dossier on harassment

Anushka Asthana
Political editor

A dossier of 43 stories of harassment, abuse and sexual violence against women at all levels of the Labour party has been submitted to Jeremy Corbyn's office, prompting calls for the party to reform the way it deals with claims of sexual misconduct.

Women who submitted their stories anonymously to the Labourtoo site over a two-month period gave examples of being raped, serially groped, inappropriate sexual comments and being urged not to report what had happened. The incidents, in settings all around the country as well as in Westminster, highlighted a number of weaknesses in the way Labour has handled the issue.

Among the problems highlighted, which the party says will be urgently fed into current reviews, were:

- Problem individuals are "common knowledge" but no action is taken against them;
- There is low or no confidence in the party's formal complaint or disciplinary processes; 2 →

Syria destroys any pretence that Europe is a moral force
Natalie Nougayrède
→ *Journal*

2018

Look, if we're going to do this whole 'Multi-Agency Support' thing, maybe we should start co-ordinating our diaries.

Home visits can be stressful, Rita, but the most important thing is not to jump to conclusions.
WOOF! WOOF! WOOF! WOOF!
See, he's a tiny little sweetie pie!

OK, Abigail, this is an Emotion Ball. We pass it to each other and it helps us express how we are feeling.
SAD
EXCI
HAPPY
Stuff it up your arse.
Come on, Abigail. How am I going to find out how you're feeling if you take that attitude?

YouTube confidential
How vloggers took over sex ed

How we made 2001: A Space Odyssey
'Hal was originally a cockney' +

→ G2

Tuesday
13 March 2018
Issue № 53,355
£2.00

The Guardian

May points the finger at Russia over 'reckless' poisoning of spy

Anushka Asthana
Andrew Roth
Luke Harding

Theresa May has given Vladimir Putin's administration until midnight today to explain how a former spy was poisoned in Salisbury before the prime minister concludes it was an "unlawful use of force" by the Russian state against the UK.

After chairing a meeting of the national security council, the prime minister told MPs yesterday that it was "highly likely" that Russia was responsible for the attack on Sergei Skripal and his daughter, Yulia.

She warned that Britain would not tolerate such a "brazen attempt to murder innocent civilians on our soil".

In a statement to the House of Commons that triggered a furious response from Moscow, May said the evidence showed that Skripal had been targeted by a "military-grade nerve agent of a type developed by Russia". Calling the incident an "indiscriminate and reckless act", she said Boris Johnson had summoned Russia's ambassador to Whitehall and demanded an explanation by midnight.

Russian officials immediately hit back, with Maria Zakharova, the spokeswoman for the Russian foreign minister, calling the remarks "a provocation" and calling the event a "circus show in the British parliament".

Andrei Lugovoi, a Russian member of parliament who is suspected of the 2006 murder of the former Russian agent Alexander Litvinenko in London, said May's decision to point the finger at Moscow so quickly was "at a minimum, irresponsible".

May addressed MPs after chairing the security council meeting, during which senior ministers were told the nerve agent used was from a group known as *Novichok*.

"Based on the positive identification of this chemical agent by world-leading experts at Porton Down, our knowledge that Russia has previously produced this agent and would still be capable of doing so, Russia's record of conducting state-sponsored assassinations, and our assessment that Russia views some defectors as legitimate targets for assassinations, the government has concluded it is highly likely that Russia was responsible for the act against Sergei and Yulia Skripal," she said.

The prime minister said that left just two plausible explanations for what happened in Salisbury. "Either this was a direct act by the Russian state against our country. Or the Russian government lost control of this potentially catastrophically damaging nerve agent and allowed it to get into the hands of others."

May made it clear she believed there was already "a backdrop of a well-established pattern of Russian state aggression" - listing the illegal annexation of Crimea, violating the airspace of European countries, and a "sustained campaign of cyber-espionage and disruption", 8 →

'We will not tolerate such a brazen attempt to murder innocent civilians on our soil'

Theresa May
Statement to the Commons

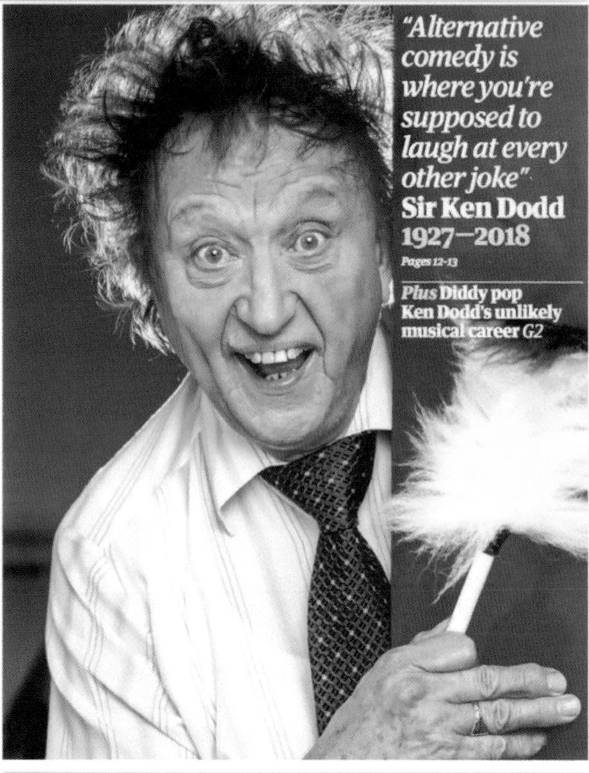

"Alternative comedy is where you're supposed to laugh at every other joke"
Sir Ken Dodd
1927—2018
Pages 12-13

Plus **Diddy pop**
Ken Dodd's unlikely musical career *G2*

University strikes may be called off as talks turn corner

Sally Weale
Education correspondent

Strikes by university staff which have caused widespread disruption on campuses across the UK in a bitter dispute over pensions could be suspended later this week after a breakthrough in talks.

Employers and union leaders have agreed a revised proposal to reform pensions, which - if endorsed by all parties - will be introduced as part of a three-year transitional arrangement.

The proposal has been sent out to members of the University and College Union (UCU) and will be considered today at a meeting of the UCU's higher education committee and at a separate meeting of branch representatives.

Universities UK (UUK), which represents university employers, is now in the process of consulting with Universities Superannuation Scheme (USS) employers on the new proposal.

In the meantime UUK is expecting union leaders to suspend industrial action from tomorrow. More than 60 universities have been hit by industrial action as a result of proposed changes to pensions that the 4 →

2018

What's this, Clare? Paper? Crayons?
Drawing helps my young client express herself, make sense of complex situations and, most importantly, tell her story exactly how she wants it told!
That's supposed to be me? That doesn't look anything like me!

Men's Group, please! This is supposed to be a 'safe space'. If Trevor finds Theresa May's dancing sexy he should be allowed to say it!

Staying Alive by The Bee Gees!
The Macarena by Los del Rio!
Staying Alive by The Bee Gees!
The Macarena by Los del Rio!
Guys...
If we can't agree on which song has the best tempo for CPR, maybe we should just call an ambulance.

2018

The 50 best pubs in Britain

→ Travel special

Saturday 27 October 2018
Issue № 53,551
£2.90

The Guardian

The return of Posy Simmonds

→ Review

Free Food magazine

→ Feast

Buy the new GCHQ puzzle book for half-price

→ Voucher page 42

PHOTOGRAPH: SIMON DAWSON/GETTY IMAGES

Exclusive
Insider tells of culture of silence at top of company over tycoon's behaviour towards women

Green paid seven-figure sums to silence abuse allegations

Owen Jones and Esther Addley

Several employees of Sir Philip Green who alleged the tycoon had sexually harassed or bullied them were given enormous seven-figure secret payouts to settle their claims, the Guardian has learned.

The huge settlements were part of a widespread culture of silence at Green's Arcadia Group, an insider said, where the billionaire owner allegedly harassed female staff but few felt able to speak up, and where senior managers frequently ignored his behaviour.

The Guardian understands there are at least seven cases in which former staff members received substantial payouts to settle complaints of sexual harassment, bullying or racist abuse against Green. In several of those cases, the sums involved reached seven figures.

The settlements, agreed by both sides, stopped them speaking out over their claims. It is not known whether these cases were among the five that were subject to a press injunction revealed this week.

One incident of alleged harassment that led to a substantial payout was dismissed by a senior manager because "he didn't really seem to think that there was anything wrong", the insider said. "I don't think he thought Philip was doing anything wrong, I think he just saw it as, that's how it is."

In that instance and others where staff raised grievances, "it was just a case of, to make sure this doesn't go to court and to make sure nobody finds out, how many zeros do you want on the end of this cheque?"

The source alleged Green's behaviour included:

- Walking into meetings and giving the women present a lingering hug.
- Asking women in meetings if they were "naughty girls", and if they "needed their bottoms slapped".
- Creeping up behind women to make them jump, before caressing their shoulders to "reassure" them.
- Calling women "sweetheart", "darling" or "love", rather than by their names.
- Telling women they were overweight and should go on a diet.
- Flying into expletive-ridden rages, abusing male and female staff in front of colleagues.

10 →

2018

'Gaslighting'? It's a form of psychological abuse in which a manipulative person gets a suggestible person to doubt their own personal experience. It comes from the Ingrid Bergman film 'Gaslight.'
I've never seen Gaslight.
Yes you have.
Yes I have.

TRAINING TODAY
You know, guys, if Megan doesn't want to do role play she shouldn't have to.

OK, everyone, before the Christmas party starts in earnest may I suggest one rule: no conversations about Brexit, football or school catchments!

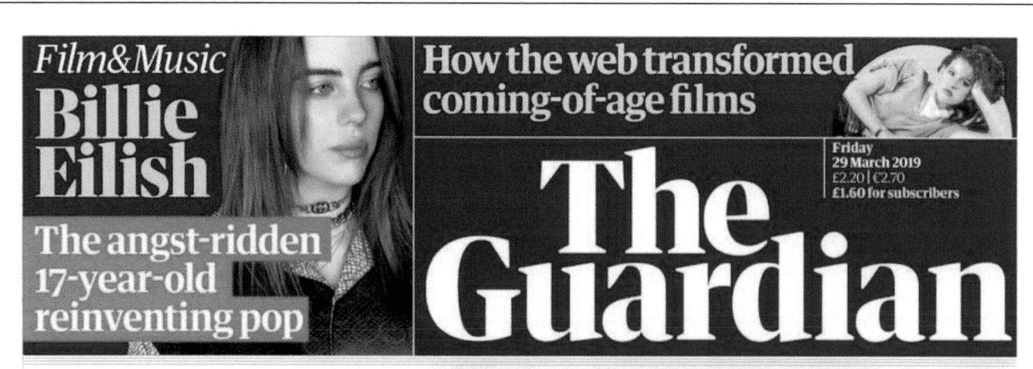

Film&Music
Billie Eilish
The angst-ridden 17-year-old reinventing pop
How the web transformed coming-of-age films
Friday
29 March 2019
£2.20 | €2.70
£1.60 for subscribers
The Guardian

May tries to buy time as ministers say: go now

Rowena Mason and Rajeev Syal

Theresa May will put only half of her Brexit deal to a vote today, in a final desperate attempt to secure MPs' support, as senior cabinet ministers made clear she must leave No 10 very soon whatever happens.

On the day Britain was originally meant to leave the EU - something the prime minister had promised more than 100 times would happen - she will put only the withdrawal agreement to a vote, having promised to step aside if the MPs give her their approval.

'She has got to go. She has fired the starting gun ... She cannot carry on and have an election. All her credibility is gone'

Conservative source

No 10 is hoping some Labour MPs will back the withdrawal agreement severing the UK's membership of the EU, without the political declaration governing Britain's future relationship with Brussels.

However, it remains extremely unlikely to pass as Labour said it would never vote for a "blindfold Brexit", while about 30 Eurosceptic Tories and the 10 Democratic Unionist MPs are also holding out against it.

MPs who support a soft Brexit are meanwhile working on a new round of votes on the alternatives on Monday, including a compromise that could combine the support of those MPs who voted for a customs union, for Labour's Brexit plan and for the Norway-style option "common market 2.0".

With European leaders sceptical that such efforts will be successful, the EU's chief negotiator, Michel Barnier, told diplomats yesterday that a no-deal Brexit was now "the most plausible outcome" and ordered work to begin on wargaming the bloc's response.

No 10 insists that it can still make progress, arguing that passing the withdrawal agreement alone will allow the UK to avoid a cliff-edge Brexit on 12 April and secure 2 →

The favourite

Michael Gove and his dog Snowy at home in London. Bookies have made him frontrunner to replace Theresa May

News *Page 9* →

PHOTOGRAPH: ANDY RAIN/EPA

Police struggling with routine crime, says chief

Exclusive
Vikram Dodd

Government cuts have left police retreating from the streets, solving just one in 10 offences and "really struggling" to deal with routine crime, the leader of Britain's police chiefs has said.

Sara Thornton is stepping down this weekend from her role as chair of the National Police Chiefs Council after a four-year tenure that saw her battle to get the government to recognise that funding cuts were leading to fewer officers and resources to fight crime.

In an interview to mark her departure as NPCC chair, Thornton, who has been in policing for 33 years, told the Guardian that she wanted to see an end to a "child"-like blame culture when policing went wrong, and for a recognition that officers were dealing with some of society's worst problems and not "running libraries".

Thornton also said the public were noticing the effects of cuts: "We can do the organised crime stuff, the big counter-terrorist stuff, but where we are really struggling is on the routine response to crime - how quickly we get in there, how many people are being investigated and how many people are then being charged or summonsed.

"What is happening is that fewer and fewer calls to the police are resulting in the deployment of an officer to the person who made the call."

She said some of that was linked to efficiencies and changes in the way the public wanted to interact, via the telephone or online. But too much of it was not, Thornton said. "I worry we have crossed the boundary between being efficient 2 →

Killing Eve leads the way at the Baftas with 14 nominations

News *Page 18* →

2019

Hi Zoe. I'm Clare, a social worker trained to work with young people like yourself. And this room is a safe space where you can share whatever it is you are feeling. But before we start...

....Can you help me set up the Bluetooth on my phone?

Fantastic cake, Megan!
It took me ages. But you know what a perfectionist I am.
Just one small thing...
30 YEARS OF THE CHILDREN'S 1989 ACT 2019
Did you really have to tell her that it was the Children Act?

I run, I swim, I paint, I write, I sing, I protest, I volunteer, I garden and I zumba. Why? Because I refuse to be an old lady fit only to be patronised!
Well, good for you!

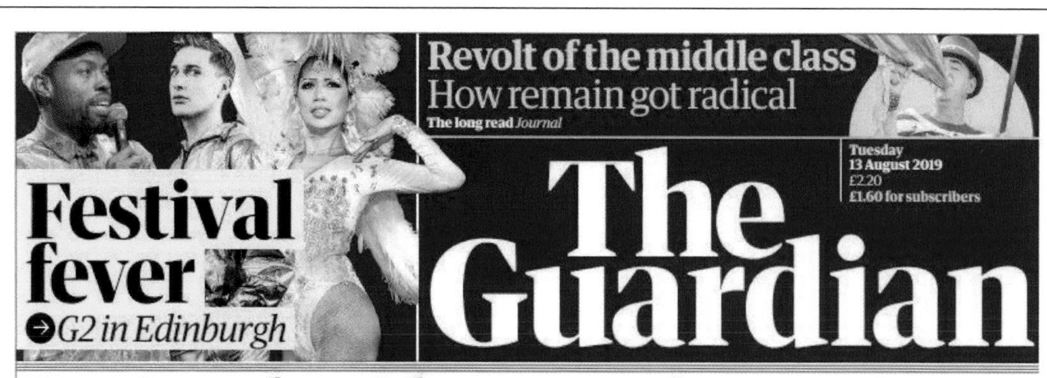

Revolt of the middle class
How remain got radical
The long read *Journal*

Festival fever
→ *G2 in Edinburgh*

Tuesday
13 August 2019
£2.20
£1.60 for subscribers

The Guardian

National Grid accused as series of blackout near-misses revealed

Exclusive
Jillian Ambrose
Energy correspondent

National Grid had experienced three blackout "near-misses" in as many months before Friday's outage left almost a million homes in the dark and forced trains to a standstill in the UK.

The system operator, already under investigation by the energy watchdog, faces criticism from within the industry that it has not done enough to guard against the risk of blackouts.

National Grid blamed the "incredibly rare" nationwide power cut on a severe slump in the grid's frequency - a measure of energy intensity - after the unexpected shutdown of two power generators.

It will face an investigation into its handling of the energy system after the first blackout in more than a decade following the shutdown of a gas-fired power plant in Bedfordshire and the Hornsea windfarm in the North Sea at about 5pm on Friday.

It said it would work with the regulator and energy companies to "understand the lessons learned" after the power plants shut down unexpectedly within minutes of each other, causing severe rush hour travel disruption across the country.

But industry sources claim National Grid has been aware of the growing potential for a wide-scale blackout "for years" and has suffered a spate of "near misses" in recent weeks.

The Guardian understands that in every month since May there has been a severe dip in the grid's frequency from its normal range around 50Hz. Industry sources have confirmed that the grid's frequency has fallen below 49.6Hz on three different occasions in recent months, the deepest falls seen on the UK grid since 2015.

'It would be easy for National Grid to write this off as a fluke, but they have been aware of this issue for many years'

Steve Shine
Anesco chairman

On Friday the blackout was triggered when the frequency slumped to 48.88Hz.

In June, the frequency of the grid plummeted to within a whisker of National Grid's legal limit of 49.5Hz after all three units of EDF Energy's West Burton gas-fired power plant in Nottinghamshire tripped offline without warning. 13 →

Showdown over no deal set for September

Rowena Mason
Peter Walker

Boris Johnson is preparing for a parliamentary battle against MPs trying to block a no-deal Brexit in the second week of September as his cross-party opponents continue to be divided about the best way to stop the UK crashing out on 31 October.

A senior government source said Downing Street believes the first legislative showdown over no deal will be on 9 September, when parliament is due to debate a progress report on power-sharing in Northern Ireland.

The expectation is that a cross-party group of MPs will try to use this to carve out time to legislate against a no-deal Brexit by requesting an extension to article 50.

The prime minister could face a confidence motion brought by Jeremy Corbyn aimed at collapsing his government as early as 3 September, when MPs return from their summer break.

Diane Abbott, the shadow home secretary, said on Monday that an early confidence 15 →

Epstein
Focus turns to British socialite

Ghislaine Maxwell has been accused of 'helping the late disgraced financier to groom girls'
News *Page 8* →

Scientists say Ebola is curable after drug trial

The World Health Organization has hailed a new treatment that drastically cuts death rates from the disease
News *Page 2* →

Farage's broadside at Harry and Meghan

Brexit party leader derides Duke and Duchess of Sussex for their 'irrelevant' social justice campaigns
News *Page 17* →

2019

Good evening everybody and welcome to the safe space that is the "People who Don't Find Fleabag Funny" support group.

PEOPLE AGAINST THE PROROGATION OF PARLIAMENT
Damn. I wish I'd thought of that.
STOP BORIS

We can't keep calling him 'Boris' anymore. From now on everyone should call him by his full title.
'That **** Boris'

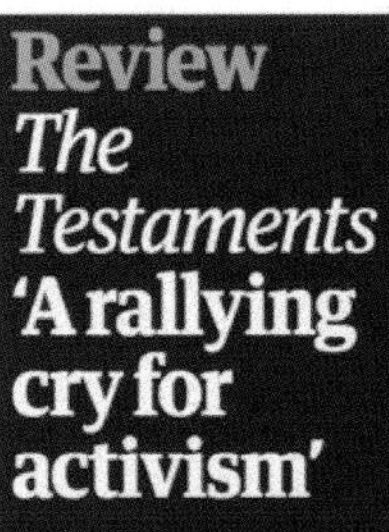

News Page 4

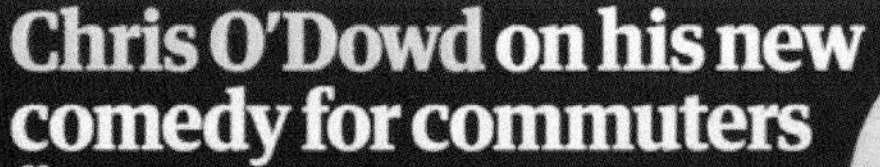

Chris O'Dowd on his new comedy for commuters
G2

Thursday
5 September 2019
£2.20
£1.60 for subscribers

The Guardian

Cornered Johnson suffers triple Commons defeat

- PM's call for snap October election rebuffed by Labour
- MPs vote twice to scupper threat of no-deal Brexit

Heather Stewart
Jessica Elgot
Peter Walker

Boris Johnson's attempt to trigger a general election next month was blocked by MPs last night after a string of heavy defeats for the government in both houses of parliament.

Immediately afterwards, the prime minister called Jeremy Corbyn "the first leader of the opposition in the democratic history of our country to refuse the invitation to an election".

But an early election still appeared inevitable last night after the Labour leader signalled he would back Johnson's call for a snap poll once the bill opposing no deal has passed.

The vote came just 48 hours after the prime minister told the public: "I don't want an election, you don't want an election."

The motion he tabled calling for an early poll was supported by 298 MPs - but that fell well short of the two-thirds required, with Labour MPs whipped to abstain.

But Corbyn made clear explicitly that Labour is ready to support a similar motion once Hilary Benn's backbench bill to block a no-deal Brexit has received royal assent - which could happen early next week if it is not scuppered by Tory peers.

Corbyn told MPs: "We want an election, because we look forward to turfing this government out!" But he claimed Johnson's proposal for a 15 October poll was "a bit like the offer of an apple to snow white by the wicked queen". Speaking after the Commons had rushed through Benn's bill - which Tory peers are now seeking to block in the Lords - the Labour leader said: "Let this bill pass, and gain royal assent: then we will back a general election."

Johnson has repeatedly called the legislation, which would oblige him to seek an extension to article 50 if he has not secured a new Brexit deal by 19 October, "Jeremy Corbyn's surrender bill". "I think it's very sad that MPs have voted like this," Johnson said, adding, "the country must decide" whether he or Jeremy Corbyn go to Brussels for the critical European council meeting on 17 October.

"He would beg for an extension; he would accept whatever Brexit demands, and we would have years more dither and delay," he said.

Benn's bill passed through all its stages in the Commons in a matter of hours yesterday as the rebels maintained their solid majority over Johnson's government, gaining a new Conservative convert in the former minister Caroline Spelman.

There were occasionally chaotic scenes. One amendment, tabled by the Labour MP Stephen Kinnock and calling for the extension to be used for the purpose of passing a Brexit deal, passed by default.

2 →

▲ *Boris Johnson during heated exchanges in the Commons yesterday*
PHOTOGRAPH: JESSICA TAYLOR/HOUSE OF COMMONS

How they voted

Bill to block a no-deal Brexit		*Motion calling for a general election*	
Yes	327	Yes	298
No	299	No	56
Majority	28	Number of votes needed	434

News Pages 6-9

2019

SAY NO TO
TRUMP
WHALING
TRIDENT
CLIMATE CHANGE
BREXIT
FOSSIL FUELS
THE CUTS
AUSTERITY
FOX HUNTING

... Joan must never know that we didn't organise this as part of her leaving drinks....
REMAIN
WE SAY REMAIN
REMAIN

My long term plan is to take all the hurt, fear, loneliness, rejection, disappointment, anxiety, despair and self-loathing and channel it into a stand-up routine...

Life after Game of Thrones Nathalie Emmanuel
→ Interview G2

In search of → G2 Ghislaine Maxwell

Thursday
12 December 2019
£2.20
From £1.60 for subscribers

The Guardian

Corbyn urges voters to deliver 'shock to the establishment'

- Labour leader uses final speech to outline 'truly historic choice'
- Johnson calls on electorate to 'put the uncertainty to bed'
- Polls suggest anything from big Tory majority to hung parliament

Heather Stewart
Rowena Mason

Jeremy Corbyn urged Britain to "shock the establishment" and "vote for hope" last night, while Boris Johnson pleaded with voters to back him and settle the issue of Brexit before Christmas, at the conclusion of a bruising election campaign.

Both leaders stressed that the result could be very close as they toured marginal seats across the country with just 24 hours to go before polling stations opened this morning.

In his eve-of-poll message, Corbyn claimed the country stood at a "fork in the road" with a "truly historic" choice between parties with widely different values and policies.

"Tomorrow you can shock the establishment, by voting for hope," the Labour leader told a rally in Hoxton in east London. "Hope for yourself. Hope for your family. Hope for your community. Hope for our NHS. Hope for our country. Tomorrow, vote for hope. Vote for real change."

He said: "The establishment doesn't want Labour to win." Corbyn also hammered home the core message he has pushed throughout the campaign, that Johnson would "open our NHS to takeover by American mega corporations and carry on with more cuts", saying that was why the US president, Donald Trump, wanted the prime minister to hold on to power.

Johnson hosted his own rally not far away from his rival, in the Olympic Park in east London, making his message all about his determination to follow through on his Brexit promises. "Enough is enough," he said in remarks released in advance of the rally last night. "This election is our chance to end the gridlock, but the result is on a knife edge."

He also repeated his claim that if the Conservatives failed to win a majority, Corbyn would have to seek a deal with the SNP, leading to second referendums on EU membership and Scottish independence.

"Today is our chance to unite as a country and put the uncertainty to bed so people can get on with their lives," the prime minister said.

"Just imagine how wonderful it will be to settle down to a turkey dinner this Christmas with Brexit decided - and how awful it would be if Corbyn and Sturgeon were in Downing Street advancing their plans for two more referendums."

Johnson criss-crossed England and Wales yesterday, taking part in a series of carefully staged business visits and photo calls, aimed at underlining his determination to press ahead with Brexit.

He has come under intense scrutiny in recent days. The father of the London Bridge attack victim Jack Merritt accused him of seeing his son's death as a political opportunity. And Johnson was also criticised for his reaction to the case of a four-year-old boy pictured sleeping on the floor of a Leeds hospital - an image he appeared reluctant to look at when asked about it by a reporter on Monday.

Corbyn also toured the country yesterday, kicking off with an early-morning rally in Glasgow and taking in Middlesbrough, South Yorkshire and Bedford on his way back to the capital.

With the Liberal Democrats urging voters to back the party most likely to defeat the Conservatives and prevent a hard Brexit, and Nigel Farage's Brexit party threatening to split the leave vote in many of the traditionally Labour seats Johnson is 2 →

▲ *The Labour leader, Jeremy Corbyn, in Dinnington, South Yorkshire, in the final hours of the campaign yesterday*
PHOTOGRAPH: CHRISTOPHER FURLONG/GETTY

Full coverage
Pages 4-15

2019

Good morning, I'm John Humphrys. Later I will be discussing the topic of 'Bias In The Today Programme' with myself, and deciding there isn't any...

Let it never be said that we don't know how to celebrate World Social Work Day.
PIZZA
PIZZA

The three golden rules of social work, Bemi: Observation, observation and observation.

'Irresistible and impossible'
Suzanne Moore on Elizabeth Wurtzel
G2

The Guardian

Thursday
9 January 2020
£2.20
From £1.60 for subscribers

Harry and Meghan to 'step back as senior royals'

Announcement follows complaints of media bullying and smears

Kevin Rawlinson

The Duke and Duchess of Sussex are to step back from public life and work towards financial self-sufficiency after a period marked by open hostilities with the media over claimed intrusion and bullying.

It is understood that no other member of the royal family was consulted before the decision was announced last night and Buckingham Palace was disappointed by the news.

The couple plan to split their time between the UK and North America, the continent of Meghan's birth, as they raise their son.

> *'We intend to ... work to become financially independent, while continuing to fully support the Queen'*
>
> Official statement

"After many months of reflection and internal discussions, we have chosen to make a transition this year in starting to carve out a progressive new role within this institution," read an official statement from Prince Harry and Meghan released yesterday.

"We intend to step back as 'senior' members of the royal family and work to become financially independent, while continuing to fully support Her Majesty the Queen. It is with your encouragement, particularly over the last few years, that we feel prepared to make this adjustment.

"We now plan to balance our time between the United Kingdom and North America, continuing to honour our duty to the Queen, the Commonwealth and our patronages.

"This geographic balance will enable us to raise our son with an appreciation for the royal tradition into which he was born, while also providing our family with the space to focus on the next chapter, including the launch of our new charitable entity.

"We look forward to sharing the full details of this exciting next step in due course, as we continue to collaborate with Her Majesty the Queen, the Prince of Wales, the Duke of Cambridge and all relevant parties. Until then, please accept our deepest thanks for your continued support."

A Buckingham Palace spokeswoman said discussions with the couple on their 9 →

▲ *The Duke and Duchess of Sussex say they will divide their time between the US and UK* PHOTOGRAPH: CHRIS JACKSON/GETTY

Trump edges away from war after Iran retaliation

Daniel Strauss *Washington*
Michael Safi *Beirut*
Ghaith Abdul-Ahad *Baghdad*

Donald Trump backed away from further military confrontation with Iran yesterday after days of escalating tensions, saying Tehran appeared to be standing down after missile attacks on two Iraqi bases hosting US and coalition troops.

Flanked by the vice-president, Mike Pence, the defence secretary, Mark Esper, and other high-ranking military officials in uniform, Trump delivered his remarks in the grand foyer of the White House, hours after Iran said the attack was retaliation for the US drone strike last week that killed the top Iranian general Qassem Suleimani.

"Iran appears to be standing down, which is a good thing for all parties concerned and a very good thing for the world," Trump said. "No American or Iraqi lives were lost because of the precautions taken, the dispersal of forces, and an early warning system that worked very well."

Trump's speech was notably more sober than his more bellicose statements and tweets in the immediate aftermath of Suleimani's killing, in which he threatened to bomb Iranian cultural sites, a potential war crime. The US, in recent days, has deployed 3,500 paratroopers to the Middle East and Americans have been urged to leave the region over safety concerns.

Even so, Trump said the United States would continue evaluating options "in response to Iranian aggression" and that additional sanctions on the Iranian regime would be imposed. He did not elaborate.

Iran is already under such heavy sanctions that few experts believe further US measures would make much economic difference. The president stressed the 2 →

Plane crash
Call for answers after 176 killed

News *Pages 6-7* →

2020

People think I'm odd for wearing the mask, I think they're odd for not. I mean, if they want to be reckless and irresponsible around their personal health that's their business, I'm not taking the risk.

So, do you ever take it off?
Never! Except when I want a fag.

PRICE CHOP
ATM
SUPAMARKET
SECUR

Is wearing a face mask inconvenient? Definitely! But I, for one, am prepared to endure my glasses being permanently steamed up...
...In the interests of safety.

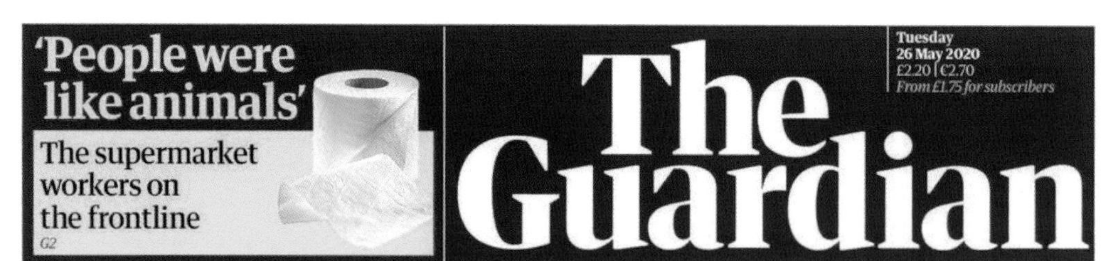

'People were like animals'

The supermarket workers on the frontline

G2

The Guardian

Tuesday
26 May 2020
£2.20 | €2.70
From £1.75 for subscribers

'I don't regret what I did.' Cummings refuses to quit

- Johnson's top adviser stages extraordinary press conference
- PM says he still backs aide amid ongoing anger over lockdown breach
- Second family trip 'necessary to check eyesight' after virus

Rowena Mason
Matthew Weaver

The crisis that has engulfed the government over the conduct of Dominic Cummings raged unabated last night after an unprecedented press conference in which he repeatedly refused to resign or apologise for breaking lockdown rules.

After an outpouring of public anger rattled No 10, Cummings attempted to explain why he drove 264 miles from London to his parents' estate in Durham despite suspecting both he and his wife had coronavirus.

No 10 had hoped the extraordinary move would draw a line under fury about Cummings' behaviour, after at least 20 Tory MPs called for him to quit and senior scientists accused him of undermining public health advice.

But his appearance in the rose garden of No 10 raised yet more questions, after the adviser admitted he suspected both he and his wife had coronavirus when they made the decision to travel across the country with their son.

During the lengthy press conference, Cummings claimed he drove to Durham because he had needed to seek possible back-up childcare for his four-year-old son from his teenage niece. He insisted they had stayed in a separate building, and had communicated with his parents by shouting a distance.

He subsequently also admitted that he made a separate trip after his family's 14-day period of isolation to Barnard Castle, a beauty spot 30 miles away from Durham, which he claimed was necessary to check his eyesight was good enough for the drive back to London. He acknowledged they got out of the car and sat for 15 minutes by a river at a time when the lockdown rules banned non-essential trips, with exceptions for shopping, exercise and picking up medication.

Both the trip from London and to Barnard Castle would appear to be breaches of the government's lockdown rules.

Refusing to apologise and saying he had not offered to quit his post, Cummings said: "I don't regret what I did ... reasonable people might disagree."

Following the press conference, Johnson once again gave his full backing to his senior adviser, who was a key architect of Brexit and the prime minister's election victory.

The prime minister took a tone of contrition at some points, saying he did "of course regret the confusion, the anger and the pain that people feel ... as a country that has been going through tremendous difficulties and sufferings".

However, he also claimed that Cummings had fully explained himself and done nothing wrong, insisting: "I don't think anyone in No 10 has done anything to undermine our messaging." He insisted it was "very, very plausible" for Cummings to have gone to Barnard Castle because of problems with his eyesight.

Johnson added: "I'm finding that I have to wear spectacles for the first time in years - because I think of the likely effects of this thing."

Numerous Tory MPs and cabinet ministers tweeted their backing to Cummings after the appearance but others remained unhappy with the explanation and feared their constituents' anger would not be assuaged.

The developments came on a day when:

- The police and crime commissioner for Durham, Steve White, formally asked the chief constable of the force he oversees to launch an investigation into Cummings. The force said it was considering complaints and issued a statement clarifying it had not given Cummings' family advice about the lockdown, but spoke to his father about security, contradicting an earlier statement.
- The retired chemistry teacher who first revealed Cummings' trip to Barnard Castle said he should resign. After hearing the prime minister's chief adviser's defence of the journey, Robin Lees said:

3 →

▲ *Dominic Cummings, the prime minister's adviser, speaks to the media at 10 Downing Street yesterday*
PHOTOGRAPH: JONATHAN BRADY/AFP/GETTY

All shops to reopen on 15 June

Outdoor markets and car showrooms will be able to reopen in England from next Monday while all other non-essential retail premises will be allowed to open in three weeks

Page 10→

2020

The key to surviving the lockdown is to accept the situation for what it is, find peace within oneself and, most importantly, to just stay calm.....

OH MY GOD! NETFLIX IS DOWN!!! NETFLIX IS DOWN!!!

These have been extremely challenging times, Men's Group. But there must have been positives amongst all the negatives. So I want each of you to take a moment and...

Not having to have to hug people.

I have to say, Megan, that I thought you'd totally unravel in isolation, but you and your flat are as immaculate as on the first day of lockdown.

Thank you, Clare, nice of you to say so.

2020

Summer on the rocks
Recreating the tastes of a lost season
G2

Gary Busey on Hollywood, drugs and seeing angels
G2
Thursday
28 May 2020
£2.20 | €2.70
From £1.75 for subscribers
The Guardian

Tories defy PM to pile pressure on Cummings

Senior minister breaks ranks to highlight 'inconsistencies' in No 10 adviser's story

Rowena Mason
Deputy political editor

More than 50 Conservative MPs stood in defiance of Boris Johnson's calls to "move on" from the Dominic Cummings crisis last night as a senior minister broke ranks to accuse the special adviser of inconsistencies in his account of his behaviour during lockdown.

The intervention of Penny Mordaunt deepened the turmoil within government following revelations by the Guardian and Daily Mirror that Cummings had travelled 260 miles to his family estate in Durham with his wife suffering coronavirus symptoms.

The former chancellor Sajid Javid, also said the journey was not "necessary or justified" as the number of backbenchers calling for Cummings to resign or be sacked grew to 43, with a total of 59 Tory MPs weighing in to criticise him. Two of those condemning Cummings are government whips.

Mordaunt, a Cabinet Office minister and former defence secretary, said there were "inconsistencies" in Cummings' account and apologised for how recent days had "undermined key public health messages".

In an email sent to constituents, Mordaunt said Cummings' continued position was a "matter for the prime minister" but she could "fully understand how angry people are" and believed there was no doubt he "took risks".

Fury among Conservative MPs has grown by the day after an investigation that also revealed how Cummings took his family on a 60-mile round trip to a beauty spot in Barnard Castle, which he says was to test whether his eyesight was good enough for him to drive back to London.

At an appearance before the liaison committee of senior MPs, Johnson declined to answer most questions about Cummings, saying repeatedly it was time to "move on".

But his pleas fell flat as Javid, who stood down as chancellor after clashing with Cummings, joined the list of those criticising him. In a letter to a constituent reported by the Bromsgrove Standard, Javid said: "I do not believe Mr Cummings' journey to County Durham to isolate on his family's estate was necessary or justified. I remain unconvinced his visit to Barnard Castle could be considered reasonable. I was also deeply concerned by his decision to return to Downing Street directly after coming into contact with a family member who was ill, potentially with coronavirus."

Other Tories who were unconvinced either by Johnson's appearance before the liaison committee or Cummings' attempts to explain himself on Monday included the former minister George Freeman.

4 →

▲ *Dominic Cummings' Durham trip was 'not justified', Sajid Javid said*

Maitlis row
Host rebuked by BBC after criticism of PM's aide
News Page 7 →
PHOTOGRAPH: RICHARD GARDNER/REX

Hancock: do your 'civic duty' over test and trace

Sarah Boseley
Heather Stewart

Matt Hancock exhorted the public to do their "civic duty" and stay at home when instructed yesterday, as he launched a new test-and-trace system.

The health secretary announced the start of the scheme in the face of warnings from council leaders that they lacked the data or powers to make local lockdowns work.

Employing Churchillian language, he called on everyone to do their bit, and warned that if they failed, the government would enforce compliance.

"It is your civic duty," said Hancock. "This will be voluntary at first because we trust everyone to do the right thing, but we can quickly make it mandatory if that's what it takes.

"Do it for the people you love. Do it for the community. Do it for the NHS and do it for all the frontline workers who have done so much and gone out every day to put themselves at risk to keep you and your family safe."

He added: "And in return for following those instructions, you'll have the knowledge that when the call came you did your bit, at a time when it really mattered."

Starting at 9am today, the test-and-trace system for England is intended to allow the nationwide lockdown to be replaced with

8 →

2020

LATE MARCH 2020
I cannot believe it took the silence of lockdown for me to notice the super abundance of birdsong in our garden.
LATE MAY 2020
SHUT THE **** UP, YOU FEATHERY ****ERS!!!

Hey, Clare, who ever would have thought my old College prom dress would come in so handy again....?
SUPA MARKET
PLEASE OBSERVE SOCIAL DISTANCING
SUPA MARKET
PLEASE OBSERVE SOCIAL DISTANCING

megan, if you haven't read the report just say so, rather than holding a pose and pretending the screen has frozen....

G2 Film & Music

Henry Golding

How the Crazy Rich Asians star conquered Hollywood

Sheila E *'I'm mad that Prince isn't here'*

Friday
11 September 2020
£2.20 | €2.70
From £1.75 for subscribers

The Guardian

Brexit talks on brink as UK rejects ultimatum

Lisa O'Carroll
Daniel Boffey *Brussels*

The Brexit talks appeared to be on the point of collapse last night after Britain flatly rejected an EU ultimatum over the government's plans to break international law by reneging on parts of the withdrawal agreement.

The clash followed an EU demand that Boris Johnson drop his plans within three weeks or face financial or trade sanctions, after the bloc's lawyers concluded Britain had already breached the withdrawal agreement by tabling the internal market bill.

In a hard-hitting statement following a meeting with Michael Gove in London, the European commission vice-president Maroš Šefčovič put the prime minister on notice that he needed to regain Brussels' trust. He also raised the prospect of both a collapse in the trade and security talks and a legal battle with the bloc.

"The EU does not accept the argument that the aim of the draft [internal market] bill is to protect the Good Friday (Belfast) agreement. In fact, it is of the view that it does the opposite," the commission said in a statement.

In a sign of the plunging prospects of a deal, Germany's ambassador to the UK, Andreas Michaelis, tweeted: "In more than 30 years as a diplomat I have not experienced such a fast, intentional and profound deterioration of a negotiation. "If you believe in partnership between the UK and the EU like I do then don't accept it."

Šefčovič had told Gove "in no uncertain terms" that the UK government must "withdraw these measures from the draft bill in the shortest time possible and in any case by the end of the month". "By putting forward this bill, the UK has seriously damaged trust between the EU and the UK. It is now up to the UK government to re-establish that trust," his statement read.

But within two hours of the tense meeting, the Cabinet Office minister said Downing Street would not climb down. "I made it perfectly clear to the vice-president of the commission we would not be withdrawing this legislation," said Gove. "I explained to vice-president Šefčovič that we could not and would not do that ... He understood that. Of course, he regretted it."

Gove said the UK was "absolutely serious about implementing the Northern Ireland 4 →

PHOTOGRAPH: GETTY IMAGES

Diana Rigg
Star of stage, cinema and The Avengers dies aged 82
News *Pages 8-9* →

Behind-the-scenes rift over legality of EU bill

Exclusive
Paul Lewis and Owen Bowcott

A behind-the-scenes rift has emerged between the government's top legal advisers over the legality of the decision to introduce legislation that overrides the EU withdrawal agreement.

Legal advice in a three-page letter marked "official - sensitive", seen by the Guardian, summarises the legal opinions of the three law officers, whose role includes ensuring ministers act in accordance with the law.

The letter appears to show Richard Keen, the advocate general for Scotland, advised that 5 →

Pandemic 'causing deep social divisions'

Robert Booth
Social affairs correspondent

Mask-wearing and lockdown rules are now causing deeper social fractures than Brexit, according to a UK-wide study that claims solidarity in the early weeks of the pandemic has given way to distrust. Polling of 10,000 people found half of mask wearers in Britain (58%) have severely negative attitudes towards non-mask wearers, and the vast majority (68%) of people who did not break lockdown rules have strong negative views about lockdown rule breakers.

Significant minorities of people who stuck to rules said they "hate" or "resent" people who do not; 12% of mask wearers said they hate those who do not wear face coverings and 14% of lockdown adherents hate rule breakers, the survey found.

The animosity created by different responses to the pandemic runs deeper than that revealed in comparable polling 2 →

2020

I know the guidelines have been relaxed, but I've made a list of people I believe we should maintain strict social distancing from.
Because they present a high health risk?
Because they talk about their kids.

According to supermarket sales during lockdown, it seems the nation has taken refuge in either baking or alcohol.
Or both, Megan. Or both.

Hey Megan, you know the group in society who must be finding this 2m social distancing most frustrating?
Who?
The strip cartoonists.
Yep, can't be easy.

Clare's final appearance in The Guardian

We shall not see her like again. Although you may see some of her jokes recycled in future strips I draw for other publications.

Acknowledgments

With thanks to David O'Connor, Ella Remande Guyard (CEO Harrivenn Corporation), Emily Wilkinson, Steve Woodgate, Paul Sweetmans, City Books Hove, Geri May, Hanaa Anwar, Philippa Mole, Robert Hahn, Alison Benjamin and all my friends and colleagues at The Annexe Studios who I have tormented for years by waving freshly drawn cartoons in their faces and demanding "Is this funny?"

If you want to contact Harry Venning • harrymvenning@gmail.com